COUNT RUMFORD OF WOBURN, MASS.

The strange career of Sir Benjamin Thompson, Knight of the White Eagle: scientist, inventor, Revolutionary War turncoat, financial wizard, philanthropist-reformer, Bavarian general.

W. J. Sparrow

Rumford's statue in the Maximilian strasse, Munich.
*(By courtesy of Herr Retzer, Landeshaupstadt München,
Fremdenverkehrsamt, München)*

W. J. SPARROW

★

Knight of the White Eagle
SIR BENJAMIN THOMPSON

COUNT RUMFORD
OF WOBURN, MASS.

Thomas Y. Crowell Company
New York · Established 1834

First published in the United States of America in 1965.

Originally published in Great Britain under the title
Knight of the White Eagle.

Copyright © 1964 by W. J. Sparrow

Printed in Great Britain.

Library of Congress Catalog Card No. 65–18565

Contents

CONTENTS

CHAPTER 5

From Aide-de-Camp to 'Excellency'

69

Thompson leaves England—Meets Prince Maximilian at Strasbourg—Vienna—Correspondence with Keith—Aide-de-camp to Charles Theodore—Knighted by King George—Death of Sackville—Reform of Bavarian army—Opposition thereto—Beggary in Bavaria—The rounding-up—Social reforms—The English Garden—Thompson ennobled—Other services to Bavaria—Travel in Italy—Meets Sir Charles Blagden and the Palmerstons—Visits Volta—First Essays—Revisits England—Robbery in St Paul's Churchyard—His daughter Sally joins him—Back to Bavaria—Strong man in Munich—Head of Police—Appointed Ambassador to the Court of St James's—Appointment annulled—Opinions of his work in Bavaria

CHAPTER 6

Founder of the Royal Institution (1)—The Days of Enthusiasm

107

Proposals for an Institution—Contact with Thomas Bernard—First meeting of the Royal Institution (1799)—Appointment of Garnett and Webster—Webster's school—Sally returns to America—Progress of the Royal Institution—Differing aims—Garnett in trouble—Appointment of Davy—Attitude of the Boultons—Modification of aims for the Royal Institution

CHAPTER 7

Founder of the Royal Institution (2)—The Days of Disillusion

131

Position in 1801—Dash to Munich—Further progress—Decides to leave London—Reasons for going—Financial difficulties in Albemarle Street—'Bernard's Institution'—Progress of the Royal Institution under Davy and Faraday

CHAPTER 8

Personal and Family Affairs

141

Aspects of Rumford's character—Rumford helps to support his mother—Sally in Munich—Her suitors—Rumford's attitude to Sally—Thinks of returning to America—In Paris—His journal—Meets Mme Lavoisier—Returns to England—Revisits Bavaria—Returns to Paris—Marries Mme Lavoisier—Assessment of his achievements

CHAPTER 9

Master of Fuel and Fire

168

'The Comforts of a Rumford Stove'—'The sublime in science'—Large-scale cooking—Roaster and fireplaces—Central heating—Applications in industry—

CHAPTER 10
Philanthropist and Reformer
184

CHAPTER 11
Man of Science—His Earlier Work
201

CHAPTER 12
Man of Science—The Nature of Heat
214

CHAPTER 13
Man of Science—Further Important Researches
227

CHAPTER 14
Man of Science—Later Researches
240

CONTENTS

CHAPTER 15

Clouded Evening

246

Marital disagreements and quarrels—Separation—Auteuil—The salons of Mme Rumford—Recall of Sally—Last visit to Bavaria—Visit of Davy and Faraday to Paris—Laplace and capillarity—Unfinished work—Last days—Death and funeral

Illustrations

Acknowledgements

I gratefully acknowledge my debt to the Managers and Librarian
of the Royal Institution for allowing me access to their Minute
Books and other records and for permission to quote from them;
to the Council and Librarian of the Royal Society for a similar
privilege, particularly in respect of Rumford's papers and the
diaries of Sir Charles Blagden; to the Master of the Birmingham
Assay Office for permission to examine and use the Boulton and
Watt Collection; to the librarian and staff of the William L.
Clements Library, Ann Arbor, who provided me with a great deal
of essential material from the Gage and Germain Papers; to Mr
Brian Connell and his publishers, Messrs André Deutsch and
Co., for allowing me to quote from *Portrait of a Whig Peer*; and
to the librarians and staffs of many other libraries in this country
and overseas, not least those of the University of Birmingham.

I am greatly indebted to the Council and Senate of the University for allowing me study leave to undertake the necessary
research and the writing of this book, and also for a grant towards
its publication.

I am grateful to Dr A. M. Wilkinson for his helpful criticism
of the manuscript, and to Miss E. R. Payne and Miss O. Daous
for help with the index.

My thanks are due to Mr and Mrs Cecil Porter of the Rumford
Historical Association in Woburn, Massachusetts, for their encouragement and hospitality; and finally to my publishers who
have been so courteous and helpful in the preparation of this book.

W. J. SPARROW

University of Birmingham

Introduction

My interest in Count Rumford dates from my schooldays when I first read in a physics textbook that 'while boring cannon at Munich Count Rumford was struck by the amount of heat evolved . . .' I, too, was struck. Why 'Count' Rumford? Somehow 'Count' and 'Rumford' didn't fit. And why was this Count boring cannon at Munich? I later found a partial answer to these questions in a footnote of Thomas Preston's remarkable book *The Theory of Heat*. As I was occupied with many other interests, it was not until about twenty years ago that I found the time and the opportunity to begin a thorough study of the man and his work. I hope that in the pages which follow I have succeeded in showing the importance of this work, and the complications of his character.

An educated person's general knowledge would be unlikely to include even enough material for a thumbnail sketch of Rumford and his work, and yet in his lifetime few men were more widely known. He had given his name to a type of fire-grate. A French soldier grumbling about the *maigreur* of his soup would refer to it disdainfully as Rumford's soup. The poor in more than one capital city would see his name or his portrait on tickets entitling them to free dinners. He was the personal friend of more than one king and well known to many others. In science his name stood high: he had received the Copley Medal from the Royal Society and honours from many other learned bodies. All these distinctions and a host of others gave him a fame almost equal to that of his contemporary and fellow countryman Benjamin Franklin. None the less Count Rumford has receded into the background of history. There are fairly obvious reasons. One lies in the emphasis placed on politics and conflict in the history taught in

13

our schools; and another in our national apathy towards the history of science.

No substantial biography of Rumford has been written and published in this country, though there are many shorter accounts of his life and work. The quarry (to use Tyndall's description) from which recent writers have hewn much of their material is the very long and now scarce memoir, written by the Reverend G. E. Ellis, which was published in 1876 in this country by Macmillan and Company for the American Academy of Arts and Sciences. Ellis's biography is scholarly, sympathetic and wide in scope, but it lacks objectivity. Moreover, although Ellis had a great range of material at his disposal, much more has been discovered in the last hundred years.

My own book has three main aims. I have tried to tell accurately the story of Rumford's life against the setting of his time, to unravel and exhibit his motives and, most important, to present a balanced account of his scientific work. My interest in this absorbing man has enriched my leisure and taken me to Munich, Paris, America and elsewhere. If what I have written contributes to his rehabilitation I shall be content.

COUNT RUMFORD

These, Virtue, are thy triumphs, that adorn
Fitliest our nature, and bespeak us born
For loftiest action; not to gaze and run
From clime to clime; or batten in the sun,
Dragging a drony flight from flower to flower,
Like summer insects in a gaudy hour;
Nor yet o'er love-sick tales with fancy range
And cry, ' 'Tis pitiful, 'tis passing strange!'
But on life's varied views to look around
And raise expiring sorrow from the ground:
And he, who thus hath borne his part assign'd
In the sad fellowship of human kind,
Or for a moment soothed the bitter pain
Of a poor brother—has not lived in vain!

S. T. COLERIDGE (1796)

I

Bright Morning

In the lexicon of youth, which fate reserves
For a bright manhood, there is no such word
As—*fail*.

LORD LYTTON

REVEALING the personality and character of his subject and evaluating the part he played in the events of his time are the acknowledged tasks of a biographer. Neither is easy with Count Rumford. His character was complex and some of his activities are still inaccessible to the student of his life and times. What is known, however, justifies our ranking him as a great man of science, a leader in technology and a philanthropist of high renown. It is true that he was in no field a genius for posterity to acclaim, but when he died he had become an international figure almost as famous as Benjamin Franklin.

Benjamin Thompson, Count Rumford to be, was born in his grandfather's house at Woburn, Massachusetts, on 26 March 1753. He was a descendant of one of the hardy early settlers who in 1630 had crossed the Atlantic with John Winthrop, the English squire who became the first Governor of Massachusetts Bay. Thompson's father, also named Benjamin, had married in 1752 a girl called Ruth Simonds, but he lived only two years to enjoy his marriage. So young Benjamin was deprived of a father in infancy and for most of his early life was brought up by his mother and stepfather, Josiah Pierce, whom Ruth married in 1756.

In middle age Rumford used to say that his stepfather was harsh and unsympathetic. His friend and admirer M. A. Pictet[1] gave wide currency to this accusation and Baron Cuvier,[2] who also knew Rumford well, went so far as to say that he owed his chance and fame to his early misfortunes. These assertions were based on nothing more than an attempt on Rumford's part to give a romantic colour to his early life. It is certain, though, that he disliked work on the family farm. No doubt he was expected to take his share in indoor and outdoor work and his unwillingness may have caused some friction. However, it is quite clear, on his own showing, that he was treated with enlightened kindness and generosity by many of his elders, including his grandfather. When considering Josiah Pierce's attitude to his stepson we should remember that in the Franklin family not many miles away, where there were seventeen children, all the boys were put 'apprentices to different trades' except Benjamin, the youngest, who was sent to a grammar school at the age of eight.[3] Josiah Franklin made the exception because he intended to devote a tithe of his sons to the Church: addiction to books when it was coupled with a distaste for homely tasks and chores was not looked upon with favour in eighteenth-century America, and continued grammar school education was exceptional. Thompson, however, like the other Benjamin, did receive early education at a grammar school; and later, when he was eleven years old, he was put under the tuition of a Mr Hill at Medford, a neighbouring town.

After two years in Medford, Thompson's formal education ended and it was decided to apprentice him to a useful trade. Accordingly, he went to live with a Mr John Appleton to learn the trade of importer and general dealer. Thompson became Appleton's apprentice in the autumn of 1766 and stayed for over two years. He was a strong, healthy, bright and intelligent lad in whom older friends took an unusual interest. He had a bent towards the sciences and ingenious mechanical contrivances, and showed increasing skill in music, drawing and engraving. A book plate he engraved at this time reveals practical skill, imagination and ambition. It is of a medallion hanging from a lopped tree. On the medallion is a shield and crest, surmounting the motto: B. Thompson. In the top right-hand corner is one-quarter of the radiating sun containing an eye. Artistically arranged round the medallion are a ship in sail, a lion cub, an open book lying on a sword, a closed book and dividers and, also hanging from the tree, a set-square and dividers. The plate is an astonishing achievement and its symbolism is prophetic of Thompson's future interests and career.

From this time of apprenticeship we can see some of the influences which helped to shape Thompson's later life. He became acquainted with Loammi Baldwin, a young man nine years older than himself, who remained a staunch and life-long friend. He acquired an interest in guns, gunpowder and mechanical contrivances, and he met the first of a line of influential people who were to recognize his ability and further his career. This was the Reverend Thomas Barnard, minister of the Free Church at Salem, and young Thompson attended his services. Barnard recognized the boy's ability and taught him some elementary mathematics.

Thompson's interest in his employment was marginal; his energies were given to his other pursuits. One was making fireworks, and this led to a serious accident in 1769 when he injured himself preparing fireworks for a display to celebrate the repeal of certain import duties.

The next fifteen years of his life were to be vastly influenced by the struggle between Great Britain and the American colonies.

Thompson was ten years old when, in 1763, the Treaty of Paris was signed. England emerged victorious from the Seven Years' War, and with a new colonial empire. France lost her North American possessions and with them her control in the territory north of the Great Lakes. The Floridas, Canada, and Louisiana as far west as the Mississippi River, now came into the possession of the British. One result of the defeat of the French was to diminish the American colonists' feeling of dependence upon British military and naval strength.

Quite apart from the gross abuse of power, whereby men in England held office in the colonies while continuing to live in England, there were many causes of friction. Colonial ports were legally open only to English ships. Although colonial industries were subsidized, colonial goods were destined for the British market; and colonial manufacturers were not allowed to compete with those at home. Then there was the matter of defence. How the colonies should be defended from the Indians and from the French, and how the cost should be divided, were important questions on both sides of the Atlantic. While the colonies had voluntarily contributed at least their fair share in the last war, it was also true that the people of England had been surprised by the extent of their material and financial resources. The Americans, now feeling less dependent upon England, could not bring themselves to accept a plan of confederation, still less to provide money to be expended in defence by the various governors. America's indecision could not restrain action in England indefinitely, however, and Charles Townshend put forward a plan to raise revenue by taxation and the planting of a standing army.

A change of government brought confirmation and extension of the same policy. Grenville wished to suppress illicit trade, to enforce the trade laws, to keep the troops in America and to raise the sum of £100,000 by means of a duty on colonial documents. A Bill was introduced; it passed both Houses and received royal assent by commission in March 1765. In England the Bill was generally thought just and commendable, but it was, in fact, hopelessly at variance with the spirit and self-respect of the Americans. 'The whole country was swayed by one universal indignation.' Resolutions denouncing the new law as unconstitutional and tyrannical were passed by the leading Assemblies; there was some rioting and patriots formed societies under the general name of Sons of Liberty. Even Franklin, who was in England at the time, seems to have been astonished at the violence of the reaction.[4] The mischief was not all undone by the repeal of the Act in the following March, for a Declaratory Act was passed maintaining the right of the central government to tax the colonies.

The repeal of the Stamp Act was the work of the Rockingham Ministry, but Britain was unstable politically, and this Ministry was superseded after holding office for less than a year. Its successor, first under the ailing Chatham, and then under the Duke of Grafton, lasted only four years.

In the new government Charles Townshend, who was brilliant but vacillating (the 'delight and ornament' of the House), was Chancellor of the Exchequer. In accordance with Chatham's theory and the prevailing temper of the House, he proposed to introduce a comprehensive series of import duties upon glass, paper, lead oxide and tea. To facilitate the collection of the duties there should be a Board of Customs Commissioners established and resident in Massachusetts Bay.[5] These proposals passed into law in 1767 and greatly increased the indignation of the incensed American people. Two regiments of the line had to be sent to Boston to ensure the safety of the Commissioners, who were working in fear and risk of physical injury or worse.

Young Benjamin, who then was thirteen years of age, was

growing up in this charged atmosphere. John Appleton, his employer, was one of those who signed the non-importation agreement by which traders showed their opposition to the British plan. No doubt the consequent decrease in business allowed Thompson more time for self-improvement and, together with the injury he received in 1769, brought to an end his employment with Appleton in the same year. Anyhow, at sixteen he was back in Woburn and putting questions to his friend Baldwin on atmospheric refraction, the firing of clay and the rise of the wind. He had also acquired an interest in the study of heat, which continued until his death. The starting point, he tells us. was Boerhaave's 'admirable Treatise on Fire'.[6]

He was not at Woburn for long. After a few months he was sent to Boston as clerk in a dry-goods store owned by a Mr Hopestill Capen. Here he was in the midst of the excitement caused by the strained political relations; and here, among other prominent citizens, he met Samuel Curwen whom he met again in London some years later in dramatically changed circumstances. It is only a tradition that he was present at the minor disturbance in Boston on 5 March 1770, subsequently known as 'the Boston Massacre', when British troops, after being pelted with snow, fired into an angry, jeering crowd, killing four citizens.

Hopestill Capen must have been impressed with Thompson's practical skill, intellectual ability and self-reliance, short as their partnership was. When, after six months, trade had diminished, Thompson decided, more ambitiously, to set out towards a career in medicine. He was determined to make his way in the world and in order to achieve his aim was quite willing to embrace a rigid discipline and to exploit the charm which led even Ellis, his charitable nineteenth-century biographer, to describe him as 'essentially a courtier'. Henceforth his career overrode all other interests. His family and friends counted less than his personal advancement and his scientific interests were made to serve his own purpose.

At this time also his growing respect for order began to be a powerful ideal. The compelling habit of organization remained with him until he died; it influenced, in fact it inspired, his philanthropy, and though sometimes it brought him ridicule it sustained much of his research in heat and light. In 1770, however, it was chiefly evident in the very careful use he made of his time. His daily programme allowed seven hours for sleep and included study, prayers and diversion. Here it is:

		'6 a.m.	..	Get up, wash hands and face
From 6 a.m.	until	8 a.m.	..	Exercise and study
„ 8 a.m.	„	10 a.m.	..	Prayers and breakfast
„ 10 a.m.	„	12 noon	..	Study
„ 12 noon	„	1 p.m.	..	Dine
„ 1 p.m.	„	4 p.m.	..	Study
„ 4 p.m.	„	5 p.m.	..	Diversion or exercise
„ 5 p.m.	„	11 p.m.	..	Follow what my inclination leads me to.'

Thompson's sense of order is also revealed by the careful record he kept of his expenses. There is one list which gives in detail the money he spent in the summer of 1771 on materials for making an electrical machine, a piece of scientific apparatus then much in use for research. The prices quoted, for example '1 yd iron wyer 1/3', throw light on contemporary scarcities. The total cost was only just under five pounds.

After leaving Boston he began studying medicine with the local physician, Dr John Hay of Woburn. He paid board at the rate of forty shillings a week and no doubt this covered his tuition. He found the money by various expedients, including barter and school-teaching. The doctor and his wife seem to have been kind, for they made an allowance for his periods of absence and even for the time 'my Mother washed for me'.[7]

Thompson had a natural aptitude for teaching. He was a particularly accomplished gymnast and his prowess was remembered by the inhabitants of Wilmington fifty years after he left. When he was able to do so he attended lectures at Harvard College where he was registered as a charity scholar. His interest in electrical machines was stimulated by Professor Winthrop's lectures on electricity. The study of electricity was receiving a good deal of attention at the time, and Franklin's work was widely known not only in America but in Europe, where he had been honoured by various universities, including Oxford and Edinburgh, and where his writings had been variously translated.

Thompson's success at Wilmington, and also at Bradford, led to his being invited to teach at Concord, New Hampshire. He went there at the invitation of Colonel Timothy Walker, whose father, the greatly respected Reverend Timothy Walker, was minister. The Walkers were well-to-do and influential and Thompson became a regular visitor at their house. He was eighteen, tall, handsome and well mannered; he was widely read, full of promise, and his experiences had given him self-reliance and a degree of maturity. He fitted easily into the family circle and realized his good fortune. His youthful success had made him conscious of his advantages and, although he was always grateful to this unselfish and perceptive country pastor, he was at the same time determined to make the most of his own gifts and opportunities.

The minister's daughter was then a little over thirty and a widow. She had a young child, Paul, and ample means left to her by her late husband Colonel Rolfe. Sarah Walker had married Rolfe when she was about thirty and he sixty. Their life together had been tragically short but she had inherited a large estate with an imposing house. Thompson's association with Walker thus brought him into contact with a comparatively rich widow of high social position, fourteen years older than himself. Sarah fell in love. Thompson was perhaps intoxicated by the aura of splendour which surrounded her and his inclinations no doubt led him instinctively in the same direction as his ambition. The minister gave his blessing to the couple and they were married in November 1772.[8]

Thompson himself told Pictet years afterwards that he was married to the widow, implying that the enthusiasm was not on his side. This may well be partly true; his motives were probably mixed and not clear even to himself. He was young, and more physically than emotionally mature. Sarah Rolfe for her part may have feared the thought of years of widowhood in trying and unsettled times. The material advantages Thompson gained from the union were not meagre. There was no more struggling to earn money to pay Dr Hay's fees; indeed he could now raise his sights to a career much higher than that of a country doctor. Events moved quickly for him, since the family took him in hand. He must dress according to his new station and his mother's consent to his marriage be obtained. The two-horse curricle was brought out and he was driven the seventy miles to Boston to be provided with a 'Hussar cloak faced with scarlet shalloon with mock-spangle metal buttons'. When young Ben (as he still was to his mother) arrived at his home with the elegant Sarah the effect was startling, but after some hesitation his mother gave her consent to the wedding.

Thompson was no longer going to train to be a doctor; he decided to be a soldier. Just before his wedding he and his wife-to-be attended a military review at Dover near Portsmouth, at which John Wentworth, the Governor of the Province, was present. This review took place on 13 November 1772 and was a muster of the Second Provincial Regiment of New Hampshire. Thompson was introduced to the Governor who was impressed by his appearance and ability. Wentworth signed the certificate authorizing the marriage on the next day, and, far more important, offered him a commission in the regiment. Thompson was stepping very easily into Rolfe's shoes; not as a colonel, but not very different since he was to be a major, and, of course, he was only one-third of Rolfe's age.

Within a few months this boy of nineteen, a struggling apprentice and untrained schoolmaster, had become Major Thompson, the Squire of Concord. He embraced his many advantages without misgiving. His own comment long afterwards to the admiring Pictet was that his ideas had not yet been fixed: 'one scheme succeeded another'; he might 'have acquired a habit of indecision and inconstancy' and 'lived poor and miserable' to the end of his days 'if a woman had not loved him, given him existence, a habitation and an independent fortune'.[9] But there is a wrong emphasis here, perhaps even a suggestion of youthful genius struggling against an unfriendly environment. The missing elements are his ambition and precocious opportunism which were to help make him, amongst other things, a gifted adventurer.

2

Royalist and Informer

But wild ambition loves to slide, not stand,
And fortune's ice prefers to virtue's land.

DRYDEN

JOHN WENTWORTH'S decision to give Thompson a commission seems, on the face of it, an error of judgement. Here was a mere youth from the country given preference in the provincial regiment over many deserving officers with normal expectation of promotion. He must undoubtedly have been regarded as an over-confident upstart looking for success at any price. Yet there is another side to the matter. Although Thompson had a remarkable knack of impressing those who were in a position to advance him, he was also able to retain their admiration and justify their confidence. His outward appearance was matched by his ability, and his enthusiasm by his performance.

He was now a soldier, though, of course, not a full-time one. As a gentleman farmer he took a keen interest in his land and crops. At the same time his interest in scientific matters was unabated. Within two months of his marriage he had waited upon His Excellency the Governor with a plan to conduct a survey of the White Mountains. He had been politely received and encouraged by an offer of help. Wentworth's instruments and library would be at the disposal of the young leader and 'if there were no public business which rendered his presence at Portsmouth *absolutely necessary*' Wentworth would himself join the party.

The quotation is from a long, high-spirited letter written to one of Thompson's friends, the Reverend Samuel Williams of Bradford, a man of learning in mathematics. In spite of its callow style the letter gives an impression of confidence and resourcefulness. It also shows that Thompson was not always serious; he could be facetious.

'But stop!', he writes, 'I will not tell you anymore till you come and see me as you promised; then we will lay the whole plan in operation, and I will tell you a charming secret—something you would give the whole world to know. 'Tis nothing about Magnetism, nor Electricity, nor Optics, nor Evaporation, nor Flatulances, nor Earthquakes. No but 'tis something twice as pretty! something entirely new; but it can't be revealed except in the town of Concord. And I do solemnly protest by the third joint of St. Peter's great toe, that unless you come and see me this winter, you shall never know this grand Arcanum.'

One can infer that Loammi Baldwin, who was still a close friend of Thompson's, was to be a third member of the surveying party, for the two men wrote regularly to each other and continued to have many common interests. But the expedition did not take place. The year was 1773 and more serious events were at hand.

In 1769 some of the import duties imposed when Townshend was Chancellor of the Exchequer had been repealed. As a result there had been a slackening in tension between the colonies and the British Parliament. Thomas Hutchinson, who became Governor of Massachusetts in 1771, believed that the storms would subside and that even in Massachusetts the remaining grievances would be forgotten, especially as New York, where trade had been seriously impaired, had shown the way. But Hutchinson was wrong, and unfortunate in having, in Boston, Samuel Adams, an able and extreme leader of the opposition to Parliament. The radical disagreement and controversies between these two Americans helped to keep alive in Massachusetts the hatred engendered by the events of the previous decade.[1]

The duty on tea had not been repealed in 1769. But this did not prevent large-scale American importation of tea. In 1773 the Prime Minister, Lord North, decided to reduce the American duty on tea as a concession both to the colonies and to the East India Company. The plan, which was superficially attractive, took no account of the fact that permission for the Company 'to export tea from its warehouses in England free of all English customs and excise duties' and subject only to a threepenny duty in America would enable it to undersell other importers, legitimate or not, and thus create a virtual monopoly. Furthermore, the American people who would benefit were those pro-English merchants who would be willing to receive the tea as agents for the Company. In pursuance of North's plan four shiploads of tea were sent to America. At Charleston the tea was unloaded and stored in cellars. New York and Philadelphia declined to receive the tea and sent the ships back to England. But in Boston, as everyone knows, the reaction was violent and theatrical. A mob of extremists disguised as Indians threw the tea into the harbour.

This action aroused high feelings in England. It was time to punish the lawless and recalcitrant colonial child. King George was not the only one to see that the die was cast and that 'the colonies must either submit or triumph'. The port of Boston was closed pending the payment of full compensation and General Gage was appointed military governor of Massachusetts. American response was immediate. A Continental Congress was called in Philadelphia, and the people of Massachusetts realized that they could count on the support of the other colonies—though when it came to proposing action the deputies were far from unanimous. Before the Congress was adjourned, however, practical measures were agreed: to stop importation of goods from Great Britain and Ireland, to limit importation from, and stop exportation to, certain other places where British influence was paramount. Town and county committees were to be formed to ensure the agreements were observed. These internal measures were complementary to a Petition to the King and an Address to the People of Great Britain.

While the problem was debated in England opposition to British policy hardened in Massachusetts. A Provincial Congress, which first met at Salem in October 1774 and then removed to Cambridge, assumed gubernatorial powers in defiance of General Gage and the British Parliament. The assumption of responsibility was accompanied by the collection of arms and ammunition and the mustering and training of the militia.

Thompson was obviously at the centre of revolt and played a significant part in American events in the next eighteen months. From the start he was a loyalist, but outwardly he adopted an equivocal attitude. His forthright statement years later that 'from principle I supported the King because I considered this to be the lawful attitude . . .' betrays an element of rationalization; so does his supporting reason, namely that he was in favour 'of a limited monarchy equally far removed from an Asiatic despotism and a dictatorship of the people'.[2]

There were many loyalists even in Massachusetts. Some were horrified by the idea of enmity towards the mother country; others saw their interests and livelihood threatened by war; all were dismayed by the belligerent actions of the extremists. The Sons of Liberty, who had taken their descriptive name from a speech delivered by Colonel Barré in the House of Commons, grew very active and, as so often happens when civil disturbance is rife, justified oppression in the name of liberty. In the words of a letter written from America, 'every consideration of affection and friendship is absolved in the name of liberty; and the Devil with all his infernal regalia can't be more obnoxious than a Tory'.[3]

From the British point of view there 'was great reason to apprehend every extravagance of behaviour from these misled violent people'.[4] Disguised mobs surrounded the houses of the newly made Councillors of Massachusetts Bay to try to compel them to resign the King's appointment. Not only the King's representatives but everyone found it dangerous 'to express the least attachment to His Majesty or Great Britain'.[5] As another letter put it: 'A man can do and say whatever he will, if he will execrate Lord North, call the Parliament a pack of corrupted rascals and speak contemptuously of all friends of Government.'[6]

Earlier in the year 1774 Thompson had written to his mother: 'all is peace and quietness in this part of the world'. Whether this was a statement of fact or an attempt at reassurance is scarcely relevant for his peace was soon broken. On 12 December 1774 he was summoned before a Committee of the People in Concord to answer a charge of being unfriendly to the cause of liberty. He demanded proof and as none was forthcoming was released. The verdict, however, was 'not proven' rather than 'not guilty', and his accusers went away unconvinced and unappeased. The immediate cause of the proceedings was Thompson's action towards certain deserters from the British regiments at Boston. By this time the training of the militia was being taken seriously and deserters from the army were valuable as instructors. Thompson, perhaps because of personal loyalty to the Governor, was rounding them up and sending them back to headquarters. At his examination he may have admitted the return of one or two deserters but he certainly did not say how fully he was implicated.

The part he played has only recently been revealed from documents unknown to Thompson's early biographers. Among them are letters he wrote to Wentworth and Gage the day after his trial. In the first he gave his account of the affair. It appears that he kept with him a soldier named Bowdidge whom he sent after deserters. Having heard that there were some at Boscawen he sent Bowdidge to persuade them to rejoin their unit with a promise of the General's pardon if they complied. By chance Bowdidge met two deserters, Riggs and Kennedy, who were already known to Thompson. They had promised to report to him at Concord but failed to do so. They now renewed their promise to Bowdidge who passed on the information to his superior. Having been deceived once Thompson again sent his orderly to fetch them in. But by this time Riggs and Kennedy had 'thrown off the mask and both now positively declared that they never intended nor would ever go back to the Army, on any conditions whatever'. The mood of the people was such that Bowdidge was lucky to escape serious bodily harm, and Thompson had to intervene to enable him to escape to Boston by a roundabout route.

The scheme was a pretty one. Thompson had obviously been empowered to offer Gage's pardon to deserters and to furnish them with money to return to Boston—a clemency which indicated their value. Bowdidge worked in plain clothes. Unfortunately for Thompson a Mr Stevens of Concord visited Boston where he met Bowdidge who had put on his uniform on returning to his regiment. This and the fact that Kennedy (now feeling quite safe) spoke openly of Thompson's activities, aroused the anger of the local Committee and, as we have already seen, they summoned him to appear before them. From Thompson's account it appears that the committee of seven members had no direct evidence, which might mean that none of the people with whom Thompson had dealt was there to give testimony. The committee had used the method not uncommon at that time of attempting to exact a confession by threats. Thompson, however, was not to be intimidated; at least not at the trial. Moreover he had influential relatives and friends who were prepared to back him. So he had been allowed to go free.

It was clear to Thompson from information he received from a friend in their confidence that his enemies would persist in their attempt to inculpate him, in order to obtain enough evidence to have him declared 'a Rebel to the State and unworthy of the benefits of Civil Society'. His anxiety was therefore intense and was the cause of his letter to Wentworth. The other letter, which he asked Wentworth to transmit to Gage, requested Gage to use his influence to keep his loyalist activities secret.[7]

Thompson was by now thoroughly alarmed and his fears were fully justified. He decided to leave Concord; and only just in time, for his house was visited by an angry mob which, ignorant of his flight, demanded that he come out and answer once more to the accusations. Had he been there he would undoubtedly have been the victim of tarring and feathering, or worse; however, learning that he had fled, the demonstrators dispersed without harming Thompson's wife and infant child or damaging their property.

From Concord he went to stay with a friend at Charlestown where he was but a mile or so from the outskirts of Boston, and near the British garrison. On 24 December 1774 he wrote a long letter to his father-in-law explaining his flight and humbly begging him to take 'kind care of his distressed family'. He asked his father-in-law to pray that in all his difficulties and troubles he might 'behave in such a manner as to approve myself a true servant of God and a sincere friend of my country'.

Thompson's motives at this point in his career have been a source of much speculation and discussion. There is little doubt that he was set upon a military career but he could, like his friend Baldwin, have fulfilled this ambition on the American side. He was ambitious, and yet there was scope for advancement in the cause of his American friends. On the other hand, his rapid rise and preferment, since his military experience was negligible, had roused envy among the commissioned officers of the provincial regiments. He was attached to Wentworth because the Governor was the source of patronage. He might all the same have overcome the suspicions of his fellow officers had he been ready to make the effort, but he was drawn to the loyalist cause by self-interest. One of the striking features of his early career, indeed, is his attachment to men who were able to promote his rise in the world. In succession there were Baldwin, Walker, Wentworth and, later, Germain, Charles Theodore (Elector of Bavaria), and

Prince Maximilian of Zweibrücken. It is only part of the truth to say that he was 'essentially a courtier'; and it is probably not the whole truth to say that, having aroused their interest in him, he was able to serve them well and justify their help and confidence. It may well be that Thompson lacking a father was unconsciously seeking one. He had few emotional attachments and undeniably gave more affection to Germain than to anyone else, including his wife and daughter.

At twenty-one, however, Thompson was more concerned to justify his actions than to analyse his motives. To his father-in-law, who wanted him to return to Concord, he wrote: 'but this you may rely and depend upon, that I never did, nor (let my treatment be what it will) ever will do, any action that may have the most distant tendency to injure the true interest of this my native country'.

Early in the next year, 1775, Thompson left Charlestown to return to his birthplace, Woburn. He lived here for a time with his mother and stepfather, and almost immediately his wife joined him bringing their child, Sarah, who was then three months old. This was an unhappy period for him and his wife. He was under pressure from his wife's father to return to Concord; she was ill and he was in a no-man's-land of doubt and anxiety. He was in and out of Boston and he was still under suspicion, for the Woburn Committee of Correspondence knew of his contacts with the British forces though not the full extent of his anti-American activities. The local minute men[8] had him on their black list and decided to pay him a visit. Ellis, his main nineteenth-century biographer, tells the traditional story of this visit. It has a touch of the comic opera about it, but mainly illustrates the loyalty and resource of Loammi Baldwin. Baldwin, who lived near where Thompson was staying, heard the rumpus outside when the minute men arrived and went out to see what was going on. As he was a major in the militia they listened to him with respect. He took the opportunity to defend his friend and invited the company into his barn for further discussion. To quote Ellis:

'They accepted the invitation, and were so generously treated with food and liquor that their errand was overlooked, and they returned without molesting Thompson, though they had previously twice sent in their summons that he should present himself, whether sick or well.'

Although Baldwin saved Thompson on this occasion he could not prevent the local committee from arresting him later. General Artemas Ward gave the Woburn Committee of Correspondence authority to constitute itself as a Court of Inquiry to examine Thompson, and the Court duly went into session on 18 May 1775. Baldwin, who was a member, recorded in his diary that he attended the sitting but that for lack of evidence the court adjourned for three days. While under remand Thompson, with remarkable assurance, petitioned the Provincial Congress for a hearing by the Provincial Committee of Safety. He wanted to bring the affair to a head and save himself, if he could, from further humiliation. In his petition, which he sent by bearer to Baldwin for transmission to Watertown where the Provincial Congress was then sitting, he asked that notice of the proposed trial should be given not only in Massachusetts Bay and the Woburn district but also in Concord where he had undergone his first examination.

The Provincial Congress received the petition on 25 May but took no action. It was busy with weightier matters and, in any event, the case was *sub judice* at Woburn where Thompson was chafing in confinement. The Woburn Committee did not sit on 22 May as planned; it could hardly do so in view of the petition waiting before Congress. A week later, however, proceedings were reopened before a large audience in the meeting-house. There was intense local interest. Thompson was twenty-two years of age, and imposing and handsome. He had been born and had spent his childhood in the place, and was known for his ability and initiative. He had made his way, had married a wealthy widow, had dined at the Governor's table and held a commission in one of the provincial regiments. Moreover in the excited atmosphere of the times Thompson's examination was a drama in which opposing loyalties and deep emotions were involved. But the result held some disappointment all round. For the accusers because there was insufficient evidence against Thompson, and for him because, although he was allowed to go free, he was not given a written acquittal. It was virtually a repetition of the verdict given at Concord. What Thompson wanted, no doubt, was a document which would procure his rehabilitation in the town and neighbouring district.

Thompson was a fortunate young man. His known offences must unquestionably have been treated as the indiscretions of youthful ambition. His elders viewed him with sympathy and indulgence, always remembering the undignified treatment accorded to those who, at the time, helped the British cause by giving service or provisions to the occupying troops. His wife returned to Concord at about this time. She had been ill, possibly sick with apprehension and dismay at the turn of events. Her coming to Woburn in the depth of winter, leaving behind the greater comfort and security of her house in Concord, was a gesture of wifely faithfulness and love which must have cost her a great deal. Thompson never saw her again.

Sarah's father, the Reverend Timothy Walker, was both saddened and hurt by his son-in-law's change of circumstances. Like others who saw in Thompson the promise of great achievement he was inclined to a lenient view of the pro-British sympathies. He was also determined to prevent his own plans for his daughter from being unfulfilled because of what he regarded as the temporary unpopularity of her husband. He therefore wrote frequently to urge a return. Thompson had fled without consulting him, although his son had known, and had, in fact, lent Thompson some ready cash and a horse.

A few months later, in August of the same year, 1775, Thompson wrote his own defence in a long, able, but equivocal and possibly hypocritical letter written from Woburn to his father-in-law at Concord. In it he defends his flight but does not excuse his departure without warning. In pleading *not guilty* at the trials, he writes that he was following the advice of his friends. He ascribes the anger of his enemies to prejudice and malice, and strongly attacks their conception of freedom which he likens to the tyranny of an '*Eastern Despot*'—a phrase similar to one he used later when describing these events.

He admits his part in returning the deserters and acknowledges a series of letters to Wentworth and the one to Gage which has already been mentioned. Taking his stand upon personal rectitude he refuses to admit guilt that he does not feel.

'Whatever prudence may dictate, yet Conscience and Honor, God and Religion forbid that my Mouth should speak what my Heart disclaims. I cannot profess my sorrow for an action which I am conscious was done from the best of motives.'

I shall refer to this letter again after describing the six months which followed his acquittal at Woburn. In passing, however, I should say that in expression, scope and composition it reaches a very high standard.

Although in April and May 1775 General Gage may have looked forward with dismay to a war between the colonies and Great Britain, he had a clear and obvious duty to seek information about stores of arms and ammunition and then to destroy them. This was no more than police action. He needed informers, of course, and the evidence shows that they were not lacking. Early in April he had received intelligence that ammunition, provisions, guns, tents and small arms had been collected at Concord, Massachusetts, 'for the Avowed Purpose of raising and supporting a Rebellion against His Majesty'.

Lieutenant-Colonel Smith of the Tenth Regiment of Foot was ordered to destroy the dumps and to command, for the expedition, corps of grenadiers and light infantry, some 700 men in all.[9] Colonel Smith was enjoined not to 'plunder the Inhabitants or hurt private property'. The night of the 18th of April was chosen for the sortie and by 1 a.m. the detachment had crossed the bay and was on its way to Lexington. The preparations were obvious to many Bostonians and the aim of the movement was guessed. Beacons were lit, alarm guns fired and William Dawes and Paul Revere were sent to Lexington to give the alarm. When the British troops arrived at Lexington just before dawn they found some sixty or seventy minute men of the provincial militia lined up on the green. There has been much debate about what happened next. The most likely explanation seems to be that a sniper, separate from those on the green, lost his head and fired a shot which provoked a British volley in return. As a result, eight of the minute men were killed and more were wounded.

Smith, however, kept his head and carried out his orders. He re-formed his detachment and continued the march to Concord, which he entered at about eight o'clock. Here the force divided. The town was held by Smith with the major force, including the grenadiers. One company of light infantry was ordered to hold the north bridge; two or three others advanced beyond it and a third group was despatched to destroy an arms store at an outlying farm. Meanwhile a provincial force hundreds strong collected on the hills and seeing that the bridge was weakly held they attacked in strength, causing the British to retreat. It is quite likely that the Americans saw smoke from the burning dumps and inferred that the town was being burnt by the grenadiers. In the skirmish at the bridge three British soldiers were killed.

So far Colonel Smith's task had been carried out with small losses, but the march back was disastrous. Using all the cover provided by trees, walls and rocks, the Americans fired relentlessly at the uniformed British troops. Longfellow pictures the action:

'You know the rest. In the books you have read
How the British Regulars fired and fled,
How the farmers gave them ball for ball,
From behind each fence and farmyard wall,
Chasing the red-coats down the lane,
Then crossing the fields to emerge again
Under the trees at the turn of the road,
And only pausing to fire and load.'

We might take exception to 'fled', for the troops were returning to base having substantially achieved their purpose, and also to 'chasing', but the tactics are accurately described. The British detachment had no answer to this mode of attack and a rescuing force sent out by Gage brought home a badly mauled force which had suffered heavy casualties. From this time the British forces in Boston were under siege from the land side.

This famous action took place while Thompson was nearby at Woburn, a month before his arrest and second trial. It is unlikely that he played an active part in it but possible that he was invited to do so by his American friends and refused. What is now beyond doubt is that he was acting as an informer for General Gage, though until the beginning of May he was unable to send information. Among the Gage Papers in the William L. Clements Library is a letter which has completely changed the outlook on his activities. This letter (see Plate 1, facing page 80) was brought to light by the late Mr Allen French in 1930. It is an astonishing document dramatically written in invisible ink. To be more precise there are two letters: one is a short covering note, the other a missive of some 700 words. Only the second part was written in invisible ink. As the document now appears both parts are legible, the covering note being clearer than the other. The signatures to both letters are missing; the signature to the shorter one has been erased, the other cut away. The paper bears clear signs of having been immersed in a liquid. The letter is reproduced here by the courtesy of the William L. Clements Library from a photostatic copy in my possession. Before considering the significance of its contents I shall examine the evidence for its authorship.

A careful examination of the letter was made by Professor Sanborn C. Brown and Mr Elbridge W. Stein.[10] After inspection by infra-red rays and X-rays they concluded that the longer letter was written with an ink made by soaking powdered nut galls in water and was subsequently developed by using ferrous sulphate solution. The covering letter and the address were written in carbon ink. Brown also made a photomicrograph of a particle of sealing wax taken from the letter and compared it with a photomicrograph of wax taken from a letter known to have been written by Thompson to Loammi Baldwin on 19 May 1775. The two specimens appear to have the same, and rather unusual, composition. Stein examined the handwriting comparing it with known examples of Thompson's hand. The similarity was striking. Furthermore, Thompson's spelling of opportunity was unusual in that he wrote 'oppertunity'. Stein showed that the same variant was present in other letters and I have come across it in many of Thompson's letters including one he wrote in 1811, thirty-six years later.

The use of invisible ink would appeal to Thompson and be within his knowledge, because of his scientific and medical background, indeed the substances used were well known in his day.

Gage had other informers but it is most unlikely that this was one of their letters. If one believed it were, one would, as French pointed out, have to explain the coincidence of a spy living in or near Woburn in circumstances similar to those of Thompson, with handwriting like his,[11] and at the same time someone with scientific knowledge who had made arrangements for the letter to be developed in Boston using ferrous sulphate.

Putting all the evidence together from handwriting, phraseology, the circumstances and location of the writer, the only reasonable conclusion is that Thompson wrote this notorious letter.

The fact that Thompson had written it three weeks before his trial at Woburn shows his astonishing self-assurance. He said to his accusers, 'I have done nothing contrary to the best interests of my country' knowing full well that his conception of the best interests was diametrically opposite to theirs and relying on them to put their construction on his words. It as as though he were contemptuous of his influential opponents and sorry for those who supported them, since twice in letters to Wentworth and Gage he refers to the deluded people or populace. He was similarly equivocal in his letter to his father-in-law.

How utterly he deceived his friends is clearly shown by the confidence they placed in him. They gave him information about the strength of the rebel army and the policy of Congress which he passed on to Gage. Why Baldwin continued to trust him and remained a faithful friend for life is not easily explained. The friendship at any rate was a credit to Baldwin and showed his nobility of character. It looks as though Thompson distinguished in his own mind between the interests of the vast majority of the provincial people and the anti-British leaders. His rationalization and self-justification may have arisen from this view. In the letter to Gage he professes himself an out-and-out royalist with a conviction that had been strengthened by what he regarded as the injustice of the treatment he had received.

After the Woburn trial Thompson still maintained contacts with both sides, particularly with Colonel Baldwin, who had recently been promoted and was on Washington's staff. Incredible though it sounds, he attempted to supply epaulets to the American forces. His plan was to get local women to make them for him and to sell them 'at about 15/-, or perhaps as low as 13/6, if a number were engaged'. What an unpleasant episode this is. There was always a touch of the huckster in Thompson. Of course he was young, and not five years since he had been obliged to support himself by selling firewood. Then his motive was laudable, but now, though he may have needed ready money, his lack of principle was execrable. Epaulets did not constitute finery in the American army. Both men and officers were often without uniform and rank was indicated by coloured armbands. Thompson knew this very well and tried to take advantage of the shortage.

It has been said that he helped to remove the library from Harvard College to Concord on 15 June.[12] This is based on a note by Baldwin and it might mean that Thompson and Baldwin were among those who prepared the college buildings for occupation by the American forces. How big an assignment the removal of the books was can only be conjectured. Anyway Thompson was not yet ready to go over to the British. As long as he was in touch with American preparations he would gather information to pass to Gage. His duplicity, perhaps, was not maintained without anxiety and mental conflict. In August he was confined to his room with 'putrid bilious disorders' possibly as a result of this conflict. He could no longer move in and out of Boston freely and this was an annoying restriction. He had not been there since mid-April and he had left his 'Hussar cloak faced with scarlet shalloon and yellow mock-spangle metal buttons' in his lodgings. Of greater value to him were his papers. In a letter to the Reverend Samuel Parker, dated 1 October, he says very significantly 'the preservation of my papers is an affair of the *utmost importance* to me', and he gives very detailed instructions about how they could be found and what should be done with them. This was necessary because his landladies had evacuated the house and left it to a caretaker.

In August, Thompson had already decided to leave America. He said so plainly in the letter that he wrote to his father-in-law from Woburn on 14 August. Ellis regarded this letter as a touching expression of noble sentiment by a misguided and unjustly treated young man. But in the light of the events just described it appears no better than a sham statement designed to palliate ignoble action and to mislead, or at best to comfort, an anxious relative. Thompson's allusions are partly scriptural, a clever touch. 'I cannot bear', he writes, 'to be looked upon and treated as the *Achan* of Society.'[13] He expresses a hope that the time may soon come when he may return to his family in peace and safety, and '*when every individual in America may sit down under his own vine, and under his own Fig-tree, and have none to make him afraid*'.[14]

Having, as it were, wound up his personal relations he proceeded to settle his financial affairs. He did this with characteristic thoroughness, even selling his share in the family pew of the new meeting-house at Woburn, a share he had inherited under a settlement made after the death of his father. Allowing for his debts and the proceeds from the sale of land at Wilmington and Woburn his balance sheet showed a credit of about £500. It was natural that he should wish to turn all his assets to ready cash which he could take away, for his move to the enemy would involve forfeiting any estate he left behind him. He had land in Maine which was unsaleable, but he did not forget it and referred to it in a letter to Baldwin twenty-three years later. He made no claim on his wife's estate, it would have been ludicrous to have done so; and he attempted no provision for his child. Having made all these preparations he took the decisive step of leaving Woburn for ever.

Describing Thompson's going Ellis says that he was driven by his stepbrother, Josiah Pierce, on 13 October, in a country cart to the boundary of the province and that he was taken on board the British frigate *Scarborough* lying in Newport harbour. This statement has frequently been repeated but in a document which Thompson himself wrote there is evidence against the date. On Sunday, 15 October, he was snooping round—I can think of no better description—a boat-building yard 'just below Cambridge Bridge' questioning the workmen about their output and the purposes for which the flat-bottomed boats were intended. Earlier on 13 October he was still in contact with some-one on the American side who had just seen a return of the carrying capacity of all the boats then available. But certainly by the beginning of November he was in Boston with the British, passing on valuable information about 'the state of the rebel army' to General Howe, who had superseded Gage on 10 October.[15]

He gave this information in a comprehensive and vivid report eleven pages long, signed B.T. and dated 4 November 1775 (see Plate 2, facing page 81 and also Appendix). The original document was among the Germain Papers. It is striking evidence of Thompson's detailed knowledge of the American army and helps to explain why his welcome was warm and his rise in favour rapid. Apart from report-ing on the number of boats and their purpose the report covers powder, firearms and shot; it deals with defence works and the location of magazines, with clothing and rations and with disease and rate of mortality among the soldiers. Altogether it presents a good picture of Washington's difficulties in creating, feeding, clothing and maintaining an army—an army which Washington himself described as 'a mixed multitude'.

Thompson's final decision to join the British was taken months before he moved over. In going exactly when he did he may have been influenced by the arrest of Dr Benjamin Church who was also an informer. The evidence seems to suggest that his conduct was even more reprehensible than Thompson's.[16] Church had risen to a position of great trust and high responsibility on the American side. He was a member of the Boston Committee of Correspondence, of the Massa-chusetts Congress and of the Continental Congress; he was Washing-ton's Surgeon-General. He was gifted and trusted, and he betrayed his trust for money. It would carry us too far from our theme to follow his career to its bitter end in disgrace and transportation, but he serves to remind us that Thompson was not alone in his unprincipled double dealing. Church was made to suffer for his treachery; Thompson, helped by luck and judgement, made his escape.

3

Junior Minister

A gentleman well versed in natural knowledge
and many branches of polite learning.
RECORDS OF THE ROYAL SOCIETY

AFTER Lexington, and before Thompson made his escape, there
was a gradual increase of tension and some military activity in
and around Boston. Thompson described the American army
as 'most wretchedly cloathed and as dirty a set of mortals as ever disgraced the name of a Soldier'. As a description of its early days this
contained some truth. As well as their other problems, the American
commanders had the difficulty of holding together an idle force. So,
when action was called for they decided to close in on Boston. Late on
the night of 16 June an American force of some 1200 men moved out
of Cambridge and occupied Breed's Hill behind Charlestown. There,
on the next day, they began to dig themselves in. This was too much
for Gage, who was willing to wait patiently for orders from London
on broader matters but was not prepared to see himself closely
besieged. General Howe was given the task of dislodging the Americans
and on the same day he landed with a numerically superior force at
Charlestown.

The day was hot and the British soldiers were encumbered with
rations and equipment. Their objective was Bunker Hill which rose
near and above Breed's Hill, and to attain it they attempted to storm
the American redoubt. The Americans held their fire until the attackers
were close enough to be picked off individually, then directed it
particularly at the officers. The British were driven back with heavy
losses, but returned to make a second direct assault which was also

unsuccessful. A third attempt, made with the help of gunfire from the British ships, scattered the Americans, and the attacking force, reduced almost to half strength, gained possession of the hill. It was a costly victory,[1] which depressed the British and put heart into their opponents, particularly Washington, who a few days later assumed full command. It was soon obvious to Howe, who succeeded Gage as commander-in-chief in October, that Boston could not be held for long. Whether a more enterprising leader who was convinced of his mission would have attacked Washington's army while it was being re-formed is a matter for debate. Howe, though competent enough, was not sure that he was fighting a war, and his own uncertainty was a distant echo of feeling in England.

In March and April 1776 the British were forced to evacuate the town. They took many loyalist refugees with them including Benjamin Thompson who, in his own words, was sent to England 'with Public Dispatches and a Letter of Recommendation from Governor Wentworth to the Secretary of State', Lord George Germain.[2] He also carried a certificate from General Howe saying that 'he had been cruelly drove from a competent estate by persecution and severe Maltreatment' and that in Boston he had 'endeavoured to be useful to His Majesty's Service'.

In April 1776 Benjamin Thompson was twenty-three years of age. He was good looking, self-confident and energetic and, what is more important, his energy was controlled and guided by an acute intelligence. Adversity did not dispirit him; it was, indeed, useful to him. He was immediately drawn to Lord George Germain partly by the attraction of aristocratic rank and partly because Germain was an obvious source of advancement.

At this time Germain was sixty years of age and still physically impressive. After the disgrace of Minden (where he was popularly believed to have shown cowardice in battle) he had stood firm against his numerous, bitter and influential enemies. He was convinced that he had been grievously wronged and strove long and hard for an honourable rehabilitation. Seldom has a public figure been the target of such vindictive obloquy and contempt. He was never broken by the treatment he received. He was fortified by detachment and a sense of family superiority; in fact he had greater confidence in his high birth than in his own abilities. It is at least arguable that he has been judged too harshly by many historians. It is also debatable that he was wronged by many of his contemporaries who publicly accused him not only of cowardice but also of culpable procrastination and private vice. Although he succeeded the Earl of Dartmouth as Secretary for the Colonies in November 1775, his rehabilitation was never complete and he began an almost impossible task under the handicaps of personal animosity and political division.

The attraction was not entirely one-sided. To Germain, who set about his task with an energy which at least compared favourably with the slackness of other ministers, Thompson came with first-hand information of American topography and affairs. What is more important, they probably shared the view that England was fighting a group of men incited by agitators like Samuel Adams. The war was not against the American people, the 'poor deluded populace', but against their leaders. Such a view frequently crops up over the centuries in an England at war, but in 1776 it was apparently real for many people here apart from Germain and Thompson. The aim was to defeat the army, give a salutary lesson and restore England's rights. There is also evidence to show that both men misjudged the strength of the loyalists and underestimated the fighting capacity of the colonial army.

Germain, impressed by this young man's knowledge and assurance, found him a post immediately. It was a sinecure which carried a small salary. Within a few days of his arrival in London Thompson[3] says he 'was appointed Secretary of the Province of Georgia with a salary of £100 per annum'. Soon malicious gossip arose about Thompson's relations with Germain and his family. 'When he was introduced', said Lord Glenbervie, writing some years later, 'he was it seems very handsome, *Formosus et centum puer artium*. Lady Glenbervie remembers him going about with Lady George and her daughters to balls as a humble dependant and dancing with the young ladies when they could get no other partners.' He goes on: 'At that time he was considered as the favourite, at once, of the father, mother and daughters, and the ill-fame of the father then, and the conduct of the daughters since have served to keep the scandal alive with regard to them' an imputation which received greater support from Germain's reputation than from reliable knowledge. This anecdote reminded Glenbervie 'of what was said of Caesar: *Omnium mulierum maritus, maritorum omnium uxor*'.[4]

43

Thompson found England a land of interest and opportunity. His friendship with Germain brought him into contact with rich and influential people. He observed minutely and stored his memories. He drank the waters of Bath and was a guest at Stoneland Lodge, Germain's rented country house. Here he took up his scientific pursuits again and with the help of the Rector of Withyham carried out an important series of experiments upon the velocities of projectiles and 'the most advantageous situation for the vent in fire-arms'.[5] This was the beginning of scientific work of high quality. He read a descriptive paper before the Royal Society in 1781, but before then he had communicated to Mr Banks (later Sir Joseph) the results of other experiments on the cohesion of bodies. Banks was then the newly elected president of the Royal Society. An enduring friendship grew up between these two men. Years later they were closely associated in founding the Royal Institution, but in the late 1770s each was busy with his individual work. Thompson was elected a Fellow of the Royal Society in 1779 'as a gentleman well versed in natural knowledge and many branches of polite learning'. This was a recognition and honour he valued highly and in return he contributed to the influence and distinction of the body that elected him. He made many friends among its Fellows and later became one of its vice-presidents.

With true versatility he turned to naval architecture, and in 1781 he contributed to *Stalkartt's Treatise* on this subject a chapter giving plans for the construction of a frigate. His design, which was for a vessel of 1000 tons displacement and 150 feet long, was submitted to and commended by Kempenfelt and other authorities. His interest in ships was quickened by a cruise he made, serving as a gentleman volunteer, on the *Victory* in the summer of 1779. His chief purpose in undertaking this cruise was to carry out experiments on the firing of guns; he had, as he says, 'opportunities of making several very interesting observations which gave him much new light relative to the action of fired gunpowder'.[6]

He was always anxious to write about his experiences and he sent some illuminating letters to Germain. These letters were highly critical of the discipline of the fleet and the skill of its commanders. 'My dear Lord,' he wrote, 'I can stand it no longer. Those who are interested in the disgrace of our Commander, may laugh at our blunders but I . . . am hurt beyond measure to find how little dependance is to be put in our skill in manœuvring this great and respectable fleet.' He had been 'put out of all manner of patience' by the wrong and contradictory signals, and he observed a lack of discipline. The picture, however, was not all black; he went on to say: 'Don't be discouraged. It has been by our bravery and not our discipline we have ever conquered and be assured there was never a braver set of men existing than our present Sea Commanders.'

He was vainly pleased at being well liked. All through life he exulted in the respect shown to him by his superiors. Years later he described to Lord Chichester, with boring repetition, how he had been treated 'with marked attention and civility' by Napoleon and his ministers. In 1779 he was honoured by the attentions of the commander of the fleet. 'Sir Charles [Hardy] continues to load me with civilities and I am a favourite with the whole fleet.'[7]

In a letter to Thomas de Grey, Germain's Under-Secretary, he wrote in similar terms about the lack of skill and seamanship of the officers and the compensating bravery of the other ranks. Speaking of the supersession of Sir Charles Hardy, he said: 'You can best tell what foundation there is for these reports and all I have to say is (and I am sure it cannot be treason to say it) that if he is recalled I hope a better will be sent out.'

The same thoughts were in another letter where after showing anxiety about his outspokenness he said that Sir Charles was not a fit person to command the fleet. His personal relations with the commander, however, seem to have remained on a pleasant and intimate footing for he wrote: 'He is good natured to a fault and it would make you die with laughing to see him kick my hat about the deck.'

Thompson's stay with the fleet was serious enough and his reputation sufficiently high for the captains of a number of ships, which he names as the *Duke* of ninety-eight guns, the *Berwick* of seventy-four guns and the *Bienfaisant* of sixty-four guns, to give co-operation in his experiments. He was concerned with the range of the shots fired and made comparisons by the simultaneous firing of many heavy guns. In a letter from the *Victory* he described the new signalling system he had devised for use at sea.

This naval episode does credit to Germain. It must have been arranged and approved by him, and his motive was probably to encourage this young scientist of twenty-six and to provide an opportunity for him to continue and extend the experiments on gunfire begun at Stoneland Lodge.

When he returned to London Thompson was promoted. In September 1780 he succeeded de Grey as Under-Secretary of State in the American Department. This was indeed a rise in the world and his post gave him close contact with the practical affairs of war. He put his knowledge of military affairs to good account in his designs 'for horse furniture and accoutrements' and light dragoon clothing.[8] For the first time in his life he was able to make a good deal of money, though almost certainly not the £7000 a year one of his detractors estimated.

This particular detractor was the loyalist Samuel Curwen. It was part of Thompson's duty to submit to the Treasury, through Germain, claims made for pensions and allowances by many unfortunate Americans who had been forced to leave home and possessions and were in dire need. The shaking up which war brings can seldom have led to a more dramatic meeting than that of Thompson and Curwen in London. Their reversal of status was striking. Here was Curwen as a suppliant to a man who had been an assistant in the shop next door. When Thompson was Appleton's apprentice in Salem, Curwen had been a Deputy Judge of Admiralty and Crown Provincial Impost Officer in the same town, and a man of influence in the Province.

Richard Cumberland, the dramatist, who was at one time Germain's secretary, had found dealings with the loyalists 'an arduous and delicate business to conduct' and one of 'some personal risque and danger'.[9] Thompson, as Under-Secretary, worked hard for his unfortunate fellow countrymen. The Treasury Records (Expired Commissions—American Claims) contain many examples of his advocacy and help for refugees. Curwen was thus one of many, and is of interest to us because he kept a diary while in London and described his meetings with Thompson. He called upon the former 'shop-lad' at his lodgings in Pall Mall on 24 May 1781, and was well received. He gives a short sketch of Thompson's career and says that 'he always breakfasts, dines and sups' with Lord George, 'so great a favourite is he'.

Curwen probably did not expect much help from Thompson and in the event he got none, which may account for the rather sour entry later that the Under-Secretary was a 'courtier of whom I never entertained favourable impressions'. To do Thompson justice he may have felt that relative to other loyalists Curwen's existing gratuity of £100 and his pension of the same amount were fair,[10] however picayune the amounts might seem to others in comparison with his own reputed £7000 a year.

Either at this time or shortly before, Thompson, with the flair he had for attracting attention in the right quarter, brought himself to the notice of the King. He gained possession of a collection of letters from Franklin to Dr Cooper, an eminent Boston minister and pamphleteer, with Dr Cooper's replies; and also of another set from Thomas Pownall, one-time Governor of Massachusetts, to Cooper. All these he had bound in gold-tooled red morocco, and presented them to King George. The letters dealt at first hand with the American political situation in the years 1769 to 1774. Thomas Hutchinson, who also was a former Governor of Massachusetts, records in his diary[11] that on 8 February 1780 Mr Thompson called on him and had 'a great curiosity to show him'. The curiosity was his copy of the letters, and in fact Hutchinson was familiar with some of them. It appears that Cooper, having fled from Boston after the battle of Bunker Hill, entrusted these letters to a friend named Jeffries. By accident Jeffries's son, who unlike his father was a loyalist, came into possession of them and later gave them to Thompson. Hutchinson, perhaps because he did not care for Thompson, insinuates that it was the wife of Jeffries's son who handed over the letters, as it was with her that Thompson was chiefly acquainted. What Pownall thought of Thompson's self-advertising action does not emerge. Certainly at the time he was a Member of Parliament. One thing is clear—Thompson had no legitimate complaint when he found that he made enemies.

Hutchinson also records that Thompson told him that the King had confided to Germain that 'the people who were determined to ruin the Constitution . . . should never make him their prisoner'. The implication of this was that the King would never resolve to leave the Kingdom but would rather 'die a King'. Hutchinson goes on to say that 'it shews that the King sees in a more serious light the present violence of the opposition than people generally imagine he does. It also shews that Lord G is extremely incautious in trusting such an account of conversation with the King to a young man, especially as it is not possible they should have lived so long together without Lord G's having discovered that T has not the faculty of retention.'

This supposed indiscretion, though serious enough, was insignificant in comparison with another accusation against Thompson. Lord Glenbervie says in his diary that Germain 'found it necessary or advisable to remove Thompson from his post as Under-Secretary' because it was 'supposed that he made some improper communication'. More specifically Rufus King, the American Minister at the Court of St James's, wrote in his Memorandum Book that Thompson was a traitor. His authority, if he can be called such, was Hammond, the American Secretary of State, who said that Lord Grenville had been told by Lord Mulgrave that 'if Lord Sandwich had lived that R [Thompson] could not have lived in England; that R was connected with La Motte the French spy who was executed in 1781'.

It is true that Thompson held his post as Under-Secretary for only just over twelve months and then went in some haste to America—an unexpected move. I will examine his motives later; his supposed complicity in the spying activities of La Motte needs attention first. On 14 July 1781 La Motte was accused at the Old Bailey of 'compassing the death of the King' and carrying out 'divers overt acts of a treasonable connection with the French Court to destroy the naval power of the country'.[12] In evidence it came out that various despatches sent to France had been intercepted and copied; but the chief evidence against La Motte was given by his former accomplice, Lutterloh, a person who, after years of straitened means, had turned to informing for money. After a variety of jobs Lutterloh drifted to Portsmouth where he became a book-keeper at the famous George Inn. In 1778 'he had embarked in a plot with the prisoner to furnish the French Court with secret intelligence of the navy'. At first La Motte paid Lutterloh for the information at the rate of eight guineas a month, but later he became so impressed with its importance and value that he raised the amount to fifty guineas a month, 'besides many valuable gifts'. Lutterloh's imagination soared to higher schemes and he put forward a plan for capturing a naval squadron.[13] This was more than La Motte could deal with as intermediary, so Lutterloh was sent to France to discuss the project with a French minister. His demands, however, were too high, for he assessed the value of his felonious services as 8000 guineas and a ninth share of the ships. He asked for a ninth share for La Motte also, and the same for an unnamed third person, *a friend in a certain office*. The French authorities, according to the evidence, were prepared to offer only an eighth share to be divided between the three confederates. Lutterloh, not satisfied but determined to profit from his villainy, went to Sir Hugh Palliser 'and offered a plan to take the French and to defeat his original project with which he had furnished the French court'. In view of such audacity one can believe the report that one of the leading counsel was so overcome that he had to leave the court and temporarily hand over the examination to his junior; and also that the evidence 'was of so serious a nature that the court seemed in a state of astonishment during the whole of his [Lutterloh's] long examination'.

The case was deemed to be proved and La Motte was condemned to death. He received his sentence with a brave and dignified bearing, merely requesting on his removal to the Tower that His Majesty might be asked to allow him to be beheaded rather than suffer the torture of being disembowelled. His prayer was unanswered. Curwen records laconically in his journal (for 27 July 1781): 'Passed two hours in Mr Waller's front dining-room to have a sight of the French spy, De La Motte, who was dragged on a hurdle to place of execution, Tyburn, to be hanged; tall and well grown—dress, black, flapped hat.'[14]

Our chief concern, however, is with the rumoured complicity of Thompson. He has been identified as the *friend in a certain office*, the third man of the trio who were to share the spoils of spying.[15] There is little substance in the suggestion. What evidence of identity there is points not to Thompson but, as the report in fact says, to a 'clerk in one of the public offices in the Naval Department'. It seems probable that Lutterloh, realizing that he had a good market for the information he could pick up at 'The George', sought an accomplice who was nearer the sources of accurate intelligence and found a helper in the naval department. Although Thompson knew a good deal about national policy in general and also about naval movements, it is scarcely credible, if he had wished to sell the information to the French government, that he would have chosen to do so through Lutterloh or anyone of his stamp. There is no evidence that Lutterloh was bribed to keep silence; nor are there any oblique or direct references to the trial in the letters which Thompson is known to have written to his patron. Why, if he were guilty, should he have left England months after the trial when in any case the dust was likely to settle? In the summer of 1781 he was working hard and competently in his office.[16] Moreover, at this time he was well known as a man of science and a member of the government and it is most improbable that Germain could have protected him from prosecution. And he was rewarded later for his services to this country by a knighthood. No, although Thompson's character and previous activities suggest we bring him forward for examination, in this instance there is no case to answer.

The environment he moved in during these years in England must have been pleasing to him and his adaptability was great. He was always eager to learn. Apart from his scientific activity he was interested in gardens and farming and he stored impressions and ideas which he later applied in Munich. Lord George, though no scholar in the literary. sense, had wide interests and was well informed. Thompson was one of his favourites and was doubtless treated with respect and considera- tion as Richard Cumberland was. It is from Cumberland that we learn of the human qualities of Germain. He gives a picture of Germain at Stoneland which is amusing and creditable. 'To his religious duties this good man was not only regularly but respectfully attentive,' writes Cumberland, 'on the Sunday morning he appeared in gala, as if he were dressed for a drawing-room; he marched out his whole family in grand cavalcade to his parish church leaving only a centinel to watch the fires at home and mount guard upon the spits.' He reminded Cumberland of Sir Roger de Coverley at church and amused him by his nods and signals of assent to the preacher. He would encourage a young preacher by calling out in the middle of the sermon some remark like, 'Well done, Harry', and rebuke one of the choir by loudly saying, 'Out of tune, Tom Baker'.

This picture of an eighteenth-century squire in his pew at church was matched by Germain's benevolence to his tenants and dependants, and by his intelligent use of cultivated land. He influenced Thompson deeply and permanently by his mode of living—Thompson wrote at a later date: 'Look back for a moment my dearest friend upon the work of your hands. *Je suis de votre ouvrage.* Does it not afford you a very sensible pleasure to find that your Child has answered your Expecta- tions. . . .'[17]

4

Regimental Commander

How shall we rank thee upon glory's page?
Thou more than soldier and much less than sage.
THOMAS MOORE
(one word altered)

THE year 1781 was crucial. England was beset in Europe by the Armed Neutrality inspired and engineered by France. She was hampered by the inefficient and short-sighted conduct of the government and by weakness at sea. Franklin was in France pleading as never before for subsidy and support and depicting America as a land of virile and freedom-loving people. Washington and his generals realized that though their forces were weak it was the moment for a final effort. Early in the year King George, Lord North and Germain still believed that England was fighting both for herself and the majority of the Americans, and that with the support of the loyalists the American forces would be defeated and order restored. It was of course a minority view and incomprehensible to the Parliamentary Opposition in spite of Cornwallis's successes in the southern colonies in the summer of the previous year.

One cannot be certain what Thompson's private views were as to the progress of the war. No doubt he too was influenced by the exaggeratedly favourable despatches from America, and it is likely that he still had confidence in British arms and resurgence of power at sea. Certainly, he must have been thinking about his future career. As matters stood his future was dependent upon Germain's position and he knew that his patron and chief was anxious to resign. In fact Germain had first hinted of resignation in 1778 and the next year tried hard to do so after North proposed to separate the offices of Secretary for the Colonies and Commissioner of Trade. The uncertainty of Germain's tenure of office unsettled Thompson. There was talk among his friends about his taking up a political career,[1] but he was unfitted for such a career by training and temperament; his versatility did not quite extend to the give and take of Parliamentary debate. Any lustre he might have gained would have been lost in the brilliance of Fox, Burke and Sheridan. He could never be a democrat in spirit or action; he had the instincts and outlook of a benevolent despot.

In those days although science brought eminence and prestige to men outstanding in research, it offered no career to those without means; and Thompson was in any case more concerned with the problems of applied science than with fundamental research, an attitude which twenty years later brought him into conflict with his collaborators at the Royal Institution. In 1781 he could not think of turning to science as a major interest. Above all else he was a soldier, but without experience in war. As a future, soldiering no doubt seemed the most promising career. In 1775, after joining the British in Boston he had apparently just missed a commission in a loyalist regiment. A document of his in the Public Record Office states that 'he was named for the command of one of the battalions of a regiment which was to have been raised in America for his Majesty's Service by Brig. General Ruggles'.[2] In the event the regiment was not raised, and Thompson was disappointed since his 'passion for the Military Service had not abated'. During his tenure of office as Under-Secretary he decided to raise a regiment of King's American Dragoons. The warrant was issued by Sir Henry Clinton, the British Commander-in-Chief, in February 1781, and Thompson was appointed titular lieutenant-colonel.[3] At this time he had plenty of money and lived in style, owning at least six horses and keeping a groom. It took time to raise a regiment and his second-in-command, Major David Murray, began the task among the loyalists. Murray was ordered 'to spare no pains or expence in raising the Men' and was given 'leave to draw upon him for any Sum of Money that might be wanted for that purpose'.

Thompson, however, departed hurriedly from London in October the same year (with servants, an armourer and a saddler). He left his affairs in some disorder and tradesmen unpaid. This behaviour was out of character and not at all like the meticulous ordering of his assets before he left America. He kept his lodgings in Pall Mall for nearly twelve months. A friend named Fisher acted as his agent in London and after a time took drastic action by stopping the agreed allowance to the wife of Thompson's regimental armourer and to his servants in America. This angered Thompson who found his credit gone and himself disgraced even in the eyes of the servants. In later correspondence he returned time and time again to money matters. In August 1782 he sold his phaeton for forty-five guineas, and was anxious to sell two horses and discharge his groom. He 'took it for granted that his chariot had long been disposed of' and the proceeds applied towards discharging his debts. The discounts on the tradesmen's bills were used by Fisher for the same purpose though Thompson claims that he intended 'in the greatness of his pride, honesty, folly or whatever else you may call it . . . to return them to the Public Treasury'. This last quotation illustrates his constant self-justification, a trait he never lost, and points to one of the sources of his considerable income. It is clear that the discounts were given on orders for the army as well as on his personal expenditure.

At this time he was still under thirty. He suffered intermittently from gastritis, though he was able to keep fit enough by careful dieting for the rigours of active service. He had made enemies by his indiscretions and his prospects were uncertain. If he were to ensure his future as a soldier, and he claimed to have 'a zeal for the service', then it was time to do some active soldiering. His decision to command his regiment in person was not a means of avoiding disgrace; it was an attempt to secure his future and to distinguish himself. There was another reason too. His letters from America would be useful to Germain, who remained a close friend. His knowledge, candour and powers of observation would all be used to supply up-to-date information on the war.

He sailed from England on 7 October aboard the *Rotterdam*, a ship of 50 guns, and landed in Charleston on 20 December. The *Rotterdam* was the biggest ship in a convoy destined for New York which had probably been driven off its course by unfavourable winds. While he was at sea the British forces suffered a major disaster. Lord Cornwallis who commanded them in the south was in difficulties. His troops had suffered from shortage of food, forced marches and sickness. Being under pressure he moved into Yorktown where he hoped to maintain his communications by sea, but his plans were upset by Washington's land forces, by French naval forces and by hesitation and misunderstanding at Clinton's headquarters. Yorktown was soon under siege and Cornwallis surrendered on 19 October. This was virtually the end of the struggle and the calamity was recognized by nearly everyone. Its significance was appreciated fully in London. The news arrived at Lord George's house on Sunday, 25 November at about noon. Germain immediately drove by hackney coach to tell Lord North. It was more than even he could stand without losing his calm. He took the news as a 'ball in his breast, for he opened his arms exclaiming wildly as he paced up and down . . . "Oh, God! it is all over!" '[4]

King George was less moved; he wrote immediately to Germain to say that he trusted 'that neither Lord George Germain, nor any Member of the Cabinet, will suppose that it makes the smallest alteration in those principles of my conduct, which have directed me in past time, and which will always continue to animate me under every event, in the prosecution of the present contest'.[5]

Thompson, of course, learned of the disaster on arriving at Charleston. Here he had his personal difficulties. He wanted to reach New York without delay. There was some discussion about the next move of the convoy. At first it was decided that the *Rotterdam* should sail on alone to New York, and Thompson prepared to embark with his baggage. The decision was then countermanded or so, at any rate, he was informed, and he returned to shore. The *Rotterdam* then put to sea and Thompson found himself stranded with four other officers. He regarded his enforced stay as a cool plan to prevent his going north; this is clearly shown in a letter he wrote later to Germain.

'I wish I dared to write to you without reserve. There is something I would give the world to tell you. If my former letters reach you, look at the Gentleman's name that is written in Cypher—*The old leven* —now do you know who I mean? My being left behind, and the *Rotterdam's* sailing for New York, as she did, without my knowledge, I am convinced was not without design, and *management*.'

It has been suggested that Thompson's enemy was John Montagu, fourth Earl of Sandwich and First Lord of the Admiralty, and further, that Sandwich was responsible for his being detained, but there is no strong evidence of this. It is more likely that Thompson was something of a responsibility and a nuisance when on board ship. His scientific work and gunfiring experiments could have irritated the ships' captains and, much worse, it is clear from letters he wrote that he exploited his influence and intimacy with Germain. He had more power than his rank warranted and an inflated idea of his own value. His personal qualities often made him unpopular with his equals and associates, however valuable his services were to his superiors.

At any rate here he was in South Carolina instead of New York, and characteristically he offered his help to General Leslie, the newly appointed officer in command of the region.[6] This offer, Thompson says 'he was so good as to accept in a manner most highly flattering to me'. Next day he was under orders as a cavalry officer. He was in good spirits. On his way out he had had two attacks of fever, 'the last occasioned by a heavy cold taken while sitting up all night upon the deck to take a lunar observation for determining the Longitude'. He was better now and the 'heavenly climate' suited him; 'oranges and myrtles grew in the hedges and it was as warm as an English July'.

He distinguished himself, and Leslie—whose situation in the area was precarious because of a shortage both of men and provisions— was genuinely glad of his services. His most important actions against the enemy were undertaken in the late February of 1782 on the Santee River. Various accounts are available including Thompson's own, written for his commanding officer. He moved out with the cavalry and some other detachments in the early hours of a Sunday morning and at daybreak heard of the presence in the district of a body of 'rebel troops' about 500 strong. Then there began a forced march of thirty-six miles, and from time to time Thompson mounted the infantry on the horses of the cavalry, a sensible but unconventional expedient. At the end of the march the cavalry, advancing alone, attacked the enemy near the river and killed at least forty without loss to themselves.

There was a second skirmish next day when, he reports: 'we had the good fortune to fall in with a chosen corps under the command of General Marion, in person, which we attacked and totally routed, killing a considerable number of them, taking sixteen prisoners and driving General Marion and the greater part of his army [sic] into the Santee where it is probable a great many of them perished'. He made an important capture of stores: 'near forty horses, twenty muskets with bayonets and Marion's canteens full of liquor'. Cattle were afterwards rounded up at leisure. Thompson carried through this action without loss of life and his only casualty was one man wounded. Leslie acknowledged its value and congratulated him upon it in his Orders for 1 March.

The letters Thompson wrote to Germain at this time show him to have been in turn confident and insecure. He thought that his own regiment would be more useful in the south where he was than near New York. It was, he thought, the only area where it would be of use, especially at that season. Combined with the forces then under him it would give him 'a very pretty command' and he was sure that General Leslie would not put anyone over his head. Thinking of his own rapid preferment he asks 'is it not ridiculous for me to talk of putting over heads? But seriously,' he continues, 'I really do believe he has that opinion of me that he would trust me and I do assure you I feel that I should not be afraid to trust myself. . . .' Yet to remain in the south would mean longer to wait before hearing from Germain and his anxiety to do so was 'beyond all description'. Germain would 'readily believe it must be great when he considered the peculiar unexpected circumstances he found upon his arrival'—an allusion, no doubt, to the fall of Yorktown.

In another letter he was critical of the administration in Charleston. But he was afraid to give full particulars because of the possibility that his letter would be intercepted. 'You remember', he says, 'the scheme for a commission of accounts in this country; believe me it is absolutely necessary. It is impossible to form any idea of the manner in which the business is done without being on the spot. I see enough to make a man less anxious and less severe than myself half mad. I *know* more than I could ever have been persuaded to believe had I not come to America. But I dare not at present trust myself upon this subject. The first good oppertunity I [will] write fully.'

As usual he had a low opinion of the American troops and a high one of his own. 'If the prisoners which we took the other day (which by-the-bye belonged to Col. Washington's regiment) are a fair specimen of their cavalry, I would venture to attack the whole with 150 of the dragoons that are under my command. They are absolutely no better than Children and their horses are as much too fat as ours are too lean. A long march would knock one-half of them up. Our horses tho' low in flesh are equal to a great deal of fatigue and our men with a little discipline will make most excellent troops. They have all been used to fire and sword and are brave to the last degree. All they want is method. . . .'

Method was one of Thompson's dominating ideas. Promoting order and precision, using resources with economy and applying his mind to the task in hand were qualities which he had possessed from childhood. If he had been in a higher command and twenty years older it is possible that the course of the war might have been very different. As it was he was too far down in the hierarchy to exert a decisive influence.

Thompson in America was in a favoured position because of his friendship with Germain. His correspondence reveals the unusual situation of a temporary lieutenant-colonel asking favours for the General Officer in charge of the area. Writing to Germain (he seldom wrote to anyone else from America) he said: 'Before I forget it my dear Lord, let me beg of you to bear in mind the Good General, a more amiable or a more honourable Man does not exist nor one more zealously attached to the King's Service. I know you wish him well and only hope you will have an oppertunity soon of rendering him a very essential Service. . . .' In another letter written nearly a fortnight later he told Germain that Leslie had had a bad fall from his horse, and again recommended him for patronage or preferment. 'He is the best man on Earth and I really wish my dear friend you would take care of him. You know his object and it certainly is a fair one. Pray patronize a man who is so very deserving of favor.'[7] By the time this letter reached England, however, Germain was no longer a fount of favour.

After the fall of Yorktown Lord North's views about the prosecution of the war differed from those of Germain. Germain would never 'put his hand to an instrument conceding independence to the colonies'; North was weary of the war and wanted to make the present best of a bad job. The King accepted Germain's resignation in late January and conferred a peerage upon him. He became Viscount Sackville of Drayton and took his seat in the House of Lords where once again he had to fight against fierce personal animosity. Despite his limitations he had served the King loyally and had endured with stoical detachment some of the most vicious attacks ever made upon a politician. Most of his remaining years were spent in active squiredom at his country house.

Thompson probably did not hear of Germain's resignation until he had left the south for New York. He was deeply involved in his friend's fate, but the broader issues of international conflict seem to have meant little to him. His emotions were not aroused by the fates of countries. He had no patriotism in the usual sense. Later in life he moved from one country to another and became an international figure, even living freely in France while France and England were at war. But in 1782 he was a professional soldier and something of a mercenary; his personal interests and obligations dictated his actions. He was deficient in feeling; he felt little love for individual people let alone countries. His career came first.

Thompson left Charleston on 1 April 1782. His fears of being left behind again were unjustified. With the Earl of Dunmore,[8] and 'other gentlemen of high rank' he arrived at Sandy Hook near New York after a ten days' voyage. His arrival was recorded by both *Rivington's Royal Gazette* and the *New York Mercury*. The fleet which made the journey was a considerable one of forty-five sail, composed of navy and army victuallers under convoy of various warships. This fleet had been forced to winter at Charleston, rather than sailing, as originally intended, directly to New York from England.

This time the despatches Thompson carried with him were from Leslie to Clinton who was at the end of his command.[9] No doubt he also carried Germain's letter, written from Stoneland Lodge, in which Germain 'begs to introduce Mr Thompson and to thank His Excellency for giving that gentleman the commmand of a Regiment of Light Dragoons. He [Thompson] shows a spirit and zeal for the service in quitting for a time an agreeable and profitable civil situation.'[10]

It was essential to his plans to bring his regiment up to strength so he advertised in *Rivington's Royal Gazette* for 'likely and spirited young lads desirous of serving their King and country and who prefer riding to going on foot'. Volunteers were offered ten guineas on enlistment. This appeal must have sounded hollow to many of those who read the *Gazette*. Yorktown had decided the outcome of the war. The months that remained were months of bitter local struggles. The fervour had died and the war was in an inglorious phase which gave rein to the worst impulses on both sides. Many of the remaining loyalists were desperate, holding to the British cause only through fear and self-interest. They had little hope now of American protection or restitution when peace came, but they might at least salvage some of their losses from a grateful Britain. The following letter was written by Thompson to Germain (now Viscount Sackville) some months later on 6 October 1782. It describes vividly the reactions of the loyalists, seen by a loyalist.

'You cannot conceive, nor can any language describe, the Distress that all ranks of people here have been thrown into by the intelligence of the Independence of America being acknowledged by Great Britain, and the loyalists being given up to the Mercy of their Enemies. The Militia who for some weeks have done the whole of the Garrison duty in this City have perem[p]torily refused to serve any longer, and the General has been obliged to relieve them by bringing regular Troops into Town. The Loyalists at Lloyds Neck and the other posts are in a state of Anarchy and confusion little short of actual rebellion. Papers have been stuck up about town, inviting Sir Guy Carleton to take the Command of the Army here and to oppose by force the measures of the New Administration and promising thousands to assist him. In short an universal Dispair and Phrenzy prevails within these lines, and I should not be surprised if very alarming consequences were to follow from the temper people are in. They seem to be as void of prudence as they are destitute of Hope, and a kind of Language is now spoken publicly in the streets that is enough to make one tremble for what is to follow from these Convulsions. The Provincial Corps will disband of themselves,—or what is infinitely more to be dreaded, they will take arms in opposition to these measures. They feel themselves deeply injured. For my own part I am at a loss what opinion to form respecting the end of all these commotions. I cannot help thinking that we are not made acquainted with the whole of the Secret. There must be something going on that we cannot get at, but what that something is I have no conception. I will not torment myself with idle conjectures. Long before this letter reaches your hands you must be acquainted with the whole matter. . . .'[11]

Before this letter was written, however, Thompson had taken over the remnants of the Queen's Rangers and the British Legion and had completed his own regiment, the King's American Dragoons. From the start the new Commander-in-Chief, Sir Guy Carleton, was 'very good to him'. Major Upham joined his regiment and brought twenty-five men with him; Captain Phillips also joined and subscribed 500 guineas to the regimental fund. He said in one of his letters that the King's American Dragoons were 'one of the crack corps in this army'. On 1 August they were greatly honoured by being reviewed by His Royal Highness Prince William Henry who presented their colours to them. The appearance of his men was such that he should not be ashamed to 'show the regiment in Hyde Park'. The event had 'set them upon very high ground in this army'. 'His Royal Highness said the other day at the Admiral's table that he might easily have mistaken us for an established British Regiment of Light Dragoons.' Perhaps the last remark spoilt the effect but Thompson was too elated to notice the fact. The review had been described in *Rivington's Royal Gazette*. Ellis in the *Memoir* grudgingly calls it 'a demonstrative rather than brilliant occasion', but to Thompson, still not thirty years of age, it must have been thrilling. Here were the Prince, Admiral Digby, General Birch and other distinguished officers gathered to review his own regiment and he was to receive the colours from the Prince's own hands.

'The regiment passed before the Prince, performing marching salutes. Then they returned, dismounted and formed a semicircle in front of the canopy.' After this manœuvre the chaplain, the Reverend Mr Odell, delivered an appropriate address. The men took off their helmets, laid down their arms, raised their right arms and took a solemn oath of allegiance and fidelity. After the chaplain's benediction Thompson, as lieutenant-colonel, received the colours and handed them to the eldest cornets. There were three cheers, the band played 'God Save the King', the guns fired a royal salute and the ceremony was over.

Thompson sent the cutting to Sackville with a request for it to be republished in the London newspapers. His motive was not entirely selfish or even self-advertising: he wanted the politicians to have a good opinion of his regiment when the time came to fight for its future. His plan was clear. It was that the regiment should be accorded permanent status, and the officers receive half pay if, subsequently, it were reduced.

Several weeks after the review he had orders to take his regiment to Long Island. He marched from Ireland Heights near Flushing on 24

September, and three days later he encamped opposite Lloyd's Neck five miles from Huntington and forty from New York. His orders were to evacuate the post at Lloyd's Neck, to remove the military stores and demolish the redoubt. He was to bring with him 'as many of the refugees as chose to remove'. In fact nearly all remained—unarmed. Having carried out his orders in two days he made his headquarters at Huntington.

In a letter to Sackville he said that 'although his regiment had been raised in the midst of an army by no means famous for its discipline' the men were 'really very orderly' and that he had scarcely had any complaint from the local inhabitants of depredations. He claimed, too, that whenever he left a district the people expressed regret, his regiment so excelled in behaviour the troops who had previously been in occupation. But local historians tell an entirely different story. They have spoken with anger and indignation about the actions of the troops under his command. The main accusation concerns the construction of blockhouses and barracks for his men's winter quarters. It seems that he decided that the most suitable location was in a burial ground belonging to a chapel. He put military need above the feelings of the church members, ignored their indignant protests and proceeded to strip the chapel of its timber. It may well be that the chapel had been out of use for some time and that Thompson, finding it derelict, completed its destruction to build his blockhouses on the most suitable site, which was the burial ground. But his action was regarded as sacrilegious. Thompson did not in any way atone for his first action, moreover, by using the tombstones to build baking ovens. Long afterwards, old men testified 'from the evidence of their own senses that they had often seen the loaves of bread drawn out with the reversed inscriptions of the tombstones of their friends on the lower crust'.[12]

He had to deal with men in whaleboats setting out from the mainland at night, bent on smuggling or raiding. He wrote on 7 October:

'I am going to carry on a little war of my own, the only war permitted here, against the rebel whaleboats which absolutely swarm in the Sound. I have raised a company of boatmen from among the Lloyd's Neck people and I intend fighting them with their own weapons. Nothing but a whaleboat can catch a whaleboat. If they come on shore I shall be ready to receive them. If they put to sea my boats will have fair play with them.'

These and other activities such as removing military stores and demolishing redoubts kept him busy. It is strange that at such a late stage in the war he should still speak of 'rebel' whaleboats. King George of course would have approved, but the word was completely out of keeping with the reality of the situation. His energy was remarkable. He escaped illness 'wonderfully'. 'Everyone tells me', he writes, 'that I cannot go on except I drink wine . . . I drink water notwithstanding (mixed with a little brandy or rum) and take as much exercise both of body and of mind as would kill a dozen of the lazy wine-bibbers that preach to me; and often laugh at them while they are quivering and shaking with ague.' From early manhood Thompson had to be careful over food and drink and without doubt his abstemiousness helped to keep him in good health. With his characteristic tendency to generalize, which was sometimes so unscientific, he said 'drinking and over-eating are . . . the cause of the greatest part of the disorders incident to these hot climates'.

Thompson's financial difficulties have already been mentioned. He had left his affairs in an unsettled state when he sailed from England and it seems that Sackville chided him over this and at the same time helped him to straighten things out. In self-justification Thompson claimed that in America his expenses 'were regulated by the strictest Œconomy'. On 8 August he could say that in future the officers would draw full pay and they would be able to repay him the money that he had advanced before the regiment was completed. He had hired no new servants since his arrival and he was considering discharging his groom when he could find a black boy who could care for his horses. He permitted 'no man to be taken from the Ranks to be made a Servant of'. All officers had black servants dressed alike except for the feathers in their turbans which were 'of different colours according to the troops their masters belonged to'.

If Mr Fisher, his agent in London, was worried, so was he. 'No one was more anxious that his affairs should be properly settled.' He regretted that he had been able to send but one remittance and that for only £200. However, he thanked God he did not owe a shilling in America, nor did he intend to. He paid as he went and that was the secret of living on one's income. He lived in too good company to run into debt. It was remarkable that since his arrival in South Carolina, except when he had been living with his officers in the mess, he had only twice dined at his own expense. His friend and commanding officer, General Robertson,[13] insisted upon his making his house in New York his home, whenever he was free to go to it—there was always a plate laid for him.

Thompson had other troubles the nature of which can only be guessed. He was probably often personally unpopular with those who were equal to him in standing because he felt himself superior to them in ability and achievement, as indeed he often was. Being so anxious to succeed as well as intelligent and energetic he usually stood high in the estimation of his superiors. He exploited, and probably paraded, the influence he had with those in authority. And so he made enemies. He lacked the security which others felt from having an aristocratic background or family fortune. This want of ease with his equals was with him throughout his life and made him unpopular with French *savants* after he married Mme Lavoisier. But in America in 1782 he had Sackville to confide in by letter. On 7 October, in the letter I have already quoted from, he noted that it was the anniversary of his leaving England and bemoaned his injuries. 'How fresh in my memory', he wrote, 'is every transaction of this day twelve months! 'Twas then I left home to come abroad. What a series of distresses I have since experienced. How cruelly some of them wounded me! I wish to heaven I could forget them but I cannot for the soul of me. But I can be silent. . . .'

He was in fact doing very well, as we have seen. His complaint had a childlike quality, for Sackville was still a father figure to him. It also had a touch of self-pity and self-dramatization, both qualities evident to a much greater degree in the letters he had written to his father-in-law when he was in trouble in New Hampshire for his anti-American activities. A more cheerful tone was adopted in a later letter, in fact a pleasing touch of gratitude, when he wrote to a Mr Gladwell and asked him to tell His Lordship (Viscount Sackville) that he had procured two fine young deer of the country, a buck and a doe, which he meant to send him 'by the first safe oppertunity'. He asked how His Lordship liked the firewood he sent him and gave instructions about its use: 'You must remember always to have two good large logs behind, one above the other, and the other wood laid up on hand Irons narrow and high.' In the spring he intended to send three fine American horses.

When Thompson sailed for Europe in 1776 he left his mother, wife and infant daughter behind, as well as other relatives. It has often been said that he did not attempt to make contact with them when he was back in America. This was Ellis's opinion and others have said the same, and considered it an example of his lack of feeling. There is, however, a paragraph in the letter he wrote to Sackville on 7 October which, of course, Ellis knew nothing of, and which sheds new light on his attitude. He says:

'I have not yet heard one syllable directly from New Hampshire tho' I have made many attempts. I begin to be at a loss to guess the reason of this dead silence. They must know I am here.'

While he was in England communication with his relatives was obviously impossible, but later when he was in or near New York he could have made contact through loyalists in Connecticut. There was a considerable traffic across Long Island Sound and Thompson had whaleboats at his disposal. No doubt some at least of his 'many attempts' were made by this route. The passage also suggests that he had information indirectly about his wife and family. It is hard to understand his inability to explain their silence. Probably they did know where he was, but he was proscribed and in disgrace. He had been named in the Alienation Act passed by the State of New Hampshire in 1778; he had deserted his country and given comfort to the enemy. Feeling which had run high before he left was bitter now. In New England there was blind hatred for loyalists of paler hue than Thompson. They were deprived of many rights: the right to sue in the courts, to will property, to collect debts, and to teach in school or practise law. Moreover, they were lucky to escape boycott, violence and plunder. It would have been highly dangerous for Mrs Thompson to communicate with her husband even if she had wished to. Her brother, Timothy Walker, probably had little use for Thompson; he would hate him as a traitor and a deserter of wife and child. Mrs Thompson's father, the estimable and revered Timothy Walker *père* who had helped Thompson so generously and had hoped for so much from his daughter's second marriage, had died in his parsonage five weeks before Thompson wrote this plaintive paragraph. Something their daughter wrote years later shows that his wife took the view, correct as far as it went, that he had put ambition before patriotism. There is no evidence that she openly resented this brilliant and polished young man's short-lived intrusion into her life. She seems to have been a mild amiable woman and for some years before her death in 1792 suffered from ill-health.

Thompson was egotistical for he could not see himself from his family's point of view, but he was not emotionally affected by their silence. It is not known whether he communicated with his mother; she lived in Woburn and he does not mention her, but several years later he made some financial provision for her.

There was much to occupy Thompson's attention in addition to his own little war and his personal relations. His major concern at this time was his fight for the future of his regiment. His own career, status and pay were directly involved in the fight; but he did not confine his efforts to ensuring his own well-being (though, in fact, he fared better than his subordinates). The full story has never been told and would be too long to tell here in detail. Thompson was at his most persistent, wringing every advantage he could from his influence and skill, going to the boundary of fact and occasionally just beyond. He fully realized the multiplicity of claims there would be on a depleted exchequer and he was aware of the disillusion many loyalists had experienced in England and elsewhere.

Great Britain and the United States signed articles of peace in November 1782, but their ratification was dependent upon an agreement between Great Britain and France, and it was not until 3 September the following year that the final treaty was signed in Paris. All concerned were weak and ready for peace. Though Britain pleaded hard for the loyalists she achieved nothing for them.[14] In fact little could be expected and as early as 6 August 1782, when his regiment was completed, Thompson began his campaign. He presented a petition to Carleton asking for confirmation of the rights and privileges due to a regiment completed according to the agreed proposals. Carleton referred the petition to a Board of Generals which met without delay and gave a favourable decision. Confirmation at Carleton's headquarters had, however, to be followed by ratification by the British government. This could by no means be taken for granted and Thompson knew it, although Carleton had given it as his private opinion that no objection would be raised.

What Thompson wanted most was to take his regiment to some active theatre of war. At one time there was a plan to carry on the fight against France in the West Indies and he undertook to raise a battalion of light infantry from among the provincial forces. Carleton gave the necessary orders and Thompson drew up a plan for raising four companies of light infantry and a company of artillery to be attached to the Dragoons. The total strength was to be 700 officers and men. Thompson said that it was Carleton's intention (unsolicited) to give him the provincial rank of colonel and to put the whole corps on the British Establishment upon their embarking for the West Indies. These proposals were dropped and Thompson's hopes dashed when the war with France came to an end in January 1783.

In March the same year Thompson sent a memorial to Carleton on his own behalf and on behalf of the officers and men of his regiment pointing out their distress 'in the event of peace and the independency of the American Provinces'. Since all the officers except the adjutants were Americans and 'had suffered very considerably by the rebellion all hopes of their returning to their former situations would be at an end'. The regiment was ready to go anywhere. But he evidently saw that active service was out of the question and early in April changed his tactics. He asked Carleton, who had sent his earlier memorial with supporting letters to London, to allow his regiment to go to Nova Scotia and also for leave for himself to go to London to press the claims of the provincial officers.

The move to Nova Scotia would have meant partial disbandment. The idea was that a grant of land would be given to all who desired to settle. Thompson also made the practical suggestion that each officer might be allowed to take a horse and that a conveyance be provided for their equipment. Nova Scotia, for obvious reasons, had no personal appeal for Thompson.

Carleton, who had a high opinion of Thompson's ability, granted leave on 11 April and Thompson set sail for England four days later. He was regarded as the spokesman of the loyalist officers, for a letter sent to him by 'an Officer of Rank in the Provincial Line' pointed out how grievous it would be if the applications of the refugees in London should be brought before Parliament and the claims of serving officers forgotten. The writer hoped that before Thompson reached London their petitions would have been granted but if not that they would depend on him to solicit for them as he knew 'the ways of Office' and could 'get access to Ministers'.

On arriving in London early in June Thompson found that no action had been taken. So he settled himself in Pall Mall and presented a long and clear petition on behalf of the officers to Lord North. He also approached other influential members of the House of Commons. His persistent advocacy caused the government to act. Lord North saw the justice of the request and placed the facts before the King. On 27 June Parliament voted half pay to the officers of the provincial corps. Next day Thompson wrote to North thanking him particularly for his 'able speech in their favour yesterday in the House of Commons'.[15]

So far so good; although the regiment was not to be placed on the British Establishment and used for active service, half pay had been secured. But Thompson wanted the rank of colonel for himself and of lieutenant-colonel for Major Murray, his second-in-command who had helped him so much. To help achieve his purpose he had already presented another petition setting out his claims and submitting various letters and documents in support of them. He stressed the fact that he had been disappointed of being colonel of the corps 'of seven hundred Light Troops upon the British Establishment which was to have been raised for service in the West Indies'. To North he wrote on 25 June: 'The favour I solicit is very trifling in itself but to me it is of infinite importance as my views are to Foreign Service (having solicited in vain for employment in this Country).'[16]

Among the various memoranda is a list of the officers of his regiment giving length of service and other relevant facts. He calculated his own from February 1781, which gave him only two years four months, including eight months while he still held office as Germain's Under-Secretary. He claimed to have been a Colonel of Militia in New Hampshire. Certainly he was a Major but there is no evidence he attained a higher rank.

Finally he petitioned the King. He gave the same reasons for his request but added a plea to be permitted to go to Germany and 'in case there should be a War between any of the European Powers and the Turks to offer his Services to the former'.[17] Lord North, who was invariably helpful to Thompson, put the petition and the supporting documents before King George on 10 July. The King agreed to Thompson's promotion without enthusiasm. On the same day he wrote: 'I can see no real right in Mr Thompson to obtaining the rank of Colonel, which ought to be granted with a most sparing hand; considering the few Years he has served that of Lieut Colonel seems very sufficient.'[18] The King was influenced by Carleton's approbation and North's support.

This episode closed with an exchange of letters between Thompson and Carleton and a letter from North to Carleton. There were congratulations all round. Thompson had got his own way, but poor Murray was not so fortunate. He remained a major.

5

From Aide-de-Camp to 'Excellency'

Costly thy habit as thy purse can buy,
But not express'd in fancy; rich not gaudy;
For the apparel oft proclaims the man
SHAKESPEARE

AT THIRTY Thompson was out of work. His assets, except for his half pay as colonel, were intangible. He had influential friends and no personal ties, abundant energy and an anxiety to use his gifts to his own advantage. He was not unknown as a man of science and he had some reputation as a soldier. But where was he to go? England had little to offer. As he said 'it was not a place for a loyalist to make his way' and 'the idea of vegetating was . . . more terrible than that of annihilation'.[1]

The war he had grown up in and served in was over. England, America, France, Spain and Holland were about to sign a peace treaty at Versailles. But in Eastern Europe an Austro-Russian alliance had been concluded with the aim of driving the Turks out of Europe and dividing their European territory. Trouble was already developing. The situation there might offer suitable opportunities and Thompson decided to make for Vienna. Lord North and William Fraser, Under-Secretary in the Foreign Office, willingly wrote him letters of introduction to Sir Robert Murray Keith, the British Ambassador there. North, after saying 'you have probably heard of Mr. Thompson', gave a short but laudatory account of his career and continued: 'having no employment or occupation in this country, he is desirous of travelling on the Continent and means to go in the first place to Vienna'.[2] Fraser spoke of him as 'proposing to set out on a Tour for his Amusement and intending to spend some time at Vienna' and as 'a Gentleman highly deserving any Marks of Kindness you may think proper to honour him with'.

Thompson wasted no time. By mid-September he was at Dover ready to embark. He had with him three fine American horses and presumably a groom and servant. On the same boat were two distinguished passengers: Henry Laurens, a former President of the American Congress, and Edward Gibbon, the historian. Laurens had been imprisoned in the Tower of London and after recuperating at Bath was on his way to Paris to meet Franklin. Gibbon was going on a holiday. It is from him[3] that we hear of their crossing. He wrote to Lord Sheffield in jocular style about it, referring to Thompson as 'Mr Secretary, Colonel, Admiral, Philosopher Thompson'. What Gibbon really thought of him we do not know. Thompson, long afterwards, in conversation with his friend Pictet, implied that Gibbon paid him a compliment for his versatility, but there may have been a touch of sarcasm in Gibbon's description. One can imagine that Laurens was very distant and aloof to someone whom he would undoubtedly regard as a traitor. The crossing was uncomfortable; the sea was rough, the boat was small and carried three horses, and most of the humans (except Gibbon) were sea-sick. They had to land at Boulogne instead of Calais.

Thompson went on to Strasbourg. His visit coincided with a military review of the garrison. This was a stroke of good fortune which changed his life, and he saw his opportunity and seized it. He may have remembered a similar occasion at Portsmouth, New Hampshire, more than ten years earlier when he attracted the attention of the Governor. Then he wore his Hussar cloak faced with scarlet shalloon. This time he appeared on one of his horses in the full uniform of a colonel of the British army, and, as before, he caught the attention of the chief person present. It was Prince Maximilian of Zweibrücken (or Deux-Ponts). An English officer was a rare sight so soon after the end of fighting and Thompson was such a fine specimen of *rara avis* that Maximilian asked for him to be presented. The two men took to each other at once. Maximilian was familiar with the course of the American war; the regiment of which he was titular head had seen service in America, particularly in the struggle for Yorktown. In fact there were officers present at this review who had fought in America. Thompson

70

had with him maps and documents relating to his own part in the campaign and hours were spent in fighting battles over again.

Prince Maximilian, who was an able young man and later became King of Bavaria, recognized Thompson's ability. A friendship was begun that day which lasted all their lives. Maximilian advised Thompson to call at Munich on his way to Vienna and make the acquaintance of his uncle, Charles Theodore, Elector Palatine and Elector of Bavaria. This he did, carrying a letter of introduction from Maximilian which ensured a cordial reception. Thompson, however, was anxious to reach Vienna not only because of the attraction of the court but because of the possibility of employment. There he received 'a flattering welcome' in court and embassy and was quickly on friendly terms with Keith, the British Ambassador. As there was no immediate prospect of a fighting commission he decided to travel for a time. He went on to Venice and Trieste writing Keith letters giving descriptions of natural features and scraps of news. After a few weeks he returned to Munich. Travelling was all very well and contacts with the nobility were flattering and amusing but he wanted permanent and satisfying employment. There still seemed no prospect of fighting in the Austrian army and he probably thought better of it in any case. He told Pictet that he 'was cured of this martial folly' by the wife of a German general who took a liking to him and 'opened his eyes to other kinds of glory'. None the less he returned to Munich and decided to ask the Elector of Bavaria to take him into his service. It has been thought by most that the Elector pressed Thompson to work for him; indeed Renwick, writing in 1845, and allowing his imagination to fill the gaps in his knowledge, said: 'At the very first audience of his Serene Highness he received the offer of a situation at the Court of dignity and importance; and when he declined respectfully any immediate decision, many flattering inducements were held out to him to remain. . . .'[4] In fact the initiative was clearly on Thompson's side. In a letter to Keith he said: 'I made a bold stroke and it has succeeded.'

Officially Thompson was to be colonel and aide-de-camp to Charles Theodore, and unofficially the tutor of Count von Bretzenheim, an illegitimate son of the Elector. It was a start. In his own words the charge was honourable and he fancied the service would be agreeable. He had no very great expectations at this time and, of course, suffered from speaking no German and little French. His pay was to be eighty florins a month which was considerably less than that of a Bavarian infantry colonel, and before he could accept the post he had to obtain the permission of King George. The Elector insisted on this. So Thompson returned to London to see the King who not only gave him the permission he sought but conferred a knighthood upon him. As he wrote to Keith on 1 March from London, he had every reason to be satisfied with the attentions that had been shown him.

The parchment diploma recording the Grant of Arms sets out his status and achievements. He is described as of 'St. James's, Westminster, Knight, Colonel of the King's American Regiment of Light Dragoons, and Fellow of the Royal Society of London, late Under-Secretary of State of the Province of Georgia, and Colonel of a Regiment of Militia in the Province of New Hampshire . . . Son of Benjamin Thompson late of the Province of Massachusetts Bay, in New England, Gent., deceased . . . of one of the most antient Families in North America; [It says] that an Island which belonged to his Ancestors, at the Entrance of Boston Harbour . . . still bears his Name; that his Ancestors have ever lived in reputable Situations in that Country where he was born, and have hitherto used the Arms of the antient and respectable Family of Thompson of the County of York, from a constant Tradition that they derived their Descent from that Source. . . .'

This document repeats his claim to a colonelcy in the Provincial Militia of New Hampshire for which there is no independent evidence. Ellis believed, moreover, that Thompson Island had no connection with Benjamin's family. The name was derived from a David Thompson who appears to have taken illegal possession of the island at the end of the sixteenth century. Apart from these inaccuracies, Garter King of Arms and Clarenceux King of Arms give a description which leaves little unsaid and which makes the most of Thompson's family and achievements, based on information supplied by himself. But he was only thirty, his rise had been rapid, his achievements were solid and creditable, and he can be forgiven for his vanity on so proud an occasion.

His shield and crest bore little resemblance to those he designed for the book plate when he was fifteen years old. In heraldic language they were described as:

'Per Fess Argent and Sable, a Fess embattled, counter-embattled, counter-changed between two Falcons, in chief of the second beked, membered and belled Or, and a Horse passant in base of the first. And for a Crest on a Wreath of the Colours, A Mural Crown Or, thereon a Mullet of six points Azure, and between the Battlements four Pine Buds Vert.'[5]

Perhaps as he looked at the fess on his shield it reminded him of the money he had earned as a boy by cutting and cording wood.

The award of this knighthood is difficult to account for. He himself says the honour was conferred 'as a public mark of His Majesty's approbation of my services', but for his military service he had been grudgingly rewarded with a colonelcy. An Under-Secretary might confidently expect a knighthood or a baronetcy—Richard Cumberland had been offered the higher of these two honours and had rejected it as a 'mere mouthful of moonshine'[6]—but Thompson had been in office so short a time that he could hardly expect such recognition and, in any case, the appropriate moment was long past. His new position in the Bavarian Court did not obviously warrant the honour; indeed the newly appointed minister there had no title, he was 'Young Mr Walpole'.[7] Professor Sanborn Brown has suggested that the fact that Thompson intended to give confidential information to Keith—to act as an informer—influenced the British goverment to make the award, but there is no evidence that the arrangement was known in London.[8] Even if it had been it would have caused no sensation. The diplomatic correspondence of the day shows time and time again how eager ambassadors and envoys were to acquire sources of information at times when the speed of communication was the speed of a horse and when press conferences were unheard of.

The most likely theory is that the generous Lord North asked for the knighthood and that in so doing he was considering the wide range of Thompson's achievements and the fact that he was a loyalist making his way. One thing is certain: this honour to Thompson explodes the notion that he had left the under-secretaryship in disgrace.

Sir Benjamin Thompson returned to Bavaria to take up his ill-defined duties feeling pleased with the past but doubtful about the future. In a cautious way he began to try to obtain information from Keith in Vienna who had given him permission to write freely to him. He would, so he said, be 'furnished regularly with the best intelligence from London' and it would be in his power from time to time to give Keith the first accounts of interesting occurrences in that country. He added certain precautions about privacy:

'As letters addressed to Persons in high Stations are sometimes subject to accidents perhaps you may think it prudent for me to write to you under cover to your Banker or to some other person in private life.'

Having given the address of his own bankers he said it would be unnecessary to sign the letters as they were acquainted with each other's handwriting. He goes on:

'To own to you the truth I am the more anxious that the arrangements for our correspondence should be made with caution as any interesting intelligence you may communicate will be of the greatest personal advantage to me. You will easily guess the rest. But you may rest assured that I shall never communicate with but one single person —and that Person is both too great and too good to betray us. . . .'

Keith probably thought Thompson a naive and forward young man and it is unlikely that he passed on information about policy and events in Vienna for Thompson to retail to the Elector—for that is what the proposal amounted to. Such information would have been particularly useful to Charles Theodore at the time, and Thompson saw his friendship with Keith as a means of self-advancement. At any rate Keith did not reply for nearly twelve months. He was in fact receiving regular information from Walpole, sometimes in code. Early in 1785, however, he was badly in need of reliable intelligence from Bavaria. This need arose from the peculiar position that country held in the diplomacy of the time.

The Emperor of Austria, Joseph II, grasped Bavaria's strategic importance for his own country and also the prestige that Austria would gain if it became part of his dominions. When Maximilian Joseph, Elector of Bavaria, died in 1777 he was succeeded by Charles Theodore of Salzbach who was already Elector Palatine. The two electorates were therefore united under one ruler. Charles Theodore had no legitimate heir and the next in order of succession was Charles II of Zweibrücken–Birkenfeld. Charles Theodore had little time or concern for Bavaria and in 1778 he recognized Austria's right to certain territories, including Lower Bavaria, and suggested that there should be an exchange of the Austrian Netherlands for the rest of Bavaria. The heir presumptive, Charles, opposed this plan and had the support of Frederick II of Prussia who appeared with an army in Bohemia to resist Austrian encroachment. The War of the Bavarian Succession

began; a war in which there was little fighting. Peace was restored in
1779 largely through the influence of Russia, but the matter was not
finally settled and shortly afterwards the Emperor Joseph returned
to his scheme for exchanging the Netherlands for Bavaria. Charles
Theodore was still willing but it was necessary to secure the approval
of Charles of Zweibrücken-Birkenfeld. It was rumoured that the
Elector was about to visit his relative with a view to persuading him
to consent. Prussia was still likely to oppose the plan, and England also
because it might lead to the opening up of the Scheldt for commerce
—this river had been sacrificed in the interests of the Thames and the
Rhine. When in February 1785 Charles Theodore denied that there
was a plan of exchange the situation became confused, for not everyone believed him. Thus Keith was anxious to find out just what were
the Elector's intentions. Remembering Thompson's offer to exchange
information and the nature of his post, he wrote to him. The reply
must have astonished and exasperated him not a little. If Thompson
was, by then, in the Elector's confidence he did not choose to divulge
the information—he had seen where his best interests lay. The only
news that Keith received was of the Elector's intention to visit Mannheim and the Low Countries. The letter was dated 13 April 1785, and
was too bland to be taken at its face value. After a paragraph of
courtesies it ran:

'Your Excellency does me too much honor by supposing that any
opinions of mine could bias your judgment upon any point, much less
upon a political subject.'

Thompson begged His Excellency to do him the justice of believing
that it would afford him real satisfaction at all times to obey his commands, but said it was beyond his power to satisfy his curiosity as he
had no authentic information. No doubt His Excellency would hear
the public news of the Elector's visit from Count Pergen, the Bavarian
minister; His Electoral Highness had done him the honour to name
him as one of his suite upon this excursion.

As if to say 'please do not write to me again for this kind of information', he concluded with the assurance that he was perfectly happy
and contented, that he had nothing left to wish for except to show his
zealous attachment to the best of masters and his unfeigned gratitude
for all his goodness to him.[9]

Keith had also written to Walpole. Walpole's reply dated 14 April was in similar terms. But he evidently either changed his mind or made special inquiries, for exactly a month later he wrote again to Keith. The Elector had suddenly departed with 'all the ladies of his kindred'. His going was interpreted by some 'as a tacit abandonment of the country' and by others as 'a step towards reconciliation with the Deuxponts [Zweibrücken] branch of the Palatine family in order to obtain their consent to the much rumoured exchange . . .'. There was consternation in the country both because of the injudicious behaviour of the Court and also because the army was to be clothed and equipped 'after the Austrian manner'.

This diplomatic incident gives an insight into the political atmosphere in which Thompson was plunged on his arrival in Bavaria. The incident ended in 1786 when Frederick the Great, with the support of the majority of the rulers of the small German states, drew up an agreement to maintain existing territorial boundaries. This move forced Joseph and Charles Theodore to give up their plan.

Thompson quickly grasped two salient facts about Bavaria. First that the country was utterly ready for social and military reform; and, secondly, that the Elector would willingly and gratefully support him if he attempted the task of reformation. The government was corrupt and extravagant. Trade and industry were not developing; they had in fact seriously decayed as a result of the granting of monopolies and the growth of privilege. There were, according to Cuvier, more monasteries than factories in the country. Taxation was heavy, justice was suspect and the administration oppressive. The army was small, wretchedly paid and consisted largely of the off-scourings of the population. Beggary was rife among the poor and immorality among the rich.

Charles Theodore was distrusted in Bavaria, partly because of his origin, and he did not have the qualities to inspire his Bavarian subjects with enthusiasm. He was more at home and more popular in the Palatinate where he had improved education and fostered the cultural interests of his people. He was old now and under the influence of his mistresses and favourites.[10] Walpole had grasped the truth of the situation when he wrote to Keith: 'The reigning Prince is inactive and unambitious—his Ministers are also of the same cast', and, earlier: 'The Elector has returned to his summer residence at Nymphenberg and does not disturb his repose with the politicks of the rest of Europe. . . .'[11]

An effective minister whom he could trust would relieve him of care and responsibility. Though not an ardent reformer himself he was prepared to support the efforts of one who was, provided they were in keeping with his own ideas and did not disturb his comfort.

It was an advantage that Thompson was not a Bavarian. Foreigners, particularly the English, were not unwelcome in the German Courts of the time and the Elector was very willing to see a man of non-Bavarian origin with power and influence. Here were all the elements for a fertile partnership. Thompson decided upon his course of action, and Charles Theodore responded by raising the standing and increasing the power of his aide-de-camp.

One of Thompson's first actions was to write to Sir Joseph Banks, who was President of the Royal Society, proposing that Charles Theodore should be elected to that body. Thompson described him as 'a most Respectable Prince famous for his amiable qualities and for his patronage of the arts and sciences'. He was anxious to ensure that the Elector had his proper place in the order of precedence; he supposed that he should appear in the list 'immediately after the last of the Kings' but he advised Banks to consult King George about this. This letter was written on 6 July 1784,[12] and it appears that Thompson had had no personal contact with the Elector until a few days before. This is a clear indication that Thompson had to make his own way. The view that he was immediately and openly welcomed as an adviser and reformer is false, and a facile inference from Thompson's own accounts written later as essays or given verbally to his friends. The true position he described in a letter to Sackville written in August 1785:

'You know my situation in this country and my prospects to the full as well as I do. I certainly stand well with my Master and I think I should have nothing to fear from his successor. I have made friends during my stay at Manheim who would have it much in their power to render me Service. Patience may be necessary but I think I cannot fail of succeeding if I can find the means of going on in the mean time. Employments here are not very lucrative but on the other hand living is cheap in proportion. The Emoluments of the place I hold are very triffling [sic] compared with the rank my Office gives me at the Court and the figure I am of consequence obliged to make. . . .'

Thompson went on to speak of his pay as a Bavarian colonel and to say he had expectations of a regiment.

This letter marked the end of a chapter in Thompson's personal relations. It was the last he wrote to Sackville who had been so true a friend and patron. In places its sentiment is cloying but Sackville was very ill at Stoneland as Thompson knew. There was deep feeling behind the words but equally evident was Thompson's self-centred concern with his own affairs. 'It is a most dreadful period to look to when we must part—the idea is almost insupportable—what must be the reallity? But I will not distress you with my melancholy reflexions. . . .'

As to his prospects he said that if his income were increased there would be little left for him to wish for. What follows accords ill with the earlier part of the letter. These sentences might have been written by a man at the end of his career:

'Titles, Decorations, Litterary Distinctions with some degree of litterary and some small degree of military fame I have acquired, (through your availing Protection) and the road is open to me for the rest. No man supports a better moral character than I do and no man is better satisfied with himself. . . .'

The letter ends: 'Adieu my Dear Lord. Pray write to me oft and let me know that you are perfectly recovered. I shall not have a moment's comfort till I hear from you again. . . .'[13]

Sackville never read the letter. He died at Stoneland Lodge ten days after it was written.

Whatever grief Thompson may have felt at the death of Sackville was quickly assuaged by his constant interests and activities. By nature, as he said, he would have preferred death to inactivity. He became friendly with a notable beauty, the Countess Baumgarten. He was also somewhat dangerously involved in the reorganization of the Bavarian Academy of Science. Some of the members of the Academy were also members of a sect known as the *Illuminati*. This movement, founded in 1776 by an ex-Jesuit named Adam Weishaupt, was republican in sympathy, rationalist in thought and had affiliations with various Masonic Lodges. Having been condemned by the Roman Catholic Church the movement was dissolved in 1785 by the Bavarian government, and the Bavarian Academy was suspect because of the complicity of some of its members. Thompson steered a course between the Jesuits on the one hand and the *Illuminati* on the other; in fact, he is said to have poked fun at both. When the end came for the

Illuminati he rescued the Academy and put it on a sound footing, at any rate for the time being.[14]

At first, however, he was mainly preoccupied with the army. He spent a long time collecting facts and making his plans and it was not until February 1788 that he presented to the Elector a Memorandum on Army Reform. This was considered by the Privy Council and he was entrusted to carry out the changes he had suggested. In the same year, in order presumably to give him authority to act, he was promoted to the rank of major-general, appointed adjutant-general and given a place on the Privy Council.

Thompson had all along two main ideas. The first was that the common soldier is the foundation of the army; the second, that the soldier should be well fed, well clothed and adequately paid. Before his reforms were made the conditions of service in the army were deplorable. A common complaint was that military service was used as a punishment for criminals; there was even a relation, established by law and publicly known, between a sentence in the house of correction and a period of military service. There was no bounty on enlistment. Far from it—the recruit started in debt. He was given certain articles of clothing and an allowance of five florins to buy the rest. But this cost at least sixteen florins and during the year he was obliged to spend on new equipment, and on maintenance of the old, far more than the further allowance of three florins given to him for this purpose. His difficulties did not end here, for his regular pay was inadequate for the food he needed. In order to make ends meet—such was the system— he did extra sentry duty for those who were away on leave. The man who was absent on leave 'was obliged to pay in money, under superintendence of the captain, the one who assumed in his stead the guard and sentry duty which fell to him'. In practice the money was generally set-off against the soldier's debts for clothing already received.

A system such as this could only work in peace-time and even then was dependent on the soldiers' earnings from other sources. It provided temptation to the officers to make profits on the transactions, and trading between officers and men fomented unrest and was bad for discipline. Thompson pointed out all this, also that man for man the Elector's army cost more than those of Prussia and Austria.

His first step was to eradicate these faults and abuses. He raised the private's basic pay slightly to five kreutzers (about three half-pence) a day and provided him with his clothing, and the equipment to keep it in repair, free of charge. This arrangement was possible because the clothing and equipment were made at the military workhouses. It was Thompson's boast that after his reforms no soldier in Europe was better clothed than the Bavarian. Furthermore, he remembered that he was concerned with an army at peace, and he arranged classes at the military schools in which the soldiers were taught reading, writing and the elements of arithmetic. He organized schools for the soldiers' children and provided employment for their wives. The paper used in schools was subsequently collected for raw material in making cartridges—an example of his flair for order and economy.

Thompson's aim was to make soldiers citizens and citizens soldiers. As much freedom as possible was given for the soldiers to work for their own profit when off duty, and he provided suitable working clothes. Like St Benedict, he believed idleness to be the great enemy of the soul, or at any rate bad for morals, and so every soldier was given an allotment to cultivate with an allowance of seeds for sowing and vegetables for planting. This work in the garden kept the soldier out of mischief, and gave him a useful craft and source of profit. The court gardener, Skell, calculated that the produce raised in one year on the Military Garden at Mannheim, where the system was also tried, was worth 10,000 florins. The same land before it was used in this way brought an income of only 500 florins a year. The crops were rotated, and unfamiliar or unusual vegetables cultivated, particularly the potato whose popularity Thompson did much to encourage in Central Europe.

For carrying out his plans he proposed to use the army to construct and repair roads, drain marshes, repair river-banks and, in his own words, where this was done 'the greatest care was taken to provide for their comfortable subsistence and even for their amusement. Good lodgings were prepared for them, and good wholesome food at a reasonable price; and the greatest care was taken of them when they happened to fall sick'.

Military bands replaced fife bands and each regiment had its own which provided music not only on military occasions but during working hours. The soldiers 'were permitted, and even encouraged, to make merry with dancing and other innocent sports and amusements'.

Woburn May 6th 1775

Sir, In compliance with your desires I embrace this
first opportunity that has offered since I left
Boston to send you some account of the
situation of affairs in this part of the Country

If you will be so kind as to deliver to
Mr. _____ of Boston, the Papers which I
left in your care and take his Receipt for the same,
You will much oblige

Your Humble Servant

The only information that I can give you
that can be of any consequence

Saturday May 6th 1775 from a Field officer
Army (if that mass of confusion may be called
an Army) & from a member of the Provincial
Congress that is now setting at Water town. By
them I learn that an Army consisting of
30,000 effective men is speedily to be raised in
the four New England Governments, & that the
quota for this Province is 13600. That as soon
as this Army shall be raised & regulated it is
generally supposed that the first movement
will be to make a feint attack upon the Town
of Boston, & at the same time to attempt the
Castle with the main body of their Army —
Whether this will be the precise plan of operation

1. The first page of Rumford's 'spy' letter.
(Reproduced, by permission, from the original manuscripts in the
William L. Clements Library in the University of Michigan)

Miscellanius Observations upon the state of the
Rebel Army.—

Upon Sunday October 15th I saw 16 flat bottom'd boats
or Batteaus lying just below Cambridge Bridge, & two more
were making on the yard.— The workmen informed me
that one was finished every day, and that more workmen
were daily expected from Newbury.— These Boats are built
of common deal Boards, & in general will contain from
50 to 60 Men, including the Rowers.— What number of them
were to be made I could not learn.

It is generally supposed in the Rebel Army that an
attack is designed upon either Charlestown, or Boston, or
or both—and that these boats are preparing to transport
Troops to those places—But many of the more intelligent
and among these some of their principal Officers, rather
suppose these preparations are only to amuse ye Kings
Troops, and by keeping them continually alarm'd with
apprehension of being attacked, prevent their going to dis
tant parts of the Country to Ravage.—

About the 13th October a return was made of the num
ber of Men, that all the boats of every denomination (ex
clusive of the flat bottom'd boats,) in the Rebel Camp were
capable of transporting—and I was told by a Person who
saw said return that the total number was 550.

From the best information I have been able to get
with respect to their Military Stores, the total quantity
of Gun-Powder that they have in their Camp, (exclusive
of

2. The first page of Rumford's *Miscellanius Observations upon
the State of the Rebel Army.*
(Reproduced, by permission, from the original manuscripts in the
William L. Clements Library in the University of Michigan)

Thompson spoke less of the reforms within the commissioned ranks. These were more difficult because of privilege, tradition and autocracy. The army was top-heavy with high-ranking officers, but Thompson none the less claimed that he increased the pay of some officers and speeded up promotion. With a view to sound, efficient training he established a military academy, and always interested in the care and condition of horses he founded a veterinary school. He also revised the arrangements for using troops for police duty. On his arrival he found, both in the Palatinate and in Bavaria, that the policing of the country was done by *chasseurs* or mobile troops who roamed at will and exacted lodging and forage from the farmers in return for inadequate payment. Thompson disbanded the corps of *chasseurs* and quartered four regiments of cavalry in garrisons to maintain law and order. He met part of the cost by a fixed charge on the farms so that the farmers knew their liability; they also knew that they were free from the obligation to provide quarters and food for men and horses at short notice. Thompson claimed that the new arrangement was far more efficient than the old, and as a measure of its success in Bavaria he stated that the cavalry arrested people at the rate of about 3000 a year—a figure to be borne in mind when we examine his frontal attack on beggary.

Many of these reforms seem enlightened, particularly when applied to a standing army which was disaffected and inefficient. But they aroused strong opposition and after four years, on 1 June 1792, Thompson presented a report on the work he had done, with a covering letter to the Elector asking him, for the satisfaction of both, to initiate a thorough investigation. He was criticized by the professional soldiers who doubted the wisdom of making soldiers citizens and citizens soldiers. His plan, some said, could only be the creation of a gifted dilettante. Looking at it impartially it is clear that the emphasis was more on the conversion of soldiers to citizens than the reverse. The professional soldiers also protested that discipline became slack. This is questionable, though, of course, the changes were designed to give independence and self-respect to the ranks. Some of the less enlightened officers, who had previously regarded men in the ranks as mere serfs, would naturally resent changes which made the private soldier less dependent upon a vicious system. There was also opposition to the new styles of uniform because they were similar to those of the

Imperial army. The Bavarians suspected that similarity meant sympathy, and they remembered vividly the Elector's earlier plan to exchange their country for part of the Netherlands.

The expense of Thompson's schemes came under fire. Complaints about the quartering of troops were violent, however much individual farmers may have been in favour. There were protests from all over the country at the number of soldiers' weddings, for the army held a new attraction for country girls. Even the Military Academy had its critics, and provoked anonymous letters, lampoons and satirical drawings. A contemporary drawing showed a picture of a soldier and below was printed this legend:[15]

> *Am Kopf ein Held,*
> *Im Sack kein Geld,*
> *Am Hals ein Kind,*
> *Der Bauch voll Wind,*
> *Hint und vorn ein armer Mann*
> *Der sich kaum bedecken Kann.**

This verse summarizes much of the criticism of Thompson's reforms. Though the soldier was given a fine helmet his pay was still small and he was burdened with family responsibilities. He was fed upon potatoes and turnips, and he depended upon the poor who—themselves dressed in rags—toiled to make his clothes.

The country was divided in its reaction to Thompson's schemes. The Elector issued an edict against those who ridiculed the new ideas but the disquiet remained. Thompson, however, was not without other strong supporters, and pamphlets were written in his favour. Moreover, he defended himself vigorously; sometimes, however, attacking his opponents by trying to brush aside criticisms when a more reasonable attitude might have served him better. For example, in his report he stated that he had spent nearly 45,000 florins on the

---

* Translated literally this reads:
> At the head a hero,
> In his purse no money,
> A child round his neck,
> A belly full of wind,
> Behind and before a poor man
> Who can scarcely cover himself.

Military Academy but his only justification was that 'no well-founded objection could be made to this expense' because in the future it must be 'of very great advantage to the military profession and . . . almost indispensable for the elevation of the same'. Similarly in defending the veterinary school he did not set out the advantages or attempt to show how the army would be getting value for money.

The Commission of Inquiry duly met and shortly afterwards published its findings. Guarded approval was given to Thompson's system which it was felt might bring important advantages to both the army and the state if various obstacles could be removed. It is said that Thompson himself thought he had been only partly justified and that he had won a Pyrrhic victory. His enemies continued to attack his scheme and, in spite of the findings of the Commission, to accuse him secretly of maladministration.[16]

Before this inquiry in 1792, Thompson had attacked another evil: beggary. His early reforms in the army were part of his campaign against the beggars who were a nation-wide scourge. The army was one of his assets; among his others were his growing ability to use his scientific knowledge for social and domestic purposes, the experience he had gained in founding a military workhouse in Mannheim, and the support of the Elector. He painted a highly coloured picture of the extent and corruption of mendicity in Bavaria. It had become ingrained in the life and economy of the people, and was now accepted by many as an unavoidable evil. Wandering beggars of both sexes were to be seen in the countryside and villages who threatened, stole and robbed for a livelihood. In the large towns, and in the capital particularly, there were swarms of these people. 'It was', said Thompson, 'almost impossible to cross the streets without being attacked and absolutely forced to satisfy their clamourous demands.' Many of them were not excused by age or infirmity, but were perfectly strong men who had chosen to live a life of idleness and debauchery rather than work for an honest living. They 'infested' the streets and the public places. They gave offence to worshippers in the churches. They stole from unguarded houses. By incitement to pity, by annoyance, threat and assault they levied a debased toll throughout the country. Young children, it was said, were stolen from their parents and were maimed, blinded or otherwise mutilated in order to arouse the pity and stimulate the generosity of the passer-by.

One section of this heinous community had become within its

ranks to some extent organized. It regulated the territories and gave each of its members his own beat and decided succession after promotion, resignation and death. This was the professional class of the confraternity, and in it beggars were married and given in marriage, passing on to their children the secrets of their trade and their black inheritance. This abuse of begging was complicated because begging by friars and nuns was an accepted method of raising money for genuine relief to the deserving poor. The directors of the leper hospital also had the privilege of begging for the public good. Students and out-of-work journeyman tradesmen, moreover, were a marginal class; they begged for themselves, but with better motives and less violence than the professional mendicant.

Cuvier blamed the rulers of Bavaria for allowing this social canker. They had encouraged devotion, he says, but had neglected industry. They supported the building of monasteries rather than factories; they had remained inactive in the face of ignorance. This judgement, however, neglects the wind of change which was blowing through Europe at the time, as well as the grave effects of prolonged war and political struggle. The problem was obviously both immense and complicated. It had many variables and demanded a lasting solution. Thompson's abilities were equal to the need. His plans and their execution show clearly the development which had taken place in his mental powers during his early years in Bavaria. Whether or not we agree with the canons, we recognize his confidence and maturity of judgement.

Rounding up the beggars, though not easy, was the least difficult part of his campaign. The core of the problem was what to do with them afterwards. Moreover, it would have been very unwise to have asked for money for his venture before beginning it. Thompson's two principal aims were to provide suitable employment for those beggars who could work, and humane assistance for the aged and the sick. He had to reassure those who would take alarm at what was certain to be regarded as a high-handed action, so he obtained the active support of the city magistrates and other well-known and respected public men. The care of the workhouses, the distribution of alms and the welfare of the poor were to be under the direction of a powerful committee on which would serve, among others, the respective presidents of the Supreme Regency, the Council of War, the Finance Council and the Head of the Ecclesiastical Council. This was an impressive array.

The city was divided into districts, for each of which a committee of charity was appointed with a priest, qualified medical men and a citizen of repute as chairman. The houses in each of the sixteen districts were numbered so that the abodes of all the beggars could be tabulated for reference. His arrangements completed Thompson acted with prompt and dramatic effect.

For this rounding-up he chose New Year's Day, 1790. It was a custom of long standing in Bavaria to give alms on New Year's Day and the beggars were out in force. Early in the morning the junior officers of three regiments of infantry were stationed in the streets of Munich. At the same time the field officers and chief magistrates were assembled in Thompson's apartments. His influence at the time can be gauged by the fact that they had gathered together without knowing what his plans were. He declared that he intended to seize all the beggars, and the procedure explained they all went into the street, Thompson leading the way. He was soon accosted by the first beggar asking for alms, and immediately told the unsuspecting man that henceforth begging was illegal, giving him into the charge of an orderly sergeant who was instructed to take him to the Town Hall. He had set the example, and Thompson now asked those with him to disperse to different parts of the city and arrest in this way all the beggars they met.

At the Town Hall the beggars had to give their names and addresses —even the hovels had been numbered. The able-bodied were ordered to present themselves on the following day at a military workhouse where they would find work, food and comfort. The others were told that after inquiry into their circumstances they might be eligible for poor relief and treatment.

Similar measures but with appropriate changes were carried out elsewhere, and Thompson employed his dispersed cavalry regiments to range over the country arresting the beggars as they showed themselves. It will be remembered that he gave the fact that his four regiments had made 3000 arrests in a year in support of his questionable use of troops as police.

The hope was that when the scheme was in full swing it would be self-supporting, but at the beginning a great deal of money was needed both for the relief of the sick and needy, and for food and working materials for the able-bodied. His first sources of income were the electoral treasury and the chest of the chamber of finance. He also used certain tolls and fines, and benefited from legacies. When he thought it prudent to ask for voluntary subscriptions he commissioned a member of the Bavarian Academy, a Professor Babo, to write an appeal. Babo's *Address and Petition* written in an ornate and florid style, and exuding self-conscious rectitude, was distributed by voluntary workers amongst the householders. With each copy there was a subscription form in a manner now commonplace but probably novel at the time. Afterwards collectors called on the subscribers monthly, district by district. Almost in the modern style provision was made for the well-to-do to subscribe directly through their bankers and for the not so well off to use collecting-boxes. Anonymous subscriptions were promptly and publicly acknowledged in the columns of the *Munich Gazette*. Poor-boxes were placed in churches, inns and coffee houses.

Considering the time and place Thompson worked on a big scale. His own accounts show that during the five years 1790–4 he received for his Institution for the Poor in Munich the sum of 320,298 florins—the equivalent then of about £30,000 sterling. More than half of this amount came from voluntary donations. He was the brain at the centre of the organization but much more besides. He was an active worker as well as a planner, devising and superintending kitchens, instructing workers and delivering subscription forms by hand.

The extent of his achievement can only be fully appreciated when his scientific work is taken into consideration and this will be examined in a later chapter. The philanthropic work that he did, however, had more than a touch of genius and it was based on exceptional ideals of order and thoroughness. Munich had never experienced anything like it; nor, in fact, had any other city. Here were the beginnings of a scientific campaign against poverty, want and squalor. The Church, of course, had always attempted relief and regeneration but Thompson's motives were different from those of the Church. He was not apparently moved by feelings of love for his fellow men; that is to say he was not impelled by Christian charity to change men's lives. He was a planner looking with benevolence rather than pity upon his fellow creatures. His own religion was deistic and he was, in his own mind, something of a minor deity manipulating impersonally but to their advantage the affairs of the unfortunate poor. He aimed at a moral regeneration of beggars; as he put it: 'to produce a . . . total and radical change in the morals, manners and customs of this debauched and abandoned race . . . to render them orderly and useful members of society'. He scorned preaching and punishment and sought to inculcate new habits. His approach was sociological and in many ways more in keeping with the ideas of the twentieth century than the eighteenth. He reversed the procedure of many reformers who, as he said, preached and acted on the assumption that happiness is the reward of virtue. It was much better, in his view, to make people first happy and then virtuous. 'If happiness and virtue be *inseparable* the end will be as certainly obtained by the one method as by the other; and it is most undoubtedly much easier to contribute to the happiness and comfort of persons in a state of misery than by admonitions and punishments to reform their morals.'

It would be dangerous to assume, however, that in his early work Thompson acted consistently upon exactly formulated moral principles. The practice came first; the principles crystallized as achievement grew. His efficiency was shown at its best in the arrangements made at the Military Workhouse. He had taken over a derelict factory situated in the Au, one of Munich's suburbs. There he had provided a kitchen, a bakehouse, a dining-room; shops for carpenters, smiths, turners, mechanics; halls for the spinning of hemp, flax, cotton, wool, worsted; rooms for weavers, clothiers, dyers, saddlers, knitters, sempstresses, wool-sorters, wool-combers, wool-carders; store-rooms and flats for officials. Spinning-wheels, looms, lathes, tools, raw materials and running water were all available.

As comfort and contentment were among his aims the workhouse was adequately lighted and heated; it was clean, tidy and freshly painted. In the middle there was a handsomely paved courtyard and the approaches were gravelled and spacious. Serving as a theme and a warning was a large notice in the corridor leading to the courtyard which said in gold letters on a black ground:

'NO ALMS WILL BE RECEIVED HERE.'

This building with all its machinery, tools, fabrics, raw materials and comforts was in itself a solid monument to Thompson's ability, power and knowledge. No one who had been nursed in a narrowly academic tradition could have done so much. His experiences in a farmer's household, in a Boston general store, and in the army contributed to the success of this undertaking.

Everything was ready for the beggars to be received. Many of them were unacquainted with any trade and some averse to work. Instructors and overseers were engaged to teach and direct without recourse to harsh language and ill-treatment. The tasks were graded and many of the workers were first taught to spin hemp, as the raw material was cheap and the skill easily acquired. In spite of his precautions Thompson lost 3000 florins during the first three months on hemp and flax alone. He paid the learners well in order to retain their interest and, to avoid the difficulties which would have followed had he later cut down the rate for the job, he used the expedient of transferring the semi-skilled to other work of a similar nature when they had reached a certain proficiency. He thoroughly understood the dangers of rate cutting and the importance, as we now say, of incentives.

Not surprisingly, even Thompson's powers of organization and planning did not prevent some confusion in the first week. But smooth working developed very quickly. Gouverneur Morris[17] when visiting the workhouse some time later was enthusiastic. He thought the kitchen 'wonderful'; the regularity, cleanness and economy of the house surpassed, he said, anything he ever saw. The poor were busy, happy and of cheerful countenance. He was moved to write 'Long may he be happy who has made them so', which was high praise from him. He continues:

'I taste of the soup given to the poor. It is very good and I see the crowd sit down to eat it with good appetite. The portion of bread, he [Thompson] tells me, is generally taken home by them for their supper. There are about one thousand people fed here at the annual expense of four hundred guineas, including everything. The contrivances for saving cloth, linen, leather, etc. in making clothes, the arrangements to prevent fraud, and to keep accounts for the regiments, etc., are all admirable. . . .'

Thompson did not have complete success with the hardened beggars. Even good pay did not compensate them sufficiently for their loss of freedom; they had lived in idleness too long. He expected to be most successful with the young; whom he could 'inspire with a true spirit of persevering industry'. He hoped to awaken in them 'a dormant passion whose influence they had never felt—the love of honest fame, an ardent desire to excel, the love of glory, or by what other or more pompous name this passion, the most noble and beneficent that warms the human heart, can be distinguished'. To encourage emulation, reward was given. Good workers were publicly encouraged, promoted, introduced to distinguished visitors and given special uniforms. The quotation throws light on Thompson's own mind and motives. His lack of warm affection is clear; the noblest motive is the desire for 'honest fame' or 'the love of glory'. The desire to distinguish himself had burned in Thompson throughout his progress from Salem to Au.

He had a way of dealing with the youngest children. They were seated round the walls of the rooms where the older children were working. This was tedious for them and they soon begged to be allowed to do light and easy work, often weeping 'if this favour was not instantly granted to them'. 'How sweet these tears were to me', he says, 'can easily be imagined.' But, to be fair to him, he had a nobler idea than achieving a high output or maintaining discipline, for he set up a school where the children had to go for two hours each day to learn reading, writing and arithmetic.

It was important to Thompson, both then and afterwards, to show that the Military Workhouse paid its way. It was not financed by voluntary subscriptions but provided with its own capital, first of 150,000 florins and later 250,000 florins. An army commission managed it and the poor supplied the labour for the manufacture of army uniforms and stores, for which they were paid. Feeding the poor at both the Military Workhouse and the separate Institution for the Poor, and the distribution of food and money to the indigent in their homes were financed from the separate fund I have already referred to. The Military Workhouse made a net profit of 100,000 florins in six years and paid an average dividend of about 8 per cent per annum. He was particularly proud of his kitchens and fed in the Workhouse over a thousand people every day at a daily cost for fuel of fourpence-half-penny. What is perhaps more astonishing is that all the kitchen work was done by three cook-maids. No wonder that many looked on him later with awe and admiration, and some with amusement, in the hungry cities of Europe.

He obtained cheaply much of the food he needed. Before the great rounding-up the beggars had regularly extorted considerable quantities of food from bakers, butchers and restaurant proprietors. Afterwards, delivered from impost and blackmail, shopkeepers and others were more than willing to make voluntary gifts in kind for the feeding of the poor. Brightly painted carts drawn by neatly harnessed ponies were sent round to collect bread, offal and other foodstuffs. Elaborate precautions were taken not only to prevent theft but also to convince the donors that theft was unlikely to occur.

In the early days the midday meal at the Military Workhouse consisted of about a pound and a quarter of rich soup of peas and barley with cuttings of fine white bread. Seven ounces of ryebread was given with the soup but, as Morris said, this was usually taken home for supper. Many worked at home because of sickness or infirmity and food was sent daily to them and to others genuinely unable to attend the Military Workhouse.

In spite of this resounding success, however, Thompson's most enduring work in Bavaria, giving the greatest pleasure to the people of Munich, was the construction of a large park on land that had previously been a marsh. It was laid out in 1789. Along the bank of the River Isar he found a 'dreary waste of pebbly strand and marshy ground', and turned it into a garden in the English style. He used a corps of the army to clear, drain and lay out the site; he gave the soldiers free lodgings, special clothing and extra pay and provided opportunity for recreation and amusement. The English Garden is still one of the glories of Munich and a boon to its citizens.

Thompson was a quick learner in many fields. During his stay in England he had become acquainted with the prevailing fashion in designing large gardens. He was also a great admirer of many aspects of Chinese life, as the pagoda in the garden bears witness. Not that it was the first of its kind. Kew already possessed an impressive example ten stories high, built in 1762. His English Garden was a magnificent achievement, particularly for a man occupied with many other affairs. Its benefits were fully recognized by the people of Munich, rich and poor alike, and during his absence from the city in 1795 a striking memorial was set up in the gardens with the following inscription:

'To him
Who eradicated the most disgraceful
public evils
Idleness and Mendicity
Who to the Poor gave Succour
Occupation, good Habits
and to the Youth of the Fatherland
So many cultural Institutions
Go Stroller and strive to match him
In Spirit and Action
And us
In Gratitude'

The garden is bigger now than Thompson originally made it, but his conception and much of his work remains. There are streams, trees, miniature waterfalls and pleasant walks; there is a small pleasure ground for the children, a lake and a monopteros. Some of its 600 acres can be enjoyed from the seat of a landau. During the Second World War the pagoda was destroyed in an air-raid but after the war it was quickly restored. The memorial to Rumford has also been rebuilt in the last few years. The care bestowed upon the English Garden is a measure of the regard the people of Munich have for it.

When the garden was first made it was the cause of a serious quarrel. Not long after it was opened some public-spirited and thankful citizens addressed a letter of thanks to the Elector, and Thompson, highly gratified by this gesture, had the letter printed, signed by officials and distributed amongst the people. The City Council strongly objected to this action holding it to be 'propaganda behind their backs', and an offence against the rules of local government; furthermore, they threatened to bring an action against the signatories. Thompson was angered by this move but too clever to come into open conflict with the city fathers. He therefore slyly protested to the Elector that they had attempted to restrict a spontaneous expression of regard for the Sovereign. The Elector, as usual, accepted Thompson's views and decided to dismiss the City Council. In spite of the indignation that the decision aroused the Elector did not relent and some months afterwards, on 21 May 1791, the members of the Council were obliged to meet the Elector and apologize for their action. They were nevertheless deprived of civic rights for life.

This episode did Thompson some harm. It was felt that he might have been magnanimous where he had been vindictive. Resentment against him grew in the city and was added to criticism from the army. The Elector's regard, however, remained undiminished and he showed his appreciation by conferring honours upon him. As far back as 1785 he had been made court chamberlain. The next year, at Charles Theodore's request, the King of Poland had made him a Knight of the Order of St Stanislaus. In 1791, the year of the quarrel with the Munich City Council, the Elector used his power as one of the Vicars of the Holy Roman Empire, during the interval between the death of Joseph II and the coronation of Leopold II, and ennobled him. Thompson was made a Count of the Holy Roman Empire and a Knight of the Order of the White Eagle. He took the title of Rumford from Concord, New Hampshire, which had previously been called Rumford. It has been said that he chose Rumford out of gratitude because it was there he had been given a start in life by the Reverend Timothy Walker. There may be some truth in this, and moreover the estate he had abandoned was in Concord. The old form was preferable to Count Concord: it was obviously more euphonious, and as Thompson had provoked a good deal of disagreement everywhere he had stayed since his youth he could scarcely have carried round with him so evocative a title! The other title, Knight of the White Eagle, was appropriate. He had soared to power and fame and if he had not reached the apogee of his flight he was, in 1791, very near it.

In 1798 Rumford virtually ended his full-time association with Bavaria. Up till then one of the projects to which he attached importance was improving the breeds of horses and horned cattle. He believed that in providing horses 'for the use of the army and particularly for the train of artillery' his plan would benefit farmers and army alike. A number of fine mares were to be bought at the expense of the army and given, after being branded, to farmers for use as their own property. The conditions were that the mares should be covered every season by an approved stallion and that, should the army take the field, either the mares or suitable alternative horses should be provided for active service. The farmers were to keep the foals. This ingenious scheme for making army horses earn their keep was not a success because, so Rumford alleges, the peasants were obstinate and suspected trickery. It was also obviously unpractical because a farmer might be asked to give up a horse on which he was relying at a moment when it was most urgently needed. Rumford bitterly blamed some of his enemies who 'from motives too obvious to require any explanation, took great pains at that time to render abortive every public undertaking in which' he 'was engaged'.

He did better, however, with his cattle. In designing the English Garden he had in mind utility as well as beauty and amenity. Within the confines of the garden he had built at intervals cottages and farmhouses. To help stock the farms he imported thirty-five head of cattle. He made one of the farms a show place, and many people who had little interest in the breeding of cattle nevertheless went to see 'the beautiful and extraordinary animals'. The cowsheds 'were concealed in a thick wood behind a public coffee house in the middle of the garden'.

Rumford, in spite of his intelligence, sometimes found it difficult to realize that other people's interests were different from his own, and his enthusiasms often clouded his judgements. He was at times naive in his advocacy of reforms. In proposing similar measures for other countries he said that such a farm as the one in the English Garden 'would soon become a place of public resort and improvements in agriculture a *fashionable amusement*. The ladies, even, would take pleasure in viewing from their carriages the busy and most interesting scenes of rural industry and it would no longer be thought vulgar to understand the mysteries of Ceres.'[18]

One side of Rumford's work in Germany which has never received attention was the part he played in introducing the steam engine into the Palatinate. In the Birmingham Assay Office, which houses the Boulton and Watt Collection of Manuscripts, there are various letters which show that in 1791 Rumford interested the Elector in a scheme to install a steam-driven pump in Mannheim. The installation was needed as part of the town's water supply and was to be used to raise water from wells and deliver it to a reservoir. At the Elector's request Joseph von Baader, the Bavarian engineer, wrote to Boulton and Watt a letter dated 27 February 1791, giving the necessary details. The engineering firm replied three weeks later, and a firm order was placed in April. In the following July Baader came over to Birmingham bringing with him Georg Reichenbach from Mannheim to be instructed in maintaining the engine. Before this one went to Western Germany the improved Watt engine was, according to Baader, totally unknown in that part of the Continent.

Rumford (then Sir Benjamin Thompson) is spoken of by Baader as one 'to whose indefatigable activity our Country, of late, owes all its greatest improvements'. He would have liked, too, a concession for the manufacture of the Watt engine, for that seems to be the implication of the following paragraph in Baader's letter of 25 April:

'His Highness being a great patron to Arts and Sciences and very desirous of adopting any new invention that may be of service to his Country, Mr Boulton may . . . propose, if he pleases, his Conditions under which he would chuse to communicate to the Elector the Secret of his Inventions in that line.'

But Mr Boulton did not choose to communicate his secrets either then or later, when he quite understandably refused Rumford's request to make specifications and models of the latest engines freely available.[19]

Early in 1793 Rumford fell ill. When he had sufficiently recovered he obtained leave to travel in Italy and set out on an extended tour. At that time there were many members of the English upper classes in Italy; it was the fashion to sojourn there, so Rumford could expect to meet old friends and make new ones. His reputation was already considerable, both as a man of science and as a social reformer. Among those making a leisurely journey in Italy were Sir Charles Blagden and the Palmerston family, travelling together. Blagden was the Secretary of the Royal Society and an intimate friend of its illustrious President, Sir Joseph Banks; the Palmerston family consisted of the second Viscount, his wife and children.

Blagden introduced the Count to his friends at Milan on 18 June, and Lady Palmerston thought him 'a great acquisition to our Society . . .'.[20] She records that he 'draws well, takes sketches as we are on the lake and has a thousand resources . . .'. She was very impressed by his history, and particularly by his work in Bavaria, which evidently he did not understate.

After a month the party separated and Rumford went to Verona where he supervised the rebuilding of the kitchens of the hospitals of

La Pieta and La Misericordia. He also undertook to supply the directors of the La Pieta hospital with clothes for its inmates. He hoped, as he said, 'soon to see the poor of Bavaria growing rich by manufacturing clothing for the poor of Italy'.[21]

Rumford was not only concerned with applied science and practical affairs, he lost no opportunity of seeing and making experiments of a fundamental nature. At Pavia he and Blagden had visited Volta who was conducting an important series of electrical experiments which later led to the discovery of the voltaic cell and the production of steady electric currents. In 1793 Rumford saw these experiments in a transitional stage when Volta's ideas were still influenced by the earlier work of Galvani of Bologna, and some years later he saw their culmination in Paris. His path crossed the Palmerstons' more than once and in Florence he persuaded them to act as observers in some experiments on the harmony of colours. He hoped to discover principles and construct instruments which would enable the eye to be entertained in a manner analogous to that by which the ear is entertained by musical sounds. He also saw the possible application of the principles of the harmony of colours to a pleasing choice of dress and furnishings.

In the spring of the year 1794 Rumford was ill in Naples. Blagden had returned home. The previous December Rumford had written from Pisa to Lady Palmerston, who was in Florence, to say that he had become so used to her company that he felt awkward when deprived of it; that he was 'lonesome and melancholy', 'an exile doomed to roam in the wide world, without a home and without a friend . . .'.[22] Later the Palmerstons came to Naples and Rumford recovered in body and spirits. Shortly afterwards he returned to Munich after an absence of sixteen months, and on their way home his friends spent a happy fortnight with him in Bavaria.

It is quite certain that while on holiday Rumford thought seriously about his family affairs and his future career. His wife had died in January 1792, and he began to think of providing for his daughter and of inviting her to join him. The admirable Lady Palmerston may have turned his thoughts to marriage, and his contact with English people to England. Bavaria had given him much, not least a stage on which to display his powers, but the years had brought bitter opposition. Should he remain there, the chamberlain and minister of an Elector who was becoming increasingly ineffective as a ruler in the political confusion of the struggle between Austria and France and the decay of the Empire? Should he attempt to return to America where, if he were politically acceptable, his experience of civil and military affairs would find ample scope? Ought he to find a field for the implementation of his philanthropic ideas, a place where he could foster the application of science to the everyday affairs of living? Was there a career for him in the diplomatic service?

There is little doubt that he made plans. But for the time being he concentrated upon writing his essays and completed the first five. Although by this time he had command of French and German he wrote most easily in English and no doubt he saw in England the most fruitful field in which to implant his ideas. The titles of the essays show his interests at this time. They were: *Public Establishments for the Poor in Bavaria*; *Fundamental Principles of Establishments for the Poor*; *Of Foods*; *Of Chimney Fireplaces*; *An Account of Several Public Institutions*. Some of their content has already been discussed; I shall come back to the rest later.

As he wrote his enthusiasm grew, and in September 1795 he again obtained leave of absence, this time to visit England. He wanted to superintend the publication of his essays and to meet his daughter whom he had summoned from America. He also wanted to put into practice his plans for economical large-scale cooking. On 3 November 1794 he had written to Lady Palmerston to describe some of his experiments and to ask her the price of coal in England. 'What a fortune I could make by coming to England and taking out a patent for my new inventions relative to the economy of fuel and entering into partnership with Boulton. . . .'

In the following June he told Lady Palmerston of the beauties of his garden, of the magnificent amphitheatre he had constructed there to hold 2000 persons and of the concerts he held in his apartments. He also expressed his deep affection for her, saying that he was in love with her but, with greater propriety, that she was his sincere and affectionate friend.[23]

But misfortune met him when he arrived in London. As he was driving in his post chaise and four he was held up in the darkness in St Paul's Churchyard 'by a gang of villains' and a large trunk was cut off from behind his carriage. He made a great fuss about this because the trunk contained many private papers and scientific notes. He wrote

3. A portrait of Count Rumford at the time he was
sent to England as Ambassador from Bavaria at the
age of forty-five.

4–5. The English Garden, Munich.

(Plates are reproduced by permission of Herr Retzer, Landeshaupstadt München, Fremdenverkehrsamt, München)

to Lady Palmerston the next day (14 October) saying that the loss was irreparable and that it was unlikely that he would ever smile again.

This incident had been the cause of much speculation. In a paper Rumford presented to the Royal Society on *Experiments to determine the Force of Fired Gunpowder* in 1799, nearly four years later, he said: 'This most severe blow has left an impression on my mind which I feel that nothing will ever be entirely able to remove. It is the more painful to me, as it has clouded my mind with suspicions that can never be cleared up.'[24] There is another reference to the loss in his essay *Of the Management of Fire and the Economy of Fuel*, where he says that he has many reasons to believe that the papers 'are still in being'.[25] These references have prompted a suggestion that the robbery might have had a political motive and even have been instigated by the British government because of dissatisfaction with his achievements 'as a British Secret Agent in Bavaria'.[26] This, however, is too fanciful an explanation. The robbery might have been the action of a jealous rival or of someone who resented some slight or injury, fancied or real. It could have been the work of someone hired by an unscrupulous tradesman who wished to pick Rumford's brains. Rumford's own words do suggest that he believed the robbery not to have been the action of a common thief or footpad, but then he was prone to exaggeration and like many very self-centred people he tended to magnify the enmity and malice of his opponents. Quite recently it has become clear that his losses were not crippling, some of his most valuable papers were not in the trunk, though his commonplace book was. Moreover, the reward of ten guineas which he offered for the recovery of the property brought forward a man who had found fragments of the papers in the street. In spite of what Rumford wrote the most likely explanation is that 'the gang of villains' were after booty of more tangible and immediate value than accounts of experiments, and that when they saw what was in the trunk they destroyed the papers in disgust.

This chapter is mainly concerned with Rumford's work in Bavaria, so his activities during the six months' leave—apart from the momentous meeting with Sally—must wait.

Long after her father's death Sally was persuaded to write an account of her life. She addressed it to Loammi Baldwin's second wife who had encouraged her in the enterprise. It was never published, but is vivid, candid and amusing. She called it *Memoirs of a Lady, written by herself*, and it affords valuable information and penetrating comments upon her father's doings and character.

Sally and her father had been writing to each other for at least three years before they met in London. Ellis infers that she had received a proposal of marriage from a Mr Stacey. If she had, since her mother was dead and she was under twenty-one years of age, her suitor would have to obtain the permission of the Count. No marriage took place. Possibly Rumford advised her against it,[27] but there is no evidence about his motives. At any rate it is likely that he began to send money for her support and also to help his mother. In a letter to Baldwin, which is dated 18 January 1793, he said that he wished exceedingly to be personally acquainted with his daughter, that he wanted to know her real character, and 'to lay a solid foundation for her future happiness'.

At the end of January 1796 Sally sailed in the *Charlestown* from Boston, and after a voyage of six weeks arrived in London. She brought with her a letter from Baldwin to her father, which was partly a testimonial on her behalf and perhaps designed to prepare him for her countrified ways. 'She possesses a noble mind,' wrote Baldwin, 'and wants nothing but the aid of her father to make her accomplished.' She had been attentive to her grandmother who 'expressed much affection for her and had assisted in her education'. In another letter, written six months later, he wrote: 'I know you will continue to be pleased with your amiable daughter. . . . She was beloved by everybody when she was here and I only regret . . . that it was not within my power to pay more attention to her education and happiness than I did.'

This meeting of father and daughter who were strangers to each other was bound to be an emotional strain for both. Sally had built up in her mind a romantic picture of a handsome, uniformed soldier carrying a sword. When she saw him, thin and pale with once red hair that had lost its colour, she wept with disappointment and would willingly have run from him. Rumford, of course, had his emotions under firmer control and said that Sally looked better than he had expected—an ambiguous remark which she explained by saying 'It is true he had had a most unfavorable likeness of me in a small miniature.'

But he had prepared for her coming with his usual thoroughness. He had brought a maid named 'Anymeetle' for her from Munich, and arranged for her to stay at a boarding house near his hotel in Pall Mall. He sent her with the maid to buy shoes and materials for dresses. This she did with a vengeance, not having, as she admitted, 'the least knowledge of the real value of money', and greatly offended her father's sense of propriety and economy. This extravagance was not her worst offence in the Count's eyes. On one occasion he took her with him to visit a particular friend of his. The lady was not at home but they saw the housekeeper. Sally, coming from a part of the world where even the best people kept house for themselves, failed to gauge this person's social status. On leaving, Sally made one of her 'very best, lowest courtesies'—and this to a *housekeeper*! 'Poor man!' she says with detached humour; and, indeed, Rumford must have shuddered miserably for he knew exactly the right tone, mode of address and degree of deference for meeting and communicating with all gradations of society, with everyone from an emperor to his own valet, Aichner.

Rumford appears to have acquired a taste for Italian opera during his tour of Italy. Not so Sally, who preferred music in simpler form:

'Poor man! He had occasion to tremble for another circumstance. I, having been promised to go with him to the Italian Opera, was, unfortunately to be with a party of high fashionables. After, I suppose, weighing matters well, instead of retracting his promise, he concludes to lecture me. Whatever my impressions of the music, I was to make no observations; preferring, it seems, insipidity to an improper remark. This music being an acquired taste, and I having had the advantage of only that which was most simple and natural, it is true I was not enchanted. I much preferred—*within myself*, of course—old Black Prince's fiddle, of Concord; particularly when a rosy lad, leading to the floor of the dance his still more rosy partner, looking sternly, said peremptorily, "Make your fiddle speak, Prince." '[28]

Lady Banks was kind to her, entertaining her for days on end, taking her to the Lord Mayor's Ball and inviting her to the select dinners of the Royal Society where she was agreeably surprised by finding excellent conversation without pedantry. Her father was slightly ashamed of her ignorance and autocratic in his attitude, so the poor girl was sometimes miserable in spite of the friendliness and lack of condescension of the Palmerstons and the Bankses. When Rumford went to Ireland at the invitation of the Hon. Thomas Pelham in order, amongst other duties, to give advice on the heating of the Irish House of Commons, Sally was sent for three months to a superior boarding school in Barnes's Terrace kept by the Marquise of Chabann.

It seems that when Sally came to England no decision had been made about the length of her stay. It was perhaps a trial period. Rumford's leave of absence had now run its course and there were urgent political reasons for his return. His future depended on the Elector and the Elector's own future was uncertain, and so late in July 1796 Rumford, his daughter and their servants began the long journey back to Munich via Hamburg. The carriage he had brought with him to London was not big enough for the party and a new one had to be acquired. It had belonged to a duke and still bore his armorial achievement. This was an embarrassment to Rumford for the postmaster, no doubt seeing the strawberry leaves, insisted that eight horses were *de rigueur* whereas Rumford wanted only five being a mere count and no doubt thinking of the expense.

After three weeks of trying travel in the ducal carriage, a roundabout route having been taken to avoid troop movements and bad roads, with either inferior accommodation or none, but a day of relaxation at the Leipzig Fair and much of interest to see, they arrived at Munich. Sally was impressed by the city and by her father's apartments. Years earlier Rumford had persuaded the Elector to reopen a mansion which had been furnished for someone of note but which had been closed since his death. The Russian Ambassador took the ground floor and Rumford the first floor. It appears to have been a distinguished house approached through a wide gateway into a courtyard enclosed by the building. It contained a magnificent wooden staircase, 'polished', according to Sally, 'like plate-glass'.

She wrote a few lines shortly afterwards to Mrs Baldwin to tell her that she was well and happy, but the letter is rather formal and quite different from the later style of her memoirs. One sentence at least, 'My reception here was highly flattering, and I have every reason to be pleased and happy with my new situation', clearly could have been dictated by her father.

Rumford was gratified by his reception. During his absence the commemorative monument had been erected in the English Garden. He wrote to Lady Palmerston to say that it was such that he 'dare not describe it' and he could not read the inscriptions engraved in Bavarian marble without blushing. 'To think how little I have deserved them. I wish you could have seen my daughter—when they were translated to her—as she stood with her eyes swimming in tears, gazing on her father's bust . . .'.[29] Although Rumford aroused the opposition and even the enmity of the City Council and the army in Munich, he was popular with the people, particularly the poor. They were grateful for many of the reforms he had introduced. During his illness, before he went to Italy, many of them walked in procession to the cathedral to pray for his recovery, although he was not of their faith. In the Military Workhouse and the Institution for the Poor, too, prayers were said daily for his recovery, both then and later.

But however pleasant Rumford found his return and reception, politically speaking, Bavaria was in turmoil. There was danger from outside and internal strife. The Peace of Basel, in 1795, had reduced the area of conflict in Europe, but the struggle between France and Austria continued. With Prussia out of the war and with the German states lacking unity the situation was dangerous for both. Late in 1795 the French forced the Austrians to retreat behind the Main. Their advance caused the surrender of Mannheim. Rumford's military reforms were blamed for this but probably without justice, for Charles Theodore was distrusted by both sides and the Austrians did not put it beyond him to attempt a separate agreement with France. However, good Austrian generalship changed the military situation and Mannheim was recaptured the same year. After a brief armistice fighting was resumed in 1796. French forces under Moreau crossed the Danube and invaded Bavaria. The Bavarians, without faith in the Elector, still suspicious of Austria and experiencing the ravages of war for the first time, were in a sorry plight. Their nearest and gravest danger was of being badly mauled in the fight between the two main powers, for the Austrians had retreated on Munich. Expediency dictated a policy of neutrality. When Rumford on 19 August returned the crisis was at its height.

The Elector had packed up and sent to Austria all his most valuable effects. On 25 August he and his wife fled to Lokwitz, a country seat in Saxony belonging to his minister in Dresden. Rumford at that time had no command but was deputed to act in Munich as the eyes and ears of the absent Elector and, should the city be invaded or occupied, to use what influence he had to preserve the buildings and institutions. As far as the Austrians were concerned the city, being a sovereign's place of residence, had the right to refuse the passage of the troops—

even those of the Emperor. The French were under no obligation to treat Munich as an open city.

Before the Elector fled, the French attacked the Austrians at Friedburg and forced them back to Dachau which is only a few miles from Munich. As a result the allied army of Prince Condé fell back to protect the left flank of the Austrian army and to give time for the baggage of both armies to cross the Isar at Munich. The troops followed, passing over the bridge, and took up new positions on high ground commanding the bridge and city. The regular Bavarian army had been brought in from the outside garrisons to protect the city and to avoid clashes and, all told, there were about 12,000 troops in the city. The gates of the city were closed and the Austrian general was brusquely told that he might cross the Isar but that if he attempted to pass through the city he would be opposed by force. The Bavarian officers, either because they were over-scrupulous or because of a traditional opposition to the Austrians, refused personal admittance to the Austrian Commander-in-Chief when he wished to pay a private visit to the city. It is likely that they feared the French most at that time and wanted to be ostentatiously neutral. The Austrian general, La Tour, resented the treatment he received and threatened to bombard the city should the French come near. This threat, the presence of so many Bavarian soldiers in the city and the Bavarian commander's lack of ability combined to destroy confidence and spread alarm. Rumford, who had been living as a private citizen without 'even putting on his regimentals', was called in at this juncture by the Regency. The move restored confidence, Rumford placated La Tour, the French withdrew and Munich was saved. Charles Theodore showed his gratitude by making Rumford head of the Police Department in Bavaria, conferring upon Sally—perhaps we should now call her Sarah— the courtesy title of Countess of the Empire and allowing Rumford to resign one-half of his pension of £400 a year in her favour, which pension she was to receive in any country in which she cared to reside.

Although Rumford's firmness and his ability to feed thousands saved the city from a good deal of trouble and perhaps destruction, that is not quite the whole story, for as a result of a treaty Bavaria, while pledging her neutrality, paid 10,000,000 livres and a heavy contribution in kind to France. The French did not negotiate from a position of strength, for Jourdan had been defeated on the Rhine and

Moreau's situation in Bavaria was insecure. The action of Bavaria at this time has been described as pusillanimous and it is true that it did not contribute to wider German unity.[30] We are not directly concerned with that aspect, however, since Rumford had little or no influence in the shaping of foreign policy.

Nearly all who have written about Rumford have misunderstood his position in Bavaria; they have exaggerated his political power. It is obvious that he had great influence with the Elector and a high position in the state. But his position was that of a state official rather than a statesman. This is well illustrated by the fact that he was not a member of the Council of Regency when Charles Theodore had fled and, moreover, he stayed in the background until called to take control. What then could he look forward to in Bavaria? Certainly not ministerial influence. He could rely on the Elector's support for his schemes of reform and welfare but the Elector was over seventy years old and a declining force. But even with the support of his patron his position *vis-à-vis* the ministers was likely to be impossible; 'battle without victory was to be his lot'. As long as three years before, in 1793, he had told Loammi Baldwin that he was 'sick of the bustle of public affairs' and earnestly hoped and longed for deliverance. Lady Palmerston had gathered from him that he had the whole country against him.

At the end of the year 1796 his prestige and influence were at their highest, and as far as he could judge must decline—the eagle had soared to his highest point. For two years, except for one crisis, he went on quietly with his scientific experiments, supervised his workhouses, looked after Sally and lived on a grand scale. He had made inquiries about returning to America and had been assured by Baldwin that he would be welcomed but he was hesitant to take the step. Then in 1798 he saw the opportunity he wanted. He asked to be appointed Bavarian Ambassador in London or, more accurately, Minister Plenipotentiary and Envoy Extraordinary to the Court of St James's in succession to Count Haslang who was retiring after many years.[31] To his great satisfaction the Elector acceded to his request. Shortly afterwards, accompanied by Sarah, he set out for England in high spirits and looking forward to his new office and duties (see Plate 3, facing page 96). They arrived in London on 19 September 1798, but in store for him was one of the greatest disappointments of his life. The last time he 'set foot on this ungrateful island' his baggage had been stolen, this time much worse befell him: he was not acceptable to the King and government as an ambassador.

He felt angry, resentful and belittled, particularly as he had made inquiries about his appointment some months earlier, without finding any objection. Five days before Rumford arrived in London the Foreign Secretary had written in unequivocal terms to Arthur Paget, the English minister in Munich, saying that Rumford's appointment was unacceptable, that His Majesty's decision was irrevocable and that because of it there was no doubt that the Elector would appoint someone else. The reasons put forward were, first, that Rumford was a British subject and, secondly, that he had 'filled a confidential Situation (that of Under-Secretary of State in the American Department) under His Majesty's Government'.

Rumford in his haste had, of course, left Munich long before the letter reached Paget and had also passed through Hamburg before Sir James Crauford, the Government's representative there, could tell him privately of the decision. Canning, the Under-Secretary at the Foreign Office, waited on Rumford at his hotel to make the King's decision known to him. It was clear that the decision was quite final. Rumford asked for an audience of the King to deliver to him a letter from the Elector. He offered to resign on the pretext of bad health in order to prevent altercation between the Elector and the British government. There was, however, no altercation. The Elector accepted the situation and after a decent interval another appointment was made, and Rumford officially retired from the service of Bavaria and became 'a free, independent citizen of the world'.[32] He retained his pension and acted as an unofficial agent for the Elector. He said later that he was 'handsomely out of a bad scrape'.[33]

Rumford had further contacts with Bavaria during the next sixteen years, but his main work there was finished. He had spent fourteen years in the service of his adopted country: when he went there he knew no German, indeed his first memorandum on Army Reform was presented to the Elector in French, but he quickly adapted himself to his circumstances. In one sense he was fortunate, for the personality of his patron and master suited him, giving him freedom and encouragement. Some of Rumford's characteristics grated on his contemporaries, but his pliancy and powers of adaptation were astonishing. He did not allow his heart to rule his head though there was, in every major phase of his youth and early manhood an attachment to a patron to whom he gave devoted and efficient service in return for advancement and favour.

State Councillor von Martius, at the centenary celebrations of the Royal Bavarian Academy, described him as 'an active philanthropist in a rough garment' working 'for the welfare of all not according to the impulses of his heart but for the sake of order and material prosperity in the state'. His roughness was not habitual, but it was quick to appear when he was crossed. He was appalled by the laxity, obstruction and inefficiency he found in Bavaria. Gouverneur Morris records an example of Rumford's forcefulness in getting things done. The Elector's ministers, Morris said, were so much under the influence of the National Assembly that on one occasion the Elector could not get a document he needed to sign copied in his own private chancery for six weeks. The Assembly had heard of its contents and they attempted to impeach the minister responsible for it, proposing to send a deputation to the Elector. Rumford was angry about this and advised the Elector, who was as timid as his minister, to go on a hunting expedition. While he was away Rumford went to the Chancery and told the secretary that if the document were not on the Elector's desk ready for signing by eight o'clock next morning he would lose his job. 'It is impossible,' said the secretary, 'there is too little time, the document is not yet begun.' Whereupon Rumford called in all the clerks, distributed the work amongst them, and repeated his threat. Needless to say, the paper was ready in time.

The Austrian general, von Werneck, though perhaps prejudiced against Rumford for personal reasons (he looked upon him as an obstacle to his brother's promotion) described him 'as a man with much genius and information and the zeal and activity of a planner'. He was, said von Werneck, 'extremely vain' and 'the hero of his own panegyric'—a just and pithy comment—and 'apt to neglect a business when he had brought it to the point of maturity'.

At the time of the controversy which was aroused by his army reforms, an enthusiastic supporter spoke of him as 'a man of noble soul, full of knowledge, full of spirit, enterprising and worthy to play one of the leading roles at the court of one of the first sovereigns of Germany'. His colleague, von Lichtenberg, considered the 'Europeanized American' to be the most useful experimenter of his age because of the success of his experiments in heating, cooking and mass feeding. But it was also said of him, that like the over-hasty reformer Joseph II of Austria, he was destined to overdo everything.

How permanent were the results of his work? His army reforms certainly did not last. His concept of an army of instructed citizens closely knit into the life of the state had no appeal for the professional officers and it is said that ten years after he left Bavaria all that remained of his system was the *raupenhelm*[34]—the type of helmet he introduced.

His work for the poor was more permanent. His institutions flourished for some years and remained in being for many more. His principles and practice of economical feeding and poor relief caught the imagination of reformers both in Bavaria and far beyond. Many changes came later with increased industrialization, and it is fair to say that Rumford accelerated them and helped to inspire men like Maximilian Joseph and his minister, Montgelas, who followed Charles Theodore.[35]

Rumford's most lasting contribution to Bavarian life was the English Garden. This, with its memorial, a street and an imposing statue in the Maximilian Strasse, remain to remind the visitor of one who made noble attempts to apply intelligence and scientific knowledge to improve the lot of soldier and citizen in a land that was not his own.

I will end this chapter with a verse which, although untrue in detail, shows how Rumford's work in Bavaria impressed one of his contemporaries in England. It was written by Thomas J. Mathias and is taken from a poem published in 1794 entitled:

The Pursuits of Literature

'Yet all shall read, and all that page approve,
When public spirit meets with public love.
Thus late where poverty with rapine dwelt,
Rumford's kind genius the Bavarian felt,
Not by romantic charities beguiled,
But calm in project and in mercy mild;
Where'er his wisdom guided, none withstood,
Content with peace and practicable good
Round him the labourers throng, the nobles wait
Friend of the poor and guardian of the state.'

6

Founder of the Royal Institution (1)

THE DAYS OF ENTHUSIASM

*I am very busy in striving to turn the disposition of the moment
to a good account for the permanent benefit of society . . .*

COUNT RUMFORD

RUMFORD'S Second Essay dealt with establishments for the
poor and had tremendous influence, not least in England
where he soon came to be regarded as a world authority in
this field of philanthropy. Amongst its suggestions was a set of *Proposals for forming by Private Subscription, an Establishment for Feeding the
Poor, and giving them Useful Employment . . . connected with an Institution
for introducing and bringing forward into general Use, new Inventions and
Improvements, particularly such as relate to the Management of Heat and the
Saving of Fuel. . . .*

His experience in Bavaria of feeding the poor and giving them
work, as well as the success of his kitchens, led him to formulate his
ideas and propound his theories with a most important addition,
namely, an institution for making known and popularizing new inventions. Being a man of science he saw what a profound change
science could make in human living. He was not alone in this but he
had a clearer grasp of its power in the fields of heat and mechanics,
and a greater urge to get things done than anyone else in his day. The
result was the formation of the Royal Institution.

The *Proposals* were made over the fictitious initials 'A.B.' within the
Essay which was not anonymous. This was Rumford's way of indicating the part the managing director, so to speak, would play in

implementing them. He said quite definitely that, interested as he was in such an undertaking, he had not then the time to assume the role of A.B. As set out, the *Proposals* were in the form of an address to the public. A.B. 'declares solemnly that he has no interested view in making these proposals, but is actuated merely and simply by a desire to do good, and promote the happiness and prosperity of society . . . that he will never demand, accept, or receive any pay or other recompense or reward for his services . . . or for anything he may do or perform in future relating to it. . . .'

This reads like a legal document. Rumford's purpose in writing in these terms was not, as the cynic might assume, to prepare a place for himself should opportunity arise; but rather to convince the public that it was important for the health and integrity of the institution that whoever managed it should not, as the saying went, make a job out of it.

After an initial appeal A.B. 'will request a meeting of twenty-five persons who stand highest on the list of subscribers'. From this meeting a committee would be formed to supervise the setting up of the Institution, to approve contracts and the spending of money, and give orders for payments. A.B. would be responsible for the general arrangement of the establishment and for its success—failure was not envisaged.

It is obvious (from Parliamentary debates and the opinions of his contemporaries) that at this time Rumford was highly regarded and looked upon as the man with the know-how. When, in December 1796, the Society for Bettering the Condition of the Poor was established under the patronage of the King, it was only natural that the founders should write to Rumford in Bavaria for advice. Letters passed between him and Thomas Bernard, one of the founders of the new society and a man of great influence and strong character. Rumford probably under-rated Bernard but later in their clash of ideas and personalities he very nearly met his match. From Munich he wrote in May 1798 that the rapid progress Bernard was making afforded him a high degree of satisfaction. 'Go on, my dear sir,' he said, 'and be assured that when you have put *doing good* in fashion you will have done all that human wisdom can do to retard and prolong the decline of a great and powerful nation that has arrived at or passed the zenith of human glory.'[1]

Rumford thought England was in decline because of 'the alarming progress of luxury and the corruption of taste and morals' but he gave no evidence for his belief, if indeed it was genuine. He had his own lapses, and Munich could hardly be described as a centre of puritan virtues. A month later he wrote again to Bernard in the same lofty and condescending tone: his 'dear sir' was still to 'go on' and to be assured that he would contribute more essentially to the revival of taste and morals in his favoured country 'than all the reformers and speculators in the three kingdoms . . .'. 'A well-arranged House of Industry was much wanted in London', and, as a master sends a schoolboy back to his text, he asked Bernard to read once more his *Proposals* in his Second Essay. He referred obliquely to the second object of the proposed institution. There must be 'something to *see* and to *touch* otherwise people in general will have but very faint, imperfect and transitory ideas of those important and highly interesting objects with which you must make them acquainted in order to their becoming zealous converts to our new philosophy and useful members of our com- munity . . .'. He promised Bernard that he would come to London to assist him in the execution of his plan whenever he would 'in good earnest undertake it'.[2]

The King's decision not to accept Rumford as an ambassador was in the long run highly beneficial to the development of science in England. It meant that Rumford had the leisure and the opportunity to attend to the project he had outlined. He could in fact become the A.B. of his *Proposals*. He may have regarded his new activity as less elevated than the one he had designed for himself, but it later brought him in direct contact with influential men of science like Banks, and with many members of the nobility. It took time to adjust himself to the new circumstances. There was no Elector behind him, but the opposition—for such there was bound to be—was less bitter and vindictive than that of the Munich City Council and the Bavarian States. At any rate he did, as usual, devote all his energy and enthusiasm to the task once he had undertaken it: to be inactive was worse than death.

On 31 January 1799, only three months after his return from Bavaria, he met a committee of eight people appointed by the Society for Bettering the Condition of the Poor. Among them were the Earl of Winchilsea, William Wilberforce, Thomas Bernard and the Reverend Dr Glasse. It is obvious that by this time the second objec- tive of his plan had taken hold of his mind. He wanted an institution for making the discoveries of science available in the form of inventions and improvements, particularly in the field of heat-management and fuel-saving. Above all, he wanted the public to be aware how much the standard of living would be improved if science were applied to the building of houses and to manufacturing processes. He realized, too, that the time had come for instructing skilled workmen in geometry, elementary mechanics and simple science.

These were new ideas and an institution to embody them could hardly be a subsidiary activity of the Society for Bettering the Condition of the Poor. The *ad hoc* committee reported back the next day in these terms and Rumford revised his original proposals putting them in a form more suitable for a public appeal. It was agreed that printed copies of the appeal should be distributed among those who were likely to support the idea. The response greatly encouraged Rumford and confirmed him in his decision to stay in England and direct the venture.

The revised proposals testify to his powers of organization and his ability to envisage the working of a new kind of institution which as yet existed only in his mind. Even more important is the evidence they give of his insight into the importance for society of the development of technology—an insight which unfortunately he alone possessed. The two great objects of the Institution were, first 'the speedy and general diffusion of the knowledge of all new and useful improvements in whatever quarter of the world they may originate'; and, secondly, the teaching of the application of scientific knowledge to arts and methods of manufacture, particularly those concerned with domestic comfort and convenience.

The first objective would be attained, or partly attained, by a large and permanent though changing exhibition of all new and mechanical inventions thought worthy of public notice. Working models of full size were intended, particularly those connected with the heating and ventilation of rooms, halls and ships and with the industrial processes of brewing, distilling, lime burning, spinning, weaving and farming. Working models 'of that most curious and most useful machine, the steam engine' were to be available. Each model was to have exhibited with it a detailed description with correct drawings. The name of the manufacturer and the price of the article were to be stated for the convenience of prospective buyers.

Rumford called this the Repository and it was a plan close to his heart. It was to be a combination of a teaching museum, a trade exhibition and a centre of technical information. The full list of the classes of goods to be on show illustrates Rumford's own interests and experience as well as the state of pure and applied science at the end of the eighteenth century.

The second objective, which was the teaching of applied science, was to be carried out by building a large lecture theatre and a fully equipped science laboratory. Lecturers 'of the first eminence in science' were to be engaged to lecture on the following subjects:

Heat and its Application to the various Purposes of Life.

The Combustion of Inflammable Bodies.

The Management of Fire and the Economy of Fuel.

The Principles of the Warmth of Clothing.

The Effects of Heat and Cold . . . on the Human Body in Sickness and in Health.

Of the Effects of breathing vitiated and confined Air.

The Means of making Dwelling Houses comfortable and salubrious.

The Methods of procuring and preserving Ice in Summer.

The Preservation of Food.

The Cooling of Liquors without Ice in hot Weather.

The Effects of Cookery on Food.

The Nature of the Digestive Processes.

Vegetation and Manures.

The Chemical Principles of Tanning, Soap-making, Bleaching, Dyeing and other manufacturing Processes.

This list is obviously Rumford's compilation; it closely reflects his interests and his scientific work, and many of the topics are dealt with in his own essays. One heading at least was probably suggested by his suffering from dyspepsia and gastritis. It is neither very systematic nor, as a scientific programme, very wide, even allowing for its being drawn up in a pre-electrical age. It is interesting but perhaps unfair to compare it with the programme Francis Bacon devised for men of science to achieve in *Sylva Sylvarum* a century and three-quarters earlier. Bacon, like Rumford, was enthralled by the idea that science could change man's lot and improve his material living, and although he was quite negligible as an experimental scientist he had a wider conception of its power. Rumford's list was practical rather than visionary and contained enough to be going on with. He himself might profitably have lectured on many of the topics but he never did and others fought shy of them.

Capital and income for the new Institution were to be assured by members' subscriptions, donations, legacies and money taken at the door from visitors to lectures and the Repository. Three classes of members were proposed. Proprietors would pay one fee of fifty guineas; life subscribers would make one payment of ten guineas; and annual subscribers were to be charged two guineas per annum.

Among the many privileges set out by Rumford are two which were common to all subscribers and which made some manufacturers suspicious of the enterprise. Although in a letter to Lady Palmerston he spoke of taking out a patent and entering into a partnership with Boulton, in fact he never seriously thought of any such thing. He made his fireplaces, cooking utensils and 'roasters' freely available, and rather unreasonably expected others whose circumstances were very different from his to do the same. In his plan all subscribers were to be entitled to have drawings of any model in the Repository made at their own expense by draughtsmen on the premises. A second privilege was that of recommending workmen or mechanics for the right of free access to models. This would, for example, enable a manufacturer of fireplaces, if he were a member of the Institution, to send his workmen to copy any model of a fireplace exhibited in the Repository. Rumford was prepared to be altruistic in this way but not many others were. What the Boulton family thought of the idea will be seen later.

Nine managers for the government of the Institution were to be chosen by the proprietors from among themselves. The first group of nine, however, were to be elected at a general meeting of the fifty or more subscribers. The first managers were to be divided into three equal groups serving respectively three years, two years and one year.

The managers were to be responsible for the property of the Institution, they were to authorize the spending of money, to serve without pay or emolument, to meet weekly and to keep regular minutes.

Rumford was most anxious that the Institution should be conducted for the benefit of society and that no one should make a profit out of it. Many educational institutions at that time, particularly ancient foundations, were at their nadir and they may have served as a warning. In order that the proprietors could be sure the managers were doing their duty, nine visitors were to be elected to report in detail once a year to the proprietors on the working of the Institution. It is worth noting that these proposals differ in some respects from those put forward in the Second Essay, particularly the absence of a constitutional place for A.B. or a managing director (unpaid). All managers were constitutionally on the same footing under the revised scheme.

Rumford's plans were clearly designed with a view to setting up an institute of technology for the spread of existing knowledge, and with the greatest prominence given to the Repository. Such an institution would be unique. He sent these modified proposals to the select committee with a long letter making two requests. The first was that the government should be made acquainted with the proposals officially and secondly that His Majesty's ministers should be informed that the founders intended to accept Rumford's services in the arrangement and management of the Institution. He set out his status in the letter as a subject of His Majesty but under a royal sign manual in the service of a foreign prince. His motive was undoubtedly to safeguard his half pay as a British army colonel and his Bavarian pension. He had no official post in Bavaria though he was still an unofficial agent of the Elector. He wished to make sure there were no obstacles in the way.

Rumford was well aware of the advantages of government sympathy in so ambitious an enterprise. It was also advisable to obtain the sympathy and support of the Great Cham of Science, Sir Joseph Banks, who was President of the Royal Society. This was much more than merely a personal matter, a question of influence. The Royal Society had had a virtual monopoly in the field of science for over a hundred years. With the advance of science legitimate sectional interests had grown up and there was a need for separate societies to cater for them. The Linnean Society, for example, had been founded in 1788. By 1799 Sir Joseph had presided magisterially over the Royal Society for more than twenty years and was naturally and rightly jealous for its standing and influence. Although the new Institution was not a rival to the Royal Society it was going to be concerned with the dissemination of scientific knowledge and therefore there was everything to be said for starting off with the approval of the older body. It was in fact at Banks's house in Soho Square that the first general meeting of proprietors took place on 7 March 1799. By that time fifty-eight people, many of whom were well known, had indicated their willingness to become proprietors and to pay the fee of fifty guineas.

At this meeting (under the chairmanship of Banks) it was unanimously decided to ask the King to show his approbation of the scheme by granting a Royal Charter to the Institution, and to lay an outline of the plans before the Prime Minister and the Duke of Portland. Nine managers were elected and charged with the task of carrying out the arrangements. They were: for three years, Earl Spencer, Count Rumford and Mr Richard Clark; for two years, the Earl of Egremont, Sir Joseph Banks and Mr Richard Joseph Sulivan; and for one year, The Earl of Morton, the Rt Hon Thomas Pelham and Mr Thomas Bernard.

Among these eminent names three stand out. Rumford's, of course, as that of the author of the plan. The others are Banks and Bernard. Banks, apart from his position as a leader in science, was a rich man and a personal friend of the King. Bernard was an indefatigable promoter of good causes. He was the third son of Sir Francis Bernard, one-time Governor of the Colonies of New Jersey and Massachusetts Bay. He founded or helped to found many philanthropic societies and institutions including the School for the Indigent Blind, the Cancer Institution, the London Fever Hospital, a society for the protection of Climbing Boys and one for the relief of Poor Neighbours in Distress. Thus the early progress of the Institution depended on Rumford, Banks and Bernard.

The inaugural meeting is not recorded in the Minute Books of the Institution, but subsequent meetings, beginning with 9 March, are recorded. Banks was elected chairman of managers, at least until the expected Royal Charter had been granted. Bernard acted as secretary for the meeting and fifteen resolutions were adopted mainly concerned with immediate administrative procedure. At the second meeting Rumford was secretary and his influence can be seen in that many of the resolutions related to procedure covering disagreement. At the third meeting at the end of March Sulivan was in the chair in Banks's absence, Bernard was again secretary and he read the draft of the charter.

In April it was decided to purchase a house in Albemarle Street at a cost of £4500 so that the work of adapting it to the needs of the managers could begin. A Mr Swan was appointed as clerk assistant and a Mr Webster as Clerk of the Works.

In May there were significant changes among the officers. The Reverend Dr Glasse was appointed secretary, though he was not on the original list of managers. Bernard became treasurer and Sir John Hippisley became a manager in his place. Both Glasse and Hippisley were friends of Bernard.

Events moved quickly. In June the managers met for the first time in their new house which, incidentally, had cost rather more than they had bargained for. The King had agreed to become the Patron and the Earl of Winchilsea to be President. In view of later developments it is important to observe that at this stage of the Royal Institution's development Bernard had a clear understanding of Rumford's intentions and apparently accepted them. His report to the Society for Bettering the Condition of the Poor on the aims and the foundation of the new Institution might have been written by Rumford himself.[3] By 6 July the treasurer reported that subscriptions amounted to £5327 14s.

The first senior teaching appointment was made on 14 September. Dr Thomas Garnett, a Professor of Natural Philosophy at the Andersonian Institution in Glasgow, and a man of high reputation as a lecturer, was appointed Professor and Public Lecturer in Experimental Philosophy, Mechanics and Chemistry. He was also to be Scientific Secretary and Editor of the Journals. His duties were to begin at the end of the year at a salary of £300 per annum with prospects of an increase, and he was to be given lodging in the house. It was for its time an academic plum and the kind of post which would appeal to an enterprising lecturer whose interests were scientific. But already there were rumbles of dissatisfaction in another quarter. At the same September meeting[4] Rumford read a long letter to the managers from Webster who was beginning to feel disappointment about his prospects. To take up his post at the Royal Institution he had given up private practice as an architect and disbanded a school of about a dozen mechanics. He was, however, a young man of sound education and training who saw great opportunities in his new position; without doubt he felt it an honour to work so closely with a man of Rumford's fame and though it meant an immediate reduction in salary he made the sacrifice. Rumford, for his part, saw in Webster a valuable acquisition for although there were no plans for a school for mechanics in the

Proposals what could be more valuable in furthering the aims of the Institution? Such a school would be a great advance on the meagre instruction available through merely attending the Repository and examining the drawings; it would be far better than the occasional lectures which were being given to artisans on Saturday evenings or on Sundays in some of the industrial centres. So Rumford, having Webster's help, decided to incorporate into the main scheme a school along the lines of the one Webster had given up; and Webster, with Rumford's backing, saw an opportunity of congenial work and of rendering public service at the same time.

This was the background to Webster's letter. He wrote very deferentially and gave an outline of his proposed syllabuses, but the matter was shelved and the managers proceeded to discuss a proposal to apply for a coat of arms for the Institution. Rumford must have been irritated by this setback though the Minutes are discreetly silent.

Some time later Webster made his account of the episode public. It was in a letter to Garnett about the dissemination of knowledge among the poorer classes, and he said that Rumford, who 'had the greatest share in establishing the Institution', always considered it 'an object of much importance'. It was Rumford's intention 'to do everything in his power to establish a school for science . . . particularly calculated for working mechanics, a class of men whose deficiency in knowledge proves one of the greatest drawbacks in the progress of the art'.

At this time there was a serious shortage of men with technical knowledge of an elementary kind. The older type of craftsman was very often averse to doing things in a new way or showing his limitations in skill and education. With the development of machinery and with improvements in building there was a new need for men who could follow written instructions and read plans and drawings. Webster said quite clearly that his 'idea was to make *good mechanics*' and not to force men 'like hot-bed plants out of the sphere in which they are so useful'. The reference is obvious. Some of the managers had political objections to the education of mechanics; they wished to keep the workmen in their places. According to Webster one of the opponents of the school for mechanics was Sir Joseph Banks. When Banks was confined to his house, probably with gout from which he suffered badly, the Minute Book of the Royal Institution was carried to him so that he might see how innocuous the proposed syllabuses were.

It seemed after this that Webster's scheme would go forward. On the ground floor of the building Rumford caused roasters, boilers, fireplaces and chimneys to be built to his own design, and a number of bricklayers were instructed in making them. The bricklayers were sent for the most part by Rumford's friends including, for example, the Earl of Aylesford who conceived 'that such an opportunity of getting a person so instructed [would] be of the greatest service to the town of Birmingham'.[5] But the more ambitious scheme came to nothing, though not at once. Much later, Rumford referred to it in one of his reports in 1801 when he said that setting up a school for about eighteen or twenty young men awaited the completion of rooms on the attic storey. The aim then was for these young men to be boarded at the house, to have practical instruction in the workshops during the day and to attend Webster's school in the evening. The course was to last three or four months.

The curriculum that Webster drew up included a basic course consisting of geometry, geometrical drawing and perspective, and mechanics and hydrostatics. After completing this course, specialization was possible in either architecture on the one hand or mathematics, physics and chemistry on the other.

It was a misfortune that this project failed. An opportunity was lost to make an early and sound beginning in this country in the field of technical education—a field in which we have so often and for so long lagged behind some other countries. It is true that Mechanics' Institutes sprang up all over the country in the next forty years and lectures were attended by many thousands of enthusiastic artisans and semi-skilled workers. But the Rumford Institution could have become the first centre of full-time scientific and technological instruction if the opportunity which Rumford held out had been taken. When Webster was told that his plan 'to instruct the lower classes in science must be dropped as quietly as possible', and that if he persisted he would 'become a marked man',[6] the voice of fear and privilege spoke and of short-sighted conservatism which has so markedly influenced our traditional and long-established places of education that even today, after over a century and a half, we still hear its echo and feel its effects. And it is true that the gradual percolation of science (and sound methods of teaching it) into the schools and older universities came about later through the influence of men like Tyndall, Huxley, Spencer and Armstrong, who stood outside the walls of the educational system of their day.

But in September 1799 there were many other things for the managers to attend to. Rumford had one of his periodic attacks of illness and for five months he was absent from their meetings. His daughter had returned to America a few weeks earlier and this relieved him of one responsibility. He spent some time with his friends the Palmerstons at Broadlands, where he had already improved the cooking arrangements, and while he was there he fitted out a kitchen at Romsey nearby, which, he said, almost 'deserved the name of a public repository'. By this time he had bought a house in Brompton and on 15 January 1800 he wrote to Banks saying he hoped to return there in about a fortnight. He was glad Banks liked Webster—the liking may have been genuine at the time. He hoped Garnett would do well though he was less prepossessed in his favour than he was in Webster's and he was anxious to strengthen the Board of Managers by the replacement of two or three who seldom attended.

He was present at the next meeting on 3 February, and his colleagues were probably very relieved to see him, for there is evidence in the Minutes of anxiety to see the Institution in active being and to fulfil the obligations to the Proprietors. During his absence Garnett had arrived and had put his plans and syllabus before the managers. He wanted to deliver two courses of lectures. One would be popular in treatment, dealing with experimental physics and chemistry, omitting mathematics, and designed to amuse, entertain and instruct. The other course would be weightier and more advanced, and directed at serious students. It would follow a university pattern and deal with mechanics, hydrostatics, hydraulics and pneumatics. He had brought with him a good deal of his own apparatus but had asked for £150 to £200 to add to it. In a letter to Garnett written on 26 January Rumford professed himself delighted with the preparations he had made and hoped that no expense would be spared in providing suitable apparatus. Very sensibly he said that he would like the experiments to be on a large scale and, he added, 'in all respects carried out in a manner worthy of the Royal Institution of Great Britain'.[7]

During the first half of the year 1800 the progress of the new

Institution was greatly accelerated. Rumford turned to the task with vigour and ardour, and was prepared to give the whole of his time to its affairs. He left his house in Brompton Row temporarily and moved to Albemarle Street. The Minutes of 10 March record 'that as long as Count Rumford continues to reside in the House of the Institution he be required to superintend all the works that are going on in the House and to see that the Servants in the House and the different Workmen employed discharge their various duties with diligence, order and due decorum. . . .' The business of the Institution was increasing. Rooms were being used by subscribers and lectures were being given, one more manservant and two maidservants had been engaged and a clerk to the managers appointed.

The extent of the undertaking exhibited great faith on the part of the sponsors, both proprietors and managers. It was courageous to go so far on the limited capital they had acquired—even by 1 May 1800 the total amount was only just over £8000 and more than half had been expended on the house. Rumford then wrote a prospectus. It was of excellent quality, informed and acute, restrained yet persuasive, and designed to appeal to thoughtful and public-spirited people who could afford to support the Royal Institution. His argument began by showing the importance of machinery in improving the condition of man: that its use to a great extent procures 'the necessaries, comforts and elegancies of life'; it aids commerce and industry; it increases man's vision.[8] But the spread of improvement is remarkably slow and its benefits are not fully enjoyed. For this there are many reasons such as the inertia of habit, unwillingness to confess to lack of skill in using new appliances, the disrepute into which new devices and machinery fall when they are unskilfully set up and used, and the human failings of suspicion, jealousy, envy and selfishness. Added to these reasons are division of function in the community and the mental detachment of men of science. 'Invention', he said, 'seems to be peculiarly the province of the man of science; his ardour in the pursuit of truth is unremitted; discovery is his harvest; utility, his reward. Yet it may be demanded whether his moral and intellectual habits are precisely such as may be calculated to produce useful practical improvements. Detached, as he usually is, from the ordinary pursuits of life—will he descend from the sublime general theories of science and enter into the detail of weight, measure, price, quality or the individual properties of materials which must be precisely known before a chance of success can be gained . . . ? The practical knowledge, the stimulus of interest, and the capital of the manufacturer are here wanting; while the manufacturer on his part is equally in want of the general information and the accurate reading of men of science. . . .'

Rumford saw three ways of diminishing these difficulties, of bridging the gap between manufacturer and man of science, factory and laboratory, industry and research. Two, the awards of premiums or prizes and the granting of temporary monopolies, were already available. But something else was needed, and what could meet the need better than an Institution whose specific aims were to spread knowledge and facilitate the introduction of inventions and improvements? Then followed an account of the plans already laid down in the revised *Proposals* and approved by the managers.

This prospectus was widely distributed both in England and overseas. Rumford asked the American Ambassador, Rufus King, to let him have 'a list of all the Universities, Academies, Colledges and other Scientific Bodies of note and respectability in the United States together with the names of their Presidents'. In the same letter, written 9 March 1800, he says: 'We are going on here most prosperously. Pray call in and see me as you go by. I am always at home. The Clerk can hardly enter the Subscribers names as fast as they come in.'9

Garnett began his lectures early in March: Experimental Philosophy on Tuesdays at 2 p.m.; Philosophical Chemistry on Thursdays and Saturdays also at 2 p.m. On Mondays, Wednesdays and Fridays at 8 p.m., he lectured on Natural Philosophy, Mechanics and Chemistry, and it was in this more advanced course that he dealt with the 'applications of science to the common purposes of life'.

Also in March much of the managers' time was taken up by a discussion of the bye-laws, which were drafted by Sir Joseph Banks and not by Rumford. They were considered paragraph by paragraph at three meetings on 17, 19 and 21 March. The enthusiasm of those who gave so much of their time is to be admired, but by the end of the month an important trend in the policy of the Institution began to be evident. The state of construction of repository, theatre and laboratory was discussed. Priority was given to the theatre and Rumford was asked to discuss the matter with the surveyor, 'the work to be carried on with the greatest expedition and suitable economy'. Webster's

Lecture Theatre, owing much to Rumford (and perhaps something to Garnett), subsequently became the most famous and effective room of its kind in the country and perhaps in the world. It is a commentary on the times to note that separate accommodation, with separate staircases, was provided for the ingenious mechanics and the people of quality.

At the same meeting it was resolved to set up a Scientific Committee of Council. This was to be a standing committee, undefined in number, with two main functions. It was to examine from time to time the syllabuses of the professors belonging to the Institution, 'to the end that no doctrines or opinion be taught or promulgated at public lectures but such as are agreeable to the actual state of knowledge in science for the time being'. Secondly, it was 'to superintend all the new philosophical experiments that shall be made at the House of the Institution', and when advisable to report to the managers with a view to the publication of the results by the Royal Society. It was perhaps a good idea to appoint such a committee, provided that it kept in the background. Individual members of a committee like this interfering with the lecturing and research might have been disastrous, but its existence gave weight and respectability to a new and experimental institution. Its members included the great Henry Cavendish, eminent physicist and chemist; Nevil Maskelyne, the astronomer-royal; Sir Charles Blagden, intimate friend of Rumford and Banks; the serving secretaries of the Royal Society; Major James Rennell, a geographer; and two professors at Cambridge.

These decisions show a trend towards pure science, and Rumford, perhaps in a massive attempt to keep the first aim of the Institution to the fore, proposed the formation of no fewer than fourteen committees to deal with processes and appliances important in everyday living. These working parties were to deal with:

1. The scientific investigation of the making of bread.
2. Preparing cheap and nutritious soups for feeding the poor.
3. The improvement of cottages and cottage fireplaces.
4. The improvement of stoves for warming dwelling houses.
5. The improvement of kitchen fireplaces and kitchen utensils.
6. The improvement of the most useful articles of household furniture.
7. The experimental investigation of the effects of cookery on cattle food.

8. The improvement of kitchens and utensils on ship board and the procuring of fresh water at sea by distillation.

9. The improvement of lime kilns.

10. The making of fireballs and combustible cakes.

11. The improvement of mortars and cements.

12. The investigation of the best methods for building in this climate cottages and farmhouses with pisé.*

13. The improvement of useful machines.

14. The extraction of iron from its ores and the working and refining of iron and steel.

This list is very impressive. If able and enthusiastic working parties had ever got under way on these problems, particularly as membership was not confined to those who were members of the sponsoring body, the benefit to industry would have been great and, far more important, the standard of living appreciably raised. Moreover, although Rumford's own abiding interests are again evident, there is no reason whatsoever to believe that what he proposed was the limit of his aims. But his was a voice crying in the wilderness, and he was looked at askance by many men of science and dubbed *dilettante* by the manufacturers.

The proposal to set up these committees could be little more than a gesture. In reality, all Rumford could report on the practical side at this time was that a 'roaster' had been set up and that a model of a public kitchen with four boilers and four ovens was nearly finished. The membership was more promising. On 3 April he reported that there were on the books 248 proprietors, 259 life subscribers, 297 annual subscribers and 97 ladies. At this meeting Bernard again changed his status. He became a visitor and Hippisley took his place as a manager.

In May 1800 Garnett was in trouble. Volta had written to Banks describing the experiments he had carried out the previous year in which continuous electrical currents had been produced for the first time from chemical cells. Their novelty was seized upon and their importance quickly became apparent. Banks showed Volta's letter to Sir Anthony Carlisle, a surgeon and anatomist, and Carlisle and William Nicholson repeated Volta's experiments and, further, decomposed water by passing a current through it. Between the time Banks received the letter and the decomposition of water by an electric current there was a short period of only six weeks. Garnett, who had

* Rammed clay.

heard of these experiments, borrowed some apparatus and, no doubt, wishing to be quite up to date, repeated them before his audience. Unfortunately he ascribed them to French men of science, which made Banks very angry, and he complained to Rumford who had not been at the lecture. Garnett was asked to read a correcting statement at the next one. Although this was only a minor slip on Garnett's part it did nothing to raise his prestige with certain of the managers. On the other hand, his lectures were being well received and he had audiences 'crowded with persons of the first distinction and fashion as well as by those who had individually contributed much to the promotion of science'.[10]

By the summer Rumford was again feeling the strain of continuous work and he went to Harrogate to bathe in and drink the waters. Later he visited Edinburgh with Lord Palmerston, and was received with honour and distinction. While he was away the structural alterations in the House at Albemarle Street went on apace with the gifted and industrious Webster in charge. When he returned he performed an action which was to prove one of the most important in his eventful career.

Early in the year 1801 the managers decided to appoint an assistant lecturer in chemistry. Rumford began to look round for someone suitable and heard of the talents of a young Cornishman named Humphry Davy from one of the proprietors, a Mr J. R. Underwood. A meeting between Rumford and Davy was arranged and as a result on 23 February 1801 the following historic entry was made in the Minute Book:

'Resolved.   That Mr Humphrey [the spelling is in error] Davy be engaged in the service of the R. I. in the capacities of Assistant Lecturer in Chemistry, Director of the Chemical Laboratory and Assistant Editor of the Journals of the Institution and that he be allowed to occupy a Room in the House and be furnished with Coal and Candles and that he be paid a salary of One Hundred Guineas per Annum.'

Davy was twenty-two years of age when he was appointed to the post at the Royal Institution. Two years earlier he had published a paper entitled *An Essay on Heat, Light and the Combinations of Light* which may have been inspired by one of Rumford's most famous contributions to the *Philosophical Transactions of the Royal Society*. The same tentative conclusion about the nature of heat could be drawn from both papers. It is possible that Rumford's interest in Davy was quickened by this. Rumford anyhow had a clear conception of the younger man's ability and promise for he told him that there were prospects of his becoming Professor of Chemistry in the course of two or three years at a salary of £300 per annum. Moreover, he wrote in most encouraging terms to say that the managers would encourage him to continue his researches and give him 'every facility which the philosophical apparatus at the Institution' could afford.

Davy was a promising man of science, but he lacked social grace and he neglected his appearance. His Cornish accent and intonation fell strangely on the ears of fashionable London and his pertness sometimes gave offence. Rumford began to wonder whether he had made a mistake; he was so anxious to make science fashionable. Davy's biographer records how Rumford asked Davy first to lecture in the small theatre because of his doubts about the ability of this young west countryman to hold the attention of a fashionable and distinguished audience in the new theatre. At the end of the lecture Davy had passed the test. Rumford was favourably impressed and somewhat in the manner of an Eastern potentate giving a boon to a dancing girl exclaimed: 'Let him command any arrangements which the Institution can afford.' On 2 March 1801 he wrote to Sally in America to tell her that they had found a 'nice able man for this place as lecturer, Humphry Davy'; he was obviously very pleased by the way his work for the Institution had been received, and gratified by the attendance at the lectures of 'crowds of the first people'. Lady Palmerston and her two daughters, Frances and Elizabeth, were 'pretty constant attendants'. He went on:

'They would not receive me as Minister here but seem now disposed to make it up to me by the respect they show for the Institution—originally and chiefly my work. Bernard says they are crazy about it. It is certainly gratifying to me to see the honorable list of Lords, Dukes, &c as fifty guinea subscribers. It is a very extensive establishment and will cost a great deal of money; but I hope it will be an equal advantage to the world as the expense and labour of forming it have been great. . . .

'. . . I am very busy indeed in striving to turn the disposition of the moment to a good account for the permanent benefit of society. . . .'[11]

Davy began his duties with enthusiasm and understanding, and 'the resolution of employing all [his] feeble powers towards promoting the true interests of the Institution'. His lectures surpassed all that had been expected of him. He became a magnet drawing fashionable London in their carriages to Albemarle Street. He combined simplicity of manner, deep knowledge of his subject, well-chosen demonstrations and a sensitive command of English. Coleridge, who himself lectured later in the same place, was asked why he so regularly attended lectures so far removed from his known interests and replied, 'I attend Davy's lectures to increase my stock of metaphors.'[12] In three months his title was changed from Assistant Lecturer to Lecturer, and in the following February Rumford himself moved a resolution at the managers' meeting that in view of his 'having given the most satisfactory proofs of his ability as a Lecturer and of his indefatigable zeal . . .' his salary be raised 'from one Hundred Pounds to two Hundred Pounds per annum'.[13]

The mood of the moment at the Royal Institution was brilliantly, if vulgarly, caught by the great satirical artist James Gillray. One of his drawings, entitled 'Scientific Researches—New Discoveries in PNEUMATICKS!—or—An Experimental Lecture on the Powers of Air', shows a lecture demonstration in progress. Dr Garnett, looking serious, is holding the nose of a member of the audience who has been asked to act as subject. This victim is inhaling by the mouth, with most embarrassing results, gas which is being prepared on the bench. Davy is assisting Garnett and has on his face the mischievous look of a practical joker. Rumford stands erect by the door of the preparation room wearing a decoration and looking on with benign amusement and approval. The reactions of the very mixed audience encompass a wide range of human emotion. The apparatus on the bench is of interest but the object which looks so much like an electric fan is of course no such thing, the magnetic effect of the electric current was not discovered until three years after Gillray died.

While Davy's star ascended, Garnett's declined. Various differences arose between him and the managers and that meant between him and Rumford. He had expected to have his family accommodated in the house at Albemarle Street and to practise in London as a physician. His anxiety about his children was acute, for he had lost his wife and they lived far away in Westmorland. He was disappointed in both these matters and adversely affected by his grief. Moreover he behaved tactlessly; it seems, for example, that he printed two pamphlets describing his syllabuses for the lectures for the year 1801 without having consulted the managers—this in spite of the existence of the Scientific Committee of Council, one of whose tasks it was to examine syllabuses. Bence Jones, in his discussion of these differences, said that Rumford had probably determined as early as February 1801 that Garnett should give up his professorship, but this is by no means likely. The fact of Davy's appointment is scarcely relevant because the engagement of two men, one professing chemistry and the other natural philosophy, was a natural result of the growing success of the Institution.

In February 1801 Garnett asked for an increase of salary but the managers felt unable to accede, though the request was not turned down flatly. It was to receive further consideration in May of the same year when the annual statement of finances would be available. Between February and May Garnett's health deteriorated and he went to pieces. On 25 May the managers unanimously refused to increase his salary, and on 15 June accepted his resignation but continued to pay his salary until the end of the year.

Garnett's successor was a scholar of the first rank, a great physicist of whom it was rightly said that had he concentrated his energies in one field of activity he must necessarily have been first in that field. His name was Thomas Young. He was then a young man of twenty-eight, a physician who was recommended to Rumford by Sir Joseph Banks. Rumford met Young, liked him, and thinking of his youth or the finances of the Institution or both, offered him the position at a salary rather less than the one Garnett had received. Young's reply was dignified but protesting: 'I confess I think it would be in some measure degrading both to me and to the Institution that the salary which appears to me to have been no more than moderate before should now be reduced by one-fourth, at the same time that the labour and responsibility of the employment are rather increased than lessened. . . .'[14] He made his point and his appointment was confirmed at a salary of £300 per annum at the meeting on 3 August 1801. He stayed only two years and left with the gratitude of the managers. He was unfitted for the role of popular lecturer. His subject matter was often abstruse and his presentation made no concession to lesser intelligence; as it was said 'he presumed on the knowledge and not on the ignorance of his hearers'. But he was greatly respected and both then and afterwards his association with the Royal Institution brought it prestige.

But to return to the year 1801. In May, Rumford presented a report to the managers which showed clearly that he still had in mind the aims that he had set before himself, his colleagues and the public two years earlier. He spoke of the staff: professor, lecturers, laboratory assistant, master of the works, mathematical instrument-maker, model-maker, cabinet-maker, metal-workers and others. One model kitchen was completed and a second planned. It would soon be possible to provide light refreshments and experimental dinners cooked on the special apparatus installed in the kitchen. Nine daily newspapers were being taken and numerous foreign and domestic, literary and scientific publications were available to members. There was a complete printing office and the House journals were promised to appear regularly. Of the Repository he spoke with subdued hope. Its furnishing and equipment must await the completion of the rest of the scheme; in the meantime a spacious and elegant room, forty-four feet long and thirty-two feet wide, with the ceiling supported by two rows of columns, had been constructed for the exhibits—it would be ready for use in a month.

All this was most creditable; considering the short time the managers had had to work in and the mode of financing the enterprise, the achievement was great. They had received £23,200 in subscriptions and they had £7000 in reserve. Who but Rumford could have conceived and directed so far-sighted and complicated a plan?

All was not well, however, with the scheme for making the Repository a centre of information about mechanical inventions. The manufacturers had been alarmed. Rumford knew this and in his report denied that it was either the managers' intention in general or his in particular to 'expose to public view models of machines of all kinds indiscriminately'. The apprehension that had been aroused by reports 'that valuable secrets would be disclosed on which the excellence of their machines depended, would be shown to be without foundation'. The apprehension was nevertheless very considerable particularly in the Boulton family.

In the Birmingham Assay Office there is a long memorandum written to his father by Matthew R. Boulton. It is dated March 1800, and is headed: *Thoughts and reflexions on Count Rumford's proposed establishment for the exhibition of models of the machinery of our manufactories at the Royal Institution, in a letter to M.B.*

The younger Boulton had no enthusiasm for the Royal Institution. He thought 'the Count's philosophy had got the better of his judgment', and 'however much support he received from the male and female nobility his scheme would not be relished by the British manufacturer'. Far from an Institution for diffusing general knowledge it seemed to him to be a means of diffusing the benefits of capital and industry.

'To the philosophical dilettante' (how often this description appears in reference to those who supported Rumford), 'who employs only his time and talent in pursuit of knowledge the fame of his discoveries may be a satisfactory reward, but to the manufacturer who expends his *Capital* as well as his skill and labour with a view to Emolument the possession of his improvements can alone afford him a proportionate remuneration.'

Matthew Boulton said it had even been proposed to prevent the public inspection of the Patent Office, where there was much less danger than there would be in the new Institution. It might be a very pleasant amusement for the nobility and other idle loungers who had never added an iota to the purse of the nation by the sweat of their brow to diffuse the inventions and advantages acquired by the perseverance and painful study of the grovelling mechanics, but how would it be relished by the inventor himself? 'Would he', asks this practical Midland manufacturer, 'think himself sufficiently rewarded for his pains and perseverance by a vote of thanks?'

Then he asked his father whether he or anyone else could have perfected the coining apparatus if he had not had the capital behind him to experiment. And would he be satisfied and repaid by having his name enrolled on a list of subscribers? Could the Institution offer any premiums equal to the fortune derived by Mr Arkwright from cotton-spinning? No. An Institution intended to disclose the secrets of machinery would be opposed by the manufacturers, and their opposition would be as powerful as the support of the patrons 'though composed of such exalted personages'. Such Institutions might be useful and necessary in Bavaria, feudal and backward as it was, but not in

England where the spirit of improvement was so marked, and which had taken the lead of all manufacturing countries without such aids as Rumford suggested.

This was the outburst of an indignant manufacturer speaking for his class and period. And there was obviously a good deal of truth in his argument. It is usually a big step from the initial discovery to the machine which produces goods, and capital is necessary for the step to be made—even more so now than in Boulton's day. 'Tooling up' for a new product is sometimes prohibitive and often a strain on resources. Without reserves progress must be halted. Reserves are built up from profits and profits from patent rights. Matthew Boulton was in no doubt about Rumford's intentions, for a Mr Lee had been told by Rumford that the Royal Institution wanted 'a specimen of a steam engine in its improved state', *not a model but a working engine of sufficient power to be applied to effective work and in which the different parts may be of such magnitude as to afford distinct patterns for the imitation of workmen. . . .*

Rumford had gone too far in his demands. This memorandum exposes the major source of the opposition, and the reverberations died slowly—as late as the year 1810 Humphry Davy referred to the incident in a lecture:

'Soon after the foundation of the Royal Institution, a request was made to one of the greatest mechanical philosophers of the age that he would examine the details of the establishment, and become in some way connected with the body. His refusal was prompt and his expression of disapprobation strong. "Your object", says he, "is one that every practical inventor ought to discountenance. You would destroy the value of the labour of the industrious; by laying open his invention you would take away the great stimulus to invention. Suppose a man, by great devotion of time and labour by skill and ingenuity has made an important combination in chemistry or mechanics, your object is to publish the details of his labours, to enable every speculator to profit by his knowledge. . . . This, could it happen, would be ruinous to individuals and would ultimately interfere with the commercial prosperity of Britain. . . ." I am not sure that these were the words of this able reasoner but I am sure that they convey his sentiments. . . .'

There was no ill feeling. The Royal Institution and its managers kept in touch with Boulton and Watt. In fact the firm was asked in

1803 to design and manufacture silver and copper medals to serve as tickets for subscribers.

Rumford's *Prospectus of the Royal Institution* was an excellent short essay on the social influence of mechanical invention, the slowness of the diffusion of knowledge and the means of accelerating the process. But in spite of this and his genius for planning, it seems that Rumford failed to plan adequately for his Repository and also that he had not thought out the implications of the scheme. He does not appear to have foreseen the opposition it would arouse; nor was he consistent when he encountered it. Though he was sincere in his desire to make improvements available to the people, and proved his sincerity by not taking out patents himself, he did not sufficiently appreciate the fact that his inventions, highly useful though they were, were in a narrow field and did not rank with many of the major inventions of his time. Fireplaces were one thing, steam engines another. He, moreover, was not financially dependent on his inventions; he had his half pay as a soldier and a substantial pension. To a manufacturer he was patently 'a philosophical dilettante'.

In any case it was impossible to realize his plans fully in Albemarle Street. Large resources and extensive workshops with a big trained staff would have been necessary to make a sustained attack on the problem. This does not mean that Rumford deserves any less credit for his ideas as a pioneer. If the enterprise of his Repository had not been still-born but partly successful, it might have thrown into relief the need for wider and similar action by the manufacturers acting as a body or even by the state. But the discovery of 'the happy art of connecting together liberal science and commercial industry' was long delayed.[15]

7

Founder of the Royal Institution (2)

THE DAYS OF DISILLUSION

But—

Exegi monumentum aere perennius
HORACE

IN the year 1801 the Royal Institution was to upper-class Londoners
a scientific club where lectures could be heard and the latest
scientific periodicals read in comfort. As such it was successful and
understood. Its other aims were not always very clear, and indeed to
some were suspect. Few people objected to increasing the efficiency of
workmen and to improving the living conditions of the poor, and yet
there were dangers, many thought, in educating the lower orders.
And there was also the unpractical and far-fetched plan, as it seemed,
to ask manufacturers to forgo their rights in order to speed up the use
of machinery.

It is likely that after the May meeting Rumford lowered his sights.
He knew he had failed with the manufacturers and he talked of con-
structing the models in the Institution rather than obtaining them
at first hand. He had not entirely discarded his design for a school of
mechanics but very little progress had been made. He still tried to give
the lectures a technological slant, as is shown by a Minute of the June
meeting when it was resolved that Davy should, in the next session,
give a course of lectures 'on the Chemical Principles of the Art of
Tanning and that Respectable persons of the trade who shall be
recommended by the Proprietors shall be admitted to these lectures
gratis'. Davy, who was interested in the process and had easy means of

acquainting himself with its practical aspects, was given three months' leave to prepare. But the scope and direction of the Institution's activities were settling down and Rumford must have accepted a limited objective. In his letter to Sally dated 2 March 1801 he said that he had been exceedingly busy but was thankful that all was nearly completed. In July he left his rooms in the House and went back to his own home in Brompton Row. In September he made a frantic dash to Munich. There was no ducal carriage this time. He took only a small portmanteau and he covered the journey of 752 English miles in nine days—a journey which involved 104 posts between Calais and the Bavarian capital. He did not go at the invitation of the new Elector as has been claimed; he went, in his own words, to pay court to his new Sovereign and 'to settle with him . . . a reasonable plan' for the rest of his life.[1] He was afraid lest the new pro-French policy of Bavaria should cut off his allowance and prevent his being of further service to that country. He was reassured on arrival. Before returning to England he spent some weeks in Paris, though England and France were still at war. He arrived back in London in December.

He did not forget the affairs of the Institution while he was away. On his outward journey he wrote to Banks from Dover[2] to request his watchful care over all that he had left behind him at Albemarle Street. He said: 'Dr Young promises to be a useful acquisition to us. Davy may do very well indeed if he gets the better of his natural disposition to be idle and procrastinate.' He also wrote to William Savage, the clerk with whom he always corresponded when away from home, and heard that nothing further had been done to the Repository, that they were having difficulties with the heating apparatus in the lecture theatre and that Davy had decided to cut down his lecture course on tanning. On the brighter side, the printing press was busy with printing the syllabuses and a paper by Davy. Altogether things were not going very well and Savage was not exaggerating when he said, 'I can perceive that the Institution begins to feel the want of you.'

On his return Rumford again threw his energies into the administration and development of the Royal Institution. An important innovation was the decision to 'make a series of experiments in the laboratory in order to ascertain with all possible precision the physical and chemical properties of metallic alloys'. This was the first substantial research project to be planned. But the finances of the whole enterprise gave cause for concern. The reserve of £7000 which Rumford had reported the previous May was being eaten into for the building extensions. A short time afterwards subscriptions were increased for the second time. The new amounts were: for proprietors, seventy guineas; for life subscribers, forty guineas; annual subscribers, four guineas; subscribers for lectures only, two guineas. These were large sums and those members who were not convinced of the social and philanthropic aims of the Institution may well have wondered whether they were getting their money's worth.

Rumford still clung to his aim to instruct mechanics and, as an experiment, proprietors were each given an extra transferable ticket for public lectures so that mechanics and others who might derive advantage from them could gain 'admittance to the gallery only of the great lecture room and to no other part of the house'. He presented his annual report on 26 April. It was expressed in more favourable terms than the situation warranted. He spoke of the achievements of the previous year and what still remained to be done 'to complete this great and interesting establishment *in all its details*'.[3]

The new lecture room, now complete, was 'acknowledged to be one of the most beautiful and convenient Scientific Theatres in Europe'. Acoustically it was almost perfect; it was heated by steam circulating in a large semicircular copper tube. The laboratory was finished and so were the workshops which were furnished with complete sets of tools. Several excellent workmen had been engaged and various articles made by them were on sale. In the great kitchen many new utensils and implements of cookery were in daily use; others were exhibited so that they could be easily understood and their merit appreciated. Rumford spoke of the second lecture room, the library and the conversation room, but said little about the Repository. There was, he claimed, enough capital to pay for the new work to be done and an adequate income for the maintenance of the Institution. He ended with the very significant sentence: 'The Royal Institution may therefore be considered as finished and freely established.'

He had decided to leave London. It was not unpremeditated. His visit to Bavaria the year before had made it clear that there was still useful work to do. Both his own allowance from the Bavarian government, and his daughter's, were insecure while he lived in England now that

Bavaria was under French influence. And he had met Mme Lavoisier in Paris. He therefore made up his mind to take a limited view of the purposes of the Royal Institution, to spend some of his time in England every year, to be available for advice if the managers needed it, but no longer to make himself responsible for the full time direction of its affairs. Before leaving he gave advice to the managers. What he said concerned mainly the parts of the establishment which had been his especial care, particularly during the time when he had lived in the house. These were undertakings which were partly commercial—the journal, the workshops and the dining-rooms. He was never averse to dealing with commercial matters and would put his hand to a manual task, never turning with distaste from the skills acquired in his New Hampshire upbringing. He had himself supervised the domestic arrangements, and the Day Book of the Royal Institution records even the Christmas boxes he gave, in 1800, to the watchman (five shillings) and the beadle (one shilling).

A great deal has been written about Rumford's break with the Royal Institution, much of it inaccurate. It has been said that he left England because of his quarrels with the managers but this, as we have seen, is untrue. His reasons for going were mainly personal. He thought of dividing his time between England and Bavaria and when he sailed from England in May 1802 he left his affairs unsettled; for example, he had on order 'a second-hand chariot' and Savage was asked to supervise his house at Brompton. This is not to deny he had serious differences with his fellow managers and proprietors. Sir Charles Blagden, who did not see eye to eye with Rumford but who knew most of what went on in scientific circles, wrote to Sally in 1804 to say that her father had quarrelled 'with Mr Bernard and others of his old friends at the Royal Institution and they do all they can to render him unpopular'.

Dr John Wolcot, who lampooned many well-known people from the King downwards, wrote in his *Epistle to Count Rumford* (part of the works of Peter Pindar, Esq.) which was published in 1802:

> 'High o'er the world Sir Joseph soars sublime,
> The great and fertile subject of my rhyme:—
> Yet higher *thou* shalt mount, whose angry toe
> Kick'd from thy shop the Hero of Soho;

And aiming too at Garnet's luckless crown,
Didst, with thy leaden journal, knock him down:
For who with sage opinion dares appear,
While Rumford's mouth of oracles is near?

But what an insolence in me to prate!
Pretend to him to open Wisdom's gate,
Who spurns advice like weeds, where'er it springs,
Disdaining counsel, though it comes from Kings.'

This was probably based on club or coffee-house gossip. When it came to opposing Bernard, Banks and Rumford stood together—though Peter Pindar might have been referring to the disagreement Banks expressed with the plan to teach science to workmen.

Dr Thomas Thomson, the editor of a monthly magazine *Annals of Philosophy*, wrote a biographical sketch of Rumford in April 1815 in which he spoke of the quarrels with the managers, supposing they were caused 'by an attempt on the part of Count Rumford to retain in his own hands the entire management of that Institution. Be that as it may', he went on, 'the result of the dispute induced him to leave London, to which he never again returned.'

The limit of outspokenness was reached in an obituary in *The Monthly Magazine or British Register* in May 1815. 'We feel it proper to state', the writer says primly, 'that the Count assumed the character of an absolute controller, as well as the projector, of this establishment, and conducted himself with a degree of *hauteur* which disgusted its patrons, and almost broke the heart of our amiable friend and its first professor, Dr Garnett.' It sounds as though the anonymous writer had been waiting fifteen years to get in that stroke. It seems also that Rumford had not enhanced his personal reputation by his unsympathetic treatment of Garnett.

Thomas Young, whose opinion always commands respect, wrote a short account of Rumford's life and work for the fifth edition of the *Encyclopaedia Britannica*.[4] He had the advantage of being a member of the staff of the Institution for a short time while Rumford was concerned with it and so he wrote with inner knowledge of its affairs and some insight into the character of its founder. After saying that with so active and diversified a career behind him it was not to be expected that Rumford would be satisfied with permanent residence in London he continues: 'He was so accustomed to labour for the attainment of some object, that when the object itself was completely within his reach, and the labour was ended, the prospect which ought to have been uniformly bright, became spontaneously clouded, or even the serenity became unenjoyable for want of clouds to afford a contrast. . . .' This judgement agrees with that of von Werneck, that Rumford was apt to neglect an enterprise when he had brought it to a certain maturity. Young also points out that the enthusiasm aroused by some of his inventions had subsided and also that he felt humiliated by the impertinent attacks of Peter Pindar—though there he suffered in elevated company. As for his going to Paris in the spring of 1802 the reason was mainly, if not entirely, 'the superiority of the climate'. Although climate may have played merely a small part in Rumford's decision, as a reason given by Young it is important evidence that the decision was not taken as a result of a flare-up in the inner circles of the Institution. Young would have known about that, but he is not likely to have been intimately aware of Rumford's personal motives and affairs.

Young's first important biographer, Dr George Peacock, speaking in 1855 of the Royal Institution, said that after managing it for a few months and editing its journals Rumford quarrelled with some of the directors and abandoned it altogether. This statement, however, shows a lack of intimate knowledge of the affairs of the Institution.

Ellis, with his usual care, anxious to obtain the most accurate information about the supposed quarrel and its importance wrote to H. Bence Jones, the secretary of the Royal Institution, in or about 1870, for full information. Jones was at that time writing his book *The Royal Institution: Its Founder and its first Professors*, and, of course, had the Minute Books available, though he lamented the Institution's failure to retain its early records and correspondence. Jones's reply is interesting. It was clear to him 'that Count Rumford fell out with Mr Bernard and Sir John Hippisley'. He told Ellis that when Rumford left England, in May 1802, he intended to return, which is true; but that he kept up *no* relations with the managers, which is not. In the same letter[5] he wrote:

'The fact was that Rumford's idea of workshops and kitchen, industrial school, mechanics institution, model exhibition, social club house and scientific committees to do everything, &c, &c, was much too big and unworkable for a private body, and was fitted only for an absolute wealthy government and was going rapidly into difficulties which, in 1803, led to the proposal to shut the affair and sell it off. Rumford seeing that he could not have his way went to Paris.'

But Bence Jones changed his mind about the last sentence, for in his book, published in 1871, he wrote that 'Differences with the managers had nothing to do with Count Rumford's departure from London. The immediate cause is seen in his letter to his daughter from Munich on 2 October 1801. He had promised the new Elector to return as soon as the Royal Institution was in order.' This, as far as it goes, agrees with the conclusions we have already reached.

It is obvious that there were differences of policy among the managers. What healthy young institution of any size is free from them? Open quarrels are a different matter and there appears to have been little personal animosity at any rate while Rumford was in England. Even in November 1803 Bernard could write to Boulton, and they had both been in opposition to Rumford: 'Having spent a very pleasant day at your house in company with our friend Count Rumford. . . .'[6]

One of the uncertain factors in the development of the Royal Institution was the availability of financial support. To ask the government of the day would have been unthinkable. It gave no grant for education until 1833, and then it voted only £20,000 for elementary education, a smaller amount than that available for the maintenance of the royal stables. The founders knew that they must rely upon private subscriptions and donations and that they must limit plans to keep within the income available. Where alternative plans were under consideration priority, as we now say, had to be decided, and Bernard, the treasurer, and Hippisley who strongly supported him, voted for the lectures which brought in the money rather than the Repository which brought in the opposition and which could only give a slow and diffuse benefit. Rumford himself must have seen by the spring of 1802 that his original plans were too ambitious and that their fulfilment was impossible in an Institution like the one taking form in Albemarle Street. It was clear by then that the lectures made the place pay and that the fashionable people who attended must be considered first. It is strange that it should have been Bernard, an energetic promoter of charitable causes who stood out most strongly against Rumford. Yet there is undeniable evidence that it was so. Rumford probably became disillusioned, having expected to be able to set afoot something of much wider influence and greater social importance. When personal preference and material interests attracted him abroad, he was probably glad to call it a day.

It is not unlikely that some of the managers and Visitors were embarrassed and angry at Rumford's withdrawal. Logic and anger are poor bedfellows. However much they might oppose his more nebulous plans, he had after all directed the Institution and here they were with the place on their hands. And while they resented his tendency to dictate and patronize, his scientific authority had to be admitted. Bernard and Hippisley took on the general control of affairs when he had gone and found themselves in difficulties. A month after his departure the subscription rates which had been raised on a motion by him were brought down to their previous amounts as a retrenchment. In December a committee of three, including Bernard, was appointed to report on means of reducing expenses. In the next year it was seriously proposed to close the Institution, wind up its affairs and sell the house and its contents to pay the debts. This drastic action was avoided by limiting activities to lecture theatre and laboratory. The workshops and the Repository fell into disuse, workmen and printers were discharged. In March 1803, obviously with the intention of satisfying the subscribers, an accountant was called in to examine the accounts 'from the first'. They were found to be in order and at the annual meeting in May Bernard reported that there was 'nothing that merited censure and much that deserves approbation'. It seems that however restrained Bernard was at the annual meeting, he and others let themselves go in public. Rumford's friend Lady Palmerston records under the date 21 May 1803: 'The Royal Institution, I fear, is on the decline by the ill-management of the present managers. They have subscribed £100 each. Their abuse of Count R is atrocious. Sir J. Banks thinks of withdrawing from it. . . .'[7]

Rumford intended to return to England for a short period in 1803; this is clear from his letters, but he was refused permission to pass through France. He was also concerned about his Bavarian pension. It seems that he always had greater faith in the British government's undertaking to pay him his allowance as a colonel on half pay than he had in the Bavarian government's arrangements for his pension or future employment. Banks wrote to him in April 1804 to say that he could not disguise that his not appearing in England in 1803 as he had expected had been a material disappointment to him 'and a great detriment to the Royal Institution'. It was 'entirely in the hands of the profane', and he had declared his dissatisfaction at the way in which it was carried on and his resolution not to attend in future. He was unable to 'keep matters in their proper level' because of his poor health and spirits.

Banks clearly regretted the turn of events and sympathized with Rumford because he wrote again in June saying much the same thing. 'The Institution has irrevocably fallen into the hands of the enemy and is now perverted to a hundred uses for which you and I never intended it. I could have successfully resisted their innovations had you been here, but, alone, unsupported, and this year confined to my house for three months by disease (gout) my spirit was too much broken to admit of my engaging singly with the host of Hs [Hippisleys] and Bs [Bernards] who had taken possession of the fortress. . . .'[8]

The fortress did not decline to a ruin. It was saved by Davy, who achieved world-wide renown during the early years of the century by his fundamental research, particularly the isolation by electrolysis of the metals sodium, potassium, calcium, barium and strontium. As a result of the discoveries made in it by Davy, and later by Faraday, its laboratory became the most famous in the world. The Royal Institution changed its character again and was noted as a centre of pure science. Rumford's Institution never fully materialized; Bernard's Institution was a caretaker's interlude; but the Institution of Davy and Faraday flourished and the fortress became not a place of defence but a centre of light and learning. A noble line of men of science have worked within its walls; apart from Rumford, Davy and Faraday there were Tyndall, Dewar, William Bragg and Lawrence Bragg. Though it developed along lines other than those laid down by its founder it was fortunate for him, for Great Britain and for the world, that when he returned to this country and found himself deprived of the ambassadorship he was able to engage upon the task of founding it. It was fortunate for him, for he found compensation in the task, and though his powers were circumscribed in comparison with those he had exerted in Bavaria, the little autocracy in Albemarle Street with the aristocracy in support brought him ample satisfaction, so much so that he once said that he considered it the most important undertaking of his life. It was fortunate for Great Britain because the Royal Institution has retained its eminence as a centre from which scientific knowledge has been diffused, not least among young people. It was fortunate for the world because it has been an inspiration to men of science everywhere and from it has gone forth the light which is kindled by the great discoveries made by those who seek steadfastly for truth.

In spite of his partial failure, therefore, Rumford might have said with truth when he left England in 1802:

I have raised a memorial more enduring than brass.

8

Personal and Family Affairs

Marriage, with peace, is this world's paradise. . . .
ANON.

JOHN TYNDALL said that Rumford's life of the intellect appeared to have interfered with his life of the affections. As a clue to much of Rumford's behaviour the comment has value. He was unloving from the start. He did write in a recipe book which he kept as a boy: 'Love is a Noble Passion of the Mind. LOVE.' But, if he meant what he wrote, this early adolescent stirring subsided.

It would also be true to say that in Rumford love of self interfered abnormally with his affection for others. He was exceptionally self-centred. His life revealed this and so did his letters. Sometimes in what he wrote the self-centredness is just below the surface, hidden or partly hidden by an expression of affection for others. The last letter he sent to Germain, when Germain was a dying man, affords a good illustration:

'Your letter . . . has alarmed me exceedingly on account of your health. What can I say to you that can express the anxiety I feel on that score. But why should I increase your uneasiness by a discription of my apprehension. I know you love me most affectionately and you cannot help feeling for my distresses. What my dearest friend should I do without you. It is a most dreadful period to look to when we must part—the idea is insupportable—what must be the reallity? But I will not distress you with my melancholy reflexions . . . Be assured my dearest friend that I shall leave nothing undone that is in my power to do to put you at your ease respecting my establishing myself permanently in this Country. . . .'[1]

It is dangerous to interpret a letter without seeing the one it answers but Rumford's concern with his own affairs, rather than with the sufferings of his friend, is obvious. He had as great an affection for Germain as for anyone in his life but the letter merely proceeds from a cloying expression of sympathy and affection, through a promise of requital, of doubtful sincerity—'I shall leave nothing undone, etc'—to an account of his pay and prospects in Bavaria.

Sometimes his self-centredness was painfully near the surface, and being aware of it he attempted camouflage, for instance in his valedictory letter to his father-in-law written before he moved into the British garrison at Boston. At other times he seems to have been obtuse in his inability to comprehend the effect his treatment must have had on others. He could not, for instance, understand why his relatives did not respond to his tentative overtures at a time when he was notoriously fighting with the enemy.

And yet he was rarely unemotional. If Tyndall's reading were correct and comprehensive one would expect a general lack of emotion. But in fact his emotions were easily aroused where he himself was concerned, which is exactly the behaviour of a self-centred person, the result of a strong self-regarding sentiment. He was greatly affected when the people of Munich went in procession to the Dom to pray for his recovery of health; he was touched when Sally read the inscription on the monument erected to him in the English Garden; he was elated when Napoleon accorded him the treatment due to an ambassador. In all these examples it is he who tells us of the incident and in all he was the person most concerned. There are many clues to self-centredness: self-pity, abnormal introspection and over-weening ambition are three symptoms. We can acquit him of morbid introspection, but he often evinced self-pity, and the desire for fame was paramount, though in his latter days he must have lamented, 'illweaved ambition, how much art thou shrunk'.

He appears to have been emotionally neutral to his first wife. It seems to have satisfied him that she was well provided for materially. Nor did he worry about his daughter until his wife died. Sally wrote one sentence which implied that the family felt he deliberately chose fame rather than reunion with his family, 'Vain honours! Is that a sufficient recompense for a separation from friends, from all that is dear on earth?'[2] But she does not appear to have resented her father's behaviour. Nor does Loammi Baldwin who had equal cause; when the time came he re-established old ties with alacrity.

The date Rumford began to send money to help to support his mother and daughter is not known. Ellis thinks he did so annually for some time before 1793 through a business man in Boston. It is more likely, however, that the death of his wife in January 1792 marked the reopening of relations. It seems probable that the Count then wrote to his brother-in-law about Sally's future. The result was highly unsatisfactory and a dispute arose which was not settled for some time. Meanwhile Baldwin, who had kept in touch with the family at Concord, though still living in Woburn, wrote a friendly letter to Rumford late in 1792 which he sent by the hands of a mysterious Mr Stacey who travelled to Munich. At this time Rumford was depressed and ill and Baldwin received in reply a letter asking *inter alia* about the prospects of his returning to his native country. Would he be kindly received? Were the remains of Party spirit and political persecutions done away? Would he have to ask leave of the State? He said it was possible that Baldwin might see him at Woburn before he was aware of it.

It was this letter which started the negotiations for Sally's visit to England. Rumford, in an access of emotion, real or feigned, wished also 'once more to have the satisfaction of seeing his kind and affectionate mother'. 'My dear, beloved Parent, what would I give to see her were it but for one hour!' By this time he had begun to send thirty pounds a year towards her support and he also made permanent arrangements for the same amount to be paid to his mother's other children after her death.

Rumford's tour in Italy improved his health, revived his spirits and turned his mind to the publication of his essays and it was not until 1796 that Sally and her father met. The meeting and Sally's stay in London have already been briefly described. After about three months in England Sally wrote a letter to Mrs Baldwin which, like the one she later wrote from Bavaria, seems to owe something to her father's composition. 'I am very happy, I should think it very strange if I was not. For I have one of the best of fathers that seems desirous to do everything that will contribute to my happiness . . . I am indulged in everything I wish, and I am under the protection of a parent that I have not only reason to love but to be proud of. On his account I receive every polite attention I could wish and had I his merit I should feel that I deserved it. . . .' It is not unfair to suspect Rumford's hand in this letter, his style is there. Furthermore the letters he had received from Sally before their meeting had been composed or heavily amended by her teacher, Mrs Snow. The truth was that at this time Sally, by her father's standards, was ill-educated. This embarrassed him greatly in London but less in Munich because there it was not nearly so evident and allowances would anyhow have been made for a foreigner.

Sally's first stay on this side of the Atlantic lasted three and a half years, and she spent most of it in Bavaria. She found much in Munich to interest and impress her, although there was internal discord in the city and danger from without. Her father's influence was great, his overt power very considerable and his prestige high with the poorer classes. When the immediate threat to the city was past and the Elector had returned, all was gaiety at court. The Elector was seventy-one and his young wife seventeen—a mere reversal of numbers, as the saying went. To Sally the ladies were 'accomplished, charming and sincere; the gentlemen, profound in knowledge, strict in probity with perfect high-breeding'. Sally's charity and lack of knowledge may account for this view, for the morals of the court were shocking.

Poor Charles Theodore! He cuts a sorry figure trying to keep up with his spirited and frivolous adolescent wife, following her from concert to reception and from reception to ball, anxious to get away to peace and quiet while she was at the centre of the rout. Bystanders, said Sally, were amused to witness the conjugal struggles, the Elector looking steadfastly to the door impatient for the moment of retiring, and she in the supplicating, artful manner of youth, saying: 'One dance more! One dance more!'

Her father's establishment impressed Sally greatly even though she was used to slaves at home. His personal retinue included two aides-de-camp, Captain Count Taxis and Lieutenant Spreti, a personal physician, a huntsman, a valet, a groom, an ostler—to say nothing of the inferior servants. He had a box at the Opera and was addressed as 'Excellency'. One of his greatest friends was the Countess Nogarola, a married woman of good breeding and insight, kindly, tactful and generous, and very different from her sister, the Countess Baumgarten, a celebrated beauty of flighty disposition about whom Sally writes:

'She was so much admired and celebrated in the world that even crowned heads confessed her charms. . . . Alas, poor lady! she ended in not sufficiently respecting herself.'

There was one amusing incident which shows the contrast between the two personalities of father and daughter. Rumford, always alert for improvement, brought back from England two side-saddles. He wanted to introduce the English style of riding to the ladies of Munich, so he arranged a semi-public demonstration. Three horses were chosen: a quiet one, aptly named Lambkin, for the Countess Nogarola who was a novice; Tancred, a good, steady goer for Sally, and a *personage* (Sally's word) of noble quality for the Count. The horses, fresh and groomed, were made ready and brought into the courtyard. The Count, 'decorated with honours, star and garter', descended the great staircase with Sally on one arm and the Countess on the other. 'Both ladies were dressed in the English style, except more richly, with feathers and ermine.'

The Count had in mind a dignified and splendid progression to the English Garden—English riding in an English setting. But the Lady Nogarola found it difficult to mount Lambkin 'on account of her being no horsewoman'. Aides and equerries stood by respectfully to help, the servants hid their smiles. The Count, conscious of the dignity of the expedition, was anxious to start. Sally, who was impatient, mounted with trifling assistance, skipped off through the *porte-cochère* and shouted 'Bo' to the cavalcade when it appeared. The Count was not amused.

The procession moved off but Sally's saddle was insecure and had to be fixed. When they moved off again, their pace slow because of the inexperience of the Countess Nogarola, Sally mischievously galloped away into the unknown roads and winding paths of the gardens. The Count looked to Spreti to follow her but Taxis, who had already gallantly recovered her whip, was away first—and this was doubtless just what Sally had planned.[3]

Rumford with habitual thoroughness turned to the task of educating Sally. She had a talent for drawing, so he engaged a drawing master. He also employed for her a teacher of French and music, and a third for the Italian language. The first was a priest and unable to marry, the second a woman, and the third ugly beyond redemption and possessing a harsh voice. But in spite of all the excitement and attention she was homesick. She was particularly upset when she thought her father was going to marry again and she watched with anxiety for the appearance of a white cockade on Aichner's hat. Her friend Countess Nogarola helped her devotedly and encouraged her to sketch and take her music lessons. Her application, loneliness and a reduced diet brought on sickness from which she recovered, but she was an obstinate patient and her convalescence was long.

All through her life Sally was changeable and lacked an enduring purpose; in consequence she was often discontented. Although she was proud of her father's achievements she did not seriously identify herself with his aims and work. Even her efforts to show her gratitude went wrong. On one occasion, with the help of her friend the Countess Nogarola, she arranged a birthday party for him. She provided the money out of her allowance and decided upon the programme. Five of the rooms in the house were decorated with flowers and a bust of her father was garlanded. Refreshments and music—'the best that Munich afforded'—were provided. The female guests wore white dresses, and Sally invited to the party six little girls from the House of Industry whom she dressed in white at her own expense. Cards, music and dancing were offered as entertainment.

This had all been contrived without his knowing but by some subterfuge Rumford was induced to dress for a formal occasion and then led over to the great hall where the reception took place. There was some anxiety as to how he would take all this—Sally no doubt remembered his annoyance when she had overspent on clothes. However, when the initial shock had passed he was pleased and amiable, 'bowing and smiling, showing his white teeth, of which he was very proud, thanking people for the trouble, as he termed it, of coming to see him'.

The children of the Countess sang; the Countess herself played a concerto with the orchestra; the poor-house children presented written expressions of gratitude and respect; and Sally, to show her dutiful progress in her studies, handed to her father a complimentary letter written in Italian.

All was going well until Sally noticed that the Count was paying great attention to one of the Baumgarten children, named Sophy. As he seemed to be neglecting everyone else Sally asked Mary Nogarola why this was. 'Well,' said Mary evasively, 'her mother's not here.'

After further observation Sally noticed how very alike in features were the child Sophy and the Count. Then, as she said, she could no longer consider herself an only child. This made her angry and miserable; so although she was hostess, and had duties to her guests, she decided to dance with the charming and attentive Taxis whom she had refused several times. This revived and calmed her and the party ended in harmony.

Next morning she received an invitation to take breakfast with her father, which was a signal honour. Obviously he wished to thank her for the part she had played in arranging the birthday party, to talk over its episodes; he might even be going to express some contrition over the existence of the 'beautiful illegitimate'. But on the contrary he had asked to see her in order to express his displeasure at her deceit in arranging the party without his knowing, and to rebuke her for encouraging Count Taxis.

His birthday party had a curious sequel. He was anxious to perpetuate the name of Rumford and the appearance of the children from the House of Industry gave him an idea. Later in the year he wrote to Baldwin giving him a different version of the story and saying that he 'was so much affected by this proof of [Sally's] affection', and by the pleasure it gave her, that 'it should not be forgotten'. He had therefore made her a present of American stock to the value of 2000 dollars on the express condition that she should appropriate it *in her will*, as a capital for clothing every year *forever*, on *her* birthday twelve poor and industrious children, namely six girls and six boys, each of them to be furnished with a complete suit of new clothing to the value of five dollars, made up in the same form and colours as the uniforms of the poor children she clothed on his birthday.[4]

Sally chose Concord as the place of benefaction and 'either the Selectmen of the Town or the Overseers of the Poor' were to be asked to take the trouble to see that the conditions were fulfilled.

Even Ellis loses his blandness when describing this offer. He says: 'The Count did not exercise his usual discretion and seems to have become well-nigh oblivious of the characteristics of his native land when he suggested the introduction here of one of the most odious customs of the Old World in associating a grotesque pauper uniform with a beneficiary institution.'[5]

The elders of Concord were duly grateful for the offer of the money, but doubtful about the terms. The plan was dropped, but when Sally (as Sarah, Countess of Rumford) made her will she left a substantial part of her ample fortune for charitable purposes in the town of Concord.

Rumford regarded his daughter as one of his possessions and, while paying lip service to her freedom of action and decision, his approach was always a humourless 'Father knows best'. He seems not to have wanted her to marry. Ellis thought that the shadowy Mr Stacey was a suitor and that he travelled from New Hampshire to Munich to obtain the Count's consent to his suit. But Sally does not mention Mr Stacey in describing her love affairs. She does, however, draw a parallel between Count Taxis and a certain William Green. It seems that Sally's and William's mothers had agreed on the desirability of a match although Sally was four or five years older than William. It is not impossible that shortly after the death of Rumford's wife, Mrs Green, who seems to have been a designing woman, prevailed on Mr Stacey to visit the Count as an intermediary, so as to obtain consent for the union. Rumford wrote to Baldwin, who knew of the affair: 'As to the main business of Mr Stacey's journey I must refer you to my Daughter to whom I have written fully on the subject. As I have no wish but for her happiness, I think she must be satisfied with the advice I have given her and I have no doubt she will receive it as it is meant and cheerfully follow it.' After finishing at school, William Green joined the American navy and was killed in a duel in which he became quixotically involved because his sister was being pressed to marry against her will. Sally heard of his unfortunate death while she was in Munich and was much grieved. The inference to be drawn from Sally's memoirs is not clear, the wording is ambiguous. Mrs Green could have changed her mind; but then Mr Stacey and his mission still have to be explained.

Her later attachment to Count Taxis was more romantic. He was a scion of a German family with which Rumford had relations over many years. She was genuinely fond of him and he of her, though from his gallantry she probably imagined his affection deeper than it was. As Taxis was in attendance on Rumford and also present at court functions, he and Sally were often in each other's company. On one occasion while out riding she fainted and he showed more concern than mere politeness or courtesy demanded. On another, he insisted that Mary Nogarola should take her home from a court ball when she was too ill to be out of her room, though she had obstinately insisted on being present. These marks of regard raised Sally's hopes and her father's opposition.

She was frequently ill. After one period of sickness Rumford's physician, Haubenel, prescribed a change of air. Rumford, using his influence with the Elector, arranged for her and Mary Nogarola to spend a holiday at the Elector's country palace at Ammersee, about twenty-five miles from the capital. No doubt he thought not only that the air would be beneficial but that she might recover from her infatuation for Taxis. He did his best to make the holiday eventful, and although he was too busy to spend all his time there he visited them occasionally. He planned expeditions and took them on sight-seeing tours and visits to monasteries. Life was strenuous when he was about; one of his ideas was to climb a mountain at night. For the ladies this could hardly have been enjoyable encumbered as they were by unsuitable clothes. Rumford, nothing daunted, apparently advised them to pull up their skirts, a fact which would not deserve mention here had it not given rise to this delicate circumlocution used by Ellis in describing the incident:

'. . . the Count's practical wisdom suggested to them such an approximation of the arrangement of their apparel to circumstances as anticipated the style of the more independent of their sex in our times.'

But the Taxis *affaire* was not over. After her return Sally was invited to a dinner party by the Countess of Lerchenfeld, Mary Nogarola's mother. She went with her father's permission, and found that Count Taxis was one of the guests. Rumford also discovered this a day or two later and suspected that an attempt had been made to bring the two young people together in spite of him. He accused Sally of deceit, and when she laughed at him he boxed her ears. She was at this time twenty-three years old. His anger was not, however, appeased, for when Taxis made an indirect proposal of marriage he ordered his regiment to take up duty in the country. Taxis, though he some-times communicated with Sally, accepted the situation. She was hurt. As a sad footnote we may add that both Taxis and Spreti lost their lives, along with many thousands of Bavarians, in Napoleon's Russian campaign.

Her next suitor was Sir Charles Blagden, the notable physician and chemist, and a friend, as we have seen, both of Banks and Rumford. He was a secretary of the Royal Society for nineteen years. Sally, often inexact in regard to age, says 'he was not so old as her father, but not young'. In truth, he was five years older than her father. He often dined with Sally and the evidence is that he wrote a letter to Rumford, pitched in a rather low key and written *rallentando* rather than *con fuoco*, saying that he would like to marry her. There was no enthusiasm on Rumford's side. He said nothing to Sally about the contents of the letter when it arrived, but used every opportunity to bring the conversation round to Blagden and speak of his less desirable qualities. He was wasting his time. Sally was quite unaware of the suit and 'shocked that the thing should be mentioned'. Blagden, with ease and good grace, exchanged the role of suitor for that of guardian. His manliness and generosity were shown over many years, in fact until he died in 1820, by his friendliness to her. He and Rumford often had disagreements and the friendship broke up because of some slight or injury Blagden experienced after they were both in Paris in 1802.[6] But Blagden behaved with magnanimity. Sally turned to him without embarrassment for advice when she had later proposals of marriage and he, who understood her better than most, treated her with brotherly tact and wisdom.[7]

Sally, though unstable and often indolent (perhaps because of her early upbringing), could be shrewdly discerning. She is helpful in assessing her father's character. She treated his continued protestations that he only had her interests in view with reserve, saying that when he was 'perplexed with cares or business or much occupied there was no living with him', but of course his attitude to her love affairs shows something deeper than mere captiousness or irascibility. Certainly all the three proposed alliances had their disadvantages. The Taxis affair, in many ways promising, was not without difficulties that Rumford was quick to see. But nevertheless one cannot help being convinced that he did not want Sally to marry. He may genuinely have felt that she was likely to be inconstant; like father, like daughter. He may not have wanted her to found a family in Europe. When she had returned to America he wrote to Baldwin: 'Perhaps my daughter may marry (which she has my leave to do whenever she pleases and with whom she pleases). . . . I do not mean to be an indulgent father in theory only.' But it is not easy to take this at its face value and

Blagden was always emphatic in his advice to her never to take a serious decision without reference to her father. An extreme suggestion is that Rumford may have wished her to transmit most of his money to philanthropic causes, perhaps the more certainly to perpetuate his name. It is fairly safe to conclude that whatever his motives he saw Sally's interests in the perspective created by his own.

Father and daughter returned to England, as already described, in September 1798. Sally stayed on for a year living in the house Rumford held on a lease at 45 Brompton Row. When she returned to America in October 1799, although it was with a pension and the courtesy title of Countess, she felt it, in her own words, to be a fall from heaven to earth.

At the time Sally left, Rumford was immersed in the task of founding the Royal Institution, and he had given up the idea of returning to America. In June 1798 his main aim had been to become Bavarian Ambassador at the Court of St. James's. He was temporarily bewildered by the refusal to accept him and his thoughts again turned to America. He had asked Baldwin more than five years earlier whether he would be welcome but Baldwin had not given a definite reply. In January 1796, no doubt after careful inquiry, he had been assured by his friend that he could freely return, with or without official leave from the American State, and that he would get a hearty welcome from his friends and the citizens in general. Baldwin added that as far as he was concerned no one on earth would be more welcome. His rehabilitation had begun. It continued when he was elected a member of the Massachusetts Historical Society in 1798. He valued this honour and wrote a reply to the Reverend Dr Belknap, the Society's secretary, in his most effusive style. 'I have ever loved my native country', he said, 'with the fondest affection; and the liberality I have experienced from my Countrymen—their moderation in success, and their consummate prudence in their use of Independence have attached me to them by all the ties of Gratitude, Esteem and Admiration.' At that moment he had given up the idea of returning but when, a few months later, he scarcely knew where to turn he remembered this encouragement and Baldwin's assurance. Either he could retire to America after purchasing a suitable small estate; or he could spend a holiday there, in the spring of 1799, and then make up his mind about his future; or he could try at once to obtain in America a position of responsibility and prestige. He decided upon the third course and went to see Rufus King, the American Ambassador in London. In December 1798 King wrote to Colonel Pickering, the American Secretary of State, a letter which was to be handed to the President. In it King said that Rumford had decided 'to return and settle himself in America ... to establish himself at or near Cambridge, to live there in the character of a German Count, to renounce all political expectations and devote himself to literary pursuits'. King said that he was writing at Rumford's request and hoped that he might be well received.

This letter[8] was of course a feeler, and King emphasized that Rumford was politically sound; but he also pointed out that Rumford had a knowledge of military matters, especially those concerned with the founding of cannon. This was a hint to the President that Rumford was willing if necessary to devote himself to scientific work and writing essays, but if the state *could* make use of his experience and talents in a practical way that was what Rumford would prefer.

There were bound to be months of waiting and having been encouraged so far by King—for officially he was still a proscribed person—he decided that he might profitably pay a short visit after all. He wrote to his publishers on 26 January 1799,[9] to say that he expected to sail early in March and he wished to take with him a dozen copies of his essays bound in the best possible binding for presents. He no doubt remembered the beautifully bound volume of letters he had presented to King George more than twenty years earlier. This time it was all his own work, and to emphasize this he asked the publishers to reproduce a portrait of the author opposite the title page of each of the first volumes.

But his plans changed immediately as a result of his meeting the delegates from the Society for Bettering the Condition of the Poor on 31 January. He decided not to visit America in the spring. He was too shrewd, however, just because of the meeting with Bernard and his associates, to break off his inquiries and negotiations. Still at Rumford's prompting, King wrote on 10 March to James McHenry, the American Secretary of War, advocating the formation in America of a Military Academy and emphasizing the value of Rumford's experience and ability if it were decided to establish such an institution. King also spoke of Rumford's military books, drawings and a field-piece of his design all of which would be available for the Military Academy if it were formed. Later when it was confirmed that Rumford could not leave this country for the time being he said he would try to make the journey in the spring of 1800. The field-piece and the rest of his professional samples he would present to the United States in any case; and there might be a slight delay as—an impressive touch— the Duke of York had the field-piece for the purpose of making a copy of it.

In America the President considered Rumford's request and in June wrote to McHenry to say that he had 'for five or six years past been attentive to the character of that gentleman' and had formed a high opinion of his 'genius, talents, enterprise, and benevolence'. If he returned to America he would be received with kindness and civility. On the other hand, he said, the difficulties were obvious in such cases. If McHenry wished, he was at liberty through Mr King to offer him the appointments mentioned. Rumford was then offered the post of Inspector-General of the Artillery of the United States and the super-intendence of the Military Academy. He was obviously flattered and gratified, but when he declined Rufus King said he had done wisely and no doubt the American President thought the same.

Characteristically Rumford, in describing these events to M. A. Pictet, gave the impression that the initiative had been on the side of America: as though the President had said, 'I hear Rumford is now in England, having left the service of Bavaria; let us invite him over here to superintend our Military Academy.' Rumford's habit of asking for employment and pressing his claims has led one biographer to say that he got on at every step by 'shameless solicitation'. *Solicitation*, yes; but *shameless* is too strong a term because the solicitation hurt no one and was backed by the ability (the metaphor is appropriate) to deliver the goods.

It was fortunate for Rumford that the Royal Institution claimed his energies at this time. A return to America would have entailed a psychological adjustment which would have taxed him to the limit. His partiality to titles, decorations and the symbols of power; his autocratic treatment of his helpers and servants; his class consciousness —even his servility to those he served—to say nothing of his record as a loyalist, would all have made for friction or conflict.

He was kept very busy, apart from short periods of illness or holiday, until the summer of 1801. His friend Pictet visited him in London and stayed at his show house in Brompton Row. Marc-Auguste Pictet was Professor of Philosophy at Geneva, President of the Society of Arts at Lausanne, a Fellow of the Royal Society and internationally famous. From London he sent back to Geneva letters describing Rumford and his works, for publication in the *Bibliothèque Britannique*. Rumford was well known to the readers of that journal. Four years earlier he had written to his publishers, Cadell and Davies, to say that the Editors of the *Bibliothèque Britannique* had ascribed to him and to him alone 'the uncommon success that periodical publication had met with'. This is not just another example of his readiness to cry his own wares, but also shows his renown when his influence was at its highest.

Pictet gave a lyrical description of Rumford's house and its fittings. During the evening he sat with his notebook ready to write down the sayings of the great man, anxious not to lose a word. How Rumford must have enjoyed this. How he must have mellowed in the evening after the day's vexations and duties. This was compensation indeed. How different the admiring Pictet was from the tiresome Bernards and Hippisleys who were always asking where the next shilling was to come from.

When Pictet left for home Rumford travelled with him to Calais. This was the journey that Rumford made in great haste to Munich to visit Prince Maximilian, revealing both his anxiety about his future and his physical endurance. He saw the new Elector the morning after his arrival on 2 October, and immediately wrote to his friend Pelham, later the Second Earl of Chichester:[10]

'[The Elector] received me in the most gracious and friendly manner and I have no longer any kind of apprehension respecting my future connection with this Country. . . .

'[He] ended by assuring me that I should always find in the Elector my old friend Prince Maxe.'[11]

His relief was obviously great. He told Pelham ten days later that 'nothing was ever more fortunate' than his journey to Bavaria at that time.

There was nothing for him to do at first. A new Academy was planned and he was promised the presidency, but Maximilian had far more pressing matters claiming his attention. The country was unsettled by war; he was busy with political negotiation for the expansion of his dominions, and peaceful reform and cultural development were put in the background. After a short stay Rumford decided to leave for home by way of Paris. For part of the journey he was to travel with the Prince of Mecklenburg, brother of the Queen of Prussia. Two days later he had changed his mind and decided not to travel via Paris. But he did so after all, and was the bearer of despatches to the Bavarian minister there. His position was a curious one. He was a British subject, a colonel on half pay, and England and France were still at war; in fact, a French invasion force was encamped at Boulogne. However, he wrote to Pelham to say that he was determined not to leave Paris 'without seeing the curiosities of the place'—it was his first visit—and 'making the personal acquaintance of several men of Science'. He asked his friend's advice on the propriety of being presented to the First Consul as a Bavarian General Officer saying, rather unconvincingly, that he was 'always apprehensive of doing what may be thought wrong, in these cases of form and etiquette'. In fact he was something of a military chameleon.

He had the time of his life. He sent a continuous stream of letters home—the postal service, though indirect, must have been highly efficient—all indicating that he was being treated with the utmost respect, kindness and attention. He had an open invitation to the meetings of the *Institut National* which had replaced the old *Académie des Sciences*, swept away in 1793. He hoped his stay would not give offence in England; it certainly would not in Bavaria.

On 9 November he acknowledged Pelham's reply and wrote one of his most interesting letters. He had attended three meetings of the *Institut* and at one of them he sat next but one to Bonaparte, only the great French mathematician Lagrange was between them. He had been presented to the First Consul the day before in flattering circumstances. The foreign ministers were to dine with Bonaparte on that day and he had sent an aide-de-camp, after the reception, with a special invitation to Rumford marked '*très pressante*'. The aide found Rumford at his lodgings and there was only just enough time for him to change back into regimentals.

This was not the end, however. When they were waiting to go in to dinner the Minister for Foreign Affairs called out the order of entrance. 'After naming the Spanish, Austrian, Prussian, Swedish and

Danish Ministers he named Mons. le Comte de Rumford.' Rumford could scarcely believe this, and he hesitated, upon which he was called again and again. The Bavarian minister and others stepped politely on one side and he took the place accorded him.

Although Rumford valued rank and precedence too highly, he can be forgiven for his pleasure at his reception by Napoleon and for making the facts known in England in letters to Banks and Pelham. It was a consolation for the treatment he had received in England both when he was refused the rank of ambassador and afterwards. More important, he was being honoured for his work. Several of his essays had been translated into French by order of the government, and his inventions were known and used as much in France as in England. But he told his correspondents that he had not forgotten the Royal Institution and he thought it would profit from his stay in Paris.

He spent his evenings 'in the first circles' and his mornings seeing the sights. For him democracy had no attraction and the word itself had a sinister sound after the excesses of the previous decade. He was therefore pleased to see 'what good company' there was to be met with and how seldom one came across anything resembling democracy, which was positively despised. The word '*citoyen*' was never heard in good company and as for '*liberty*' it was 'quite obsolete'. He walked out in the morning with a star on his coat—the mark of his knighthood—and he found that it commanded respect everywhere. This he would hardly venture to do in London in places where he was 'exposed to the lowest class of people'.

In another letter to Pelham, written on 15 November, he spoke of a journal he had kept since he left London. He sent it to his friend 'although it was certainly not meant to be read by anyone' but himself. As far as I am aware there are no references to this journal in any biography of Rumford or in any other published work, but a short while ago a valuable copy of the journal came to light.[12] It was advertised in the catalogue of a well-known London bookseller. Also advertised was a collection of letters, those in fact which Mr Brian Connell had used in the book *Portrait of a Whig Peer* to which I have referred from time to time. The copy of the journal had been bought from Broadlands and is now in the Library of the University of Birmingham. What happened to the original it is impossible to say but the copy has, if anything, greater interest for it was made by Lady Palmerston, Rumford's great friend. Lord Palmerston died on 16 April 1802. His gracious and loving wife was stricken with grief. One of her occupations almost immediately after her husband's death was to copy Rumford's journal. It is 124 quarto pages in length, bound in red morocco, and has the following inscription on the first page:

'Journey from London to Munich and from Munich to London by Paris in the Autumn of 1801.

'Copied at the Lavender House. Began the 29th of April and finished Tuesday evening 4th of May, 1802 by M.P.

'An occupation which has served to beguile some moments which otherwise would have pass'd in ceaseless sorrow. The knowledge of which would have given the author no small degree of gratification whose benevolence and friendship ever lead him to lend his Talents to the comfort of the Poor or the Afflicted.'

The journal indicates that Rumford's health was good at this time and his vitality unbounded. In Paris he met and commented on most people of eminence. He visited charitable institutions. He proposed the formation of a new Society for the Encouragements of Arts and Manufactures. Bonaparte fascinated him. He wrote various letters about him. His mind was clear and capacious; his apprehension uncommonly quick. Rumford thought him the most able man he had ever known; the most ambitious of mortals, said to be insensible to the allurements of pleasure, and with an uncommonly strong constitution.

On 7 November there was a meeting of great historical importance at the *Institut*. Laplace was in the chair, Lagrange on his right and Rumford by Lagrange. Volta was reading a paper on his recent electrical experiments when Bonaparte entered, taking his place next to Laplace. After Volta had finished, the First Consul rose to congratulate him, to suggest that he should be presented with a gold medal and to propose the repetition of the experiments on a large scale without regard to expense. This is a striking early example of a genuine interest in science by the head of a state, though polite patronage had long existed.

Rumford spent an evening with Talleyrand. Nobody 'had more wit or facility of expression'. He was 'naturally very caustic but his language and manner were those of a high bred gentleman'. 'If he does not give himself the trouble to refute the nonsense he is obliged to hear, it is easy to perceive by the stedfastness of his looks that he knows how to appreciate it and I never saw a face better calculated to impose silence on prating fools than his.'

Mme Grand, a divorcée with whom Talleyrand was living—the two married in 1803—was a blonde with fine flaxen hair and no wig. She had a fine figure and 'was potelée without being too much *en-bon-point*'. Rumford could not determine whether she had wit or no since she conversed little in company. Obviously she had been a most beautiful woman, and though nearly forty still retained the freshness of youth; evidently one of a long line of dumb blondes.

Talleyrand presented him to Mme Bonaparte, who received him with a bow but neither rose nor spoke. Rumford explained this apparent slight by Bonaparte's resolution that 'ladies should not be suffered to interfere in the Government of France'.

Laplace had arranged a dinner party in his honour. Later he called on Mme Laplace at two o'clock in the afternoon. She was in bed but he stayed with her for an hour and a half. She was under thirty, very pretty and dressed with an uncommon degree of taste and elegance. 'Her bed-dress and night-cap were *recherchés* and everything about her displayed the charms of refined luxury.' She received him without the slightest embarrassment and conversed animatedly on various subjects without any fatigue or loss of vivacity. Her daughter of eight or nine was present.

By this time Lord Cornwallis had arrived in Paris as British plenipotentiary in the negotiations which preceded the Peace of Amiens. Rumford presented his respects and later was a guest at a magnificent banquet arranged to lubricate the discussions. He was impressed by the 'magnificent salloon' in which the banquet was held and by the chamber music which followed.

He went to the Opera to see *'Les Mystères d'Isis* and Mozart's *The Magic Flute'*. 'The decorations were grand and very beautiful and the dancing fine. The stage was well filled and the spectacle in all respects magnificent. There was one decoration—a momentary view of the Elysian fields—which was quite enchanting. Beautiful living figures draped in white were seen distributed among the trees and the whole of the scenery was illuminated in the most resplendent manner by light perfectly white, the source of which was not seen. This most striking effect was probably produced by Bengal Lights placed on one side behind the scenes.' Did this recall the accident he had suffered years ago when as a boy of sixteen he had been injured while making fireworks to celebrate the repeal of the hated import duties? His expert interest in fireworks is obvious. His description goes on:

'The shadows cast by the gently moving figures on one another produced an effect that was fine beyond all description. We were not indulged with this enchanting view of Paradise [for more than] about half a minute. The Turkish Ambassador who sat in one of the front Boxes seemed to enjoy it more than anything else. It seemed indeed contrived to give him an idea of what his religion teaches him to expect in the other world. It was the only object that seemed in the smallest degree to disturb his secret meditations, or alter the solid gravity of his Excellency's most stupid countenance.'

One of the best things in the journal is his description of his meeting with the Russian minister.

'I stood and conversed with him', he said, 'near an hour on various scientific and political subjects. He appeared to me to be much animated in conversation and to speak without the smallest degree of reserve. On coming home alone in my carriage I amused myself by recalling to my mind the whole of our conversation in order to see if I had learnt anything from the political part of our conversation, when I found that the cautious negociator, so far from having committed himself in the smallest degree in this conversation, so rapid and so apparently unrestrained, had contrived to converse freely and with every sign of the most engaging confidence and animation without communicating to me a single new idea. I had the satisfaction to think that we parted on an equal footing in that respect.'

But the meeting which meant most to Rumford's personal life was with the widow Mme Lavoisier. They met on 19 November, and again two days later. They had many common interests. She had translated for her husband a chemical treatise written by the mineralogist Richard Kirwan, who was a friend of Rumford. Her interest in science was deep and genuine; and by her charm she had drawn round herself a group of leading French mathematicians and men of science. She was also fond of travelling. Rumford was forty-eight and she was forty-three; he had been a widower for nine years and she a widow for seven.

Mme Lavoisier had lost her husband and her father on the same day; both were victims of the guillotine. She was the daughter of M Paulze, receiver and farmer-general of the revenues, and was brought up in a refined and cultured environment. Her father's house was the meeting place of many well-known philosophers whose conversation and interests had a lasting influence on her. But she did not grow up a sickly blue stocking; her intellectual development was matched by a strengthening both of will and emotions. She was married before she was fourteen to Antoine Laurent Lavoisier, who was then twenty-eight. For almost twenty-three years she shared the scientific work of her brilliant husband, helping with translation, preparing diagrams and making notes.

After Lavoisier's death and a short period in obscurity she returned to Paris during the Directoire and drew round her some of her old and many new friends. Her salons were brilliant and of wide renown. Great mathematicians and men of science like Laplace, Lagrange, Cuvier and Arago met there. It was natural for Rumford to go. On the second occasion she was alone and received him in an elegant room 'quite filled and even crowded with Philosophical and Chemical apparatus'. He noted with approval that 'the various instruments were constructed on the largest scale and finished with great care and accuracy'. He delicately avoided referring to her late husband.

He found time to visit her a third time and they clearly liked each other. He recorded in the journal, under 2 December:

'Mme Lavoisier is a very friendly, chearful good natured woman and she is rich and independant. Speaking of my philosophical pursuits and intended publications I observed that nothing amused me so much as making experiments but that it was tiresome to write an account of them. She said to me "*Venez vous établir ici et je veux être votre secrétaire, vous travaillerez et moi j'écrirai*". That would be charming indeed was my answer.'

This was the beginning of a long courtship which suffered interruptions but was consummated in marriage. Rumford makes it sound as though the initial proposal came from the lady, which was certainly ungallant and probably inaccurate.

Rumford was reluctant to leave Paris but at the same time anxious to continue his work at the Royal Institution. He arrived back in England on 20 December 1801. Early in 1802 he decided not to make London his permanent home. His duties in Bavaria were not fixed but he still had hopes of taking active part in the reform of the country. The reception he had had in Paris genuinely astonished him and threw into relief his treatment in England. Sally said once that it was 'something of a come-down' for him when he was refused the office of ambassador, and we know how deeply he felt it. There was, however, a further cause for chagrin. During the years which followed he was never received at court. There is a reference to his request to see the King personally when he arrived in England from Bavaria, and also evidence that he was the bearer of proposals for a treaty, but as far as I am aware, there is no evidence that he did any more than transmit his despatches to the Foreign Office. He was friendly, and even intimate, with many titled families and he would eagerly have embraced any opportunity of moving near the throne, yet in England he seems to have found a social barrier which he could not cross. Another verse written by Peter Pindar suggests that this was widely known. The first six lines are not strictly apposite but are a reminder that Rumford was no exception to the rule that whoever takes himself too seriously will earn ridicule.

'I know they mock thee (in their laughter loose)
Because thou sweep'st a chimney with a goose;
I know the world a jealous spirit fosters
And christens thee the weakest of Imposters:
Stead of a war-horse, one of Folly's *hacks*;
The *Prince*, The *King*, The *Emp'ror* of the Quacks
Sir Joseph of the journals makes his sport;
Laughs at thy dinners, keeps thee from our Court,
Or long, *long* since had'st thou received commands
To come and lounge at levees, and kiss hands.'

In Bavaria, when at the height of his influence, he was second only in authority to the Elector; in France he was treated as the minister of a major power; in Prussia as a friend of the Royal Family; but at the Court of St James's he was *persona non grata*.

Whatever kept Rumford from the court, however, it was not likely to be opposition from Sir Joseph Banks. The two men were different in temperament, habits and background, and Banks, without question, had a great influence in court circles, but they were friends. Moreover, Banks was not the kind of man to injure another behind his back. A possible explanation is the difficulty over Rumford's rank and standing. Where would this British knight who had become a Count of the Empire and a member of two European orders of knighthood, this British colonel who was a Bavarian lieutenant-general, stand in the order of precedence? He was touchy about such things.

Many of Rumford's decisions were prudential. Having been away from Bavaria for six months he decided to return to see whether the Elector Maximilian and his minister Montgelas were ready to accept his help. He left London on 9 May 1802, and arrived in Paris five days later. Sir Charles Blagden[13] whom he met there accompanied him to Munich and was impressed to see the respect and affection in which he was held in Bavaria. Blagden told Banks that he was considered a public benefactor by the great mass of the people and that they would like to see the government in his hands. But many of his reforms had decayed. His Institution for the Poor was still in being, though not well attended. The English Garden, however, looked more beautiful than ever.

The Elector was still occupied with the political aggrandizement of his country and the plans for the revived Academy were in abeyance. Blagden left at the beginning of October and on his return journey wrote to Banks to say Rumford was still in great favour but had no settled position. The country was 'rather in a state of alarm', and Rumford hoped to spend some months in England during the next year. This was confirmed by Rumford himself who on 5 November 1802, wrote this letter to his housekeeper, Miss Williams, at 45 Brompton Row; the letter shows him in slacks and slippers rather than court dress and decorations.

'Dear Bessey,

I desire you would write to me once a fortnight that I may know how you do and how you are going on. I shall most likely come to England before the next Spring. If my daughter should come to England from America she will come and lodge in my house, and you must take great care of her. I a good deal expect she will come in about two or three months. If she comes she will most probably chuse to lodge in the attics, where I lodged; but she may lodge wherever she pleases; and you must tell her so. Adieu, my dear Bessey. Be a good girl and all will be well. Write to me soon and tell me all about yourself.'[14]

He was fond of Bessey. Earlier in the year he had written twice from Paris to Savage at the Royal Institution asking him to look after her. Evidently her spelling was not all it might have been for she was to be given a good spelling book and a small spelling dictionary. She was also to drink Cheltenham water for her health and to receive a present of three or four guineas to cover the expense of mourning clothes bought when her sister died. Savage paid her wages of 'half a guinea a week and one guinea a month extra, for her private use . . .'. In both letters Rumford said she was a very good girl and he wanted her to be treated with kindness. He heard that she kept his house very clean and neat and this gave him much pleasure.[15]

Rumford did not return to England in the spring. The Peace of Amiens, uneasy to all and unsatisfactory to England, was showing signs of strain. Rumford was refused permission to travel through France. He could have taken the northern route but there was insufficient incentive. He was mainly concerned with his scientific experiments and with Mme Lavoisier. She met him in the summer and they spent a holiday together touring in Switzerland and the French Alps. Afterwards he stayed on at Mannheim, where he was presented to and dined with the King and Queen of Sweden, and she returned to Paris.

Whether it was through his own or the influence of Mme Lavoisier is not known, but he was given permission in October to return to Paris, although England and France were again at war. He was unsettled at this time and somewhat irritable with his friends. He told Sally he wanted quiet for his health's sake. He refused an Imperial invitation to visit St Petersburg. What he wanted most was to marry Mme Lavoisier. Sally was made very anxious by the turn of events because she wanted to return to Europe and stay with her father. Her anxiety was increased because her father did not choose to confide in her, though he hinted that Mme Lavoisier was very fond of him. She depended for her information upon Blagden, who tried to keep her fully up to date with her father's movements and intentions. He wrote to her on 5 December to say that Rumford continued very intimate with the lady but that his own opinion was that they would not marry. If they did, however, he did not think it would be unfortunate for Sally.

'The lady is rich and most probably will have no children. If you should have no other home you would naturally live with them, and in that situation would enjoy every kind of comfort belonging to a single state. Whether that would make you amends for the want of conjugal felicity you can best judge from your own feelings. . . .'[16]

Rumford quite clearly had set his mind on marriage but Blagden thought that Mme Lavoisier would not yield. At the beginning of the year 1804 Sally was informed that her father was spending most of his time with the widow, that he had lost interest in English affairs, that his continued residence in Paris was giving offence and that his numerous enemies were making the most of it. It was hurtful to her to have to rely on her friend Blagden for information but her father did not reveal his plans until he was sure of their fulfilment. In view of the assiduity with which he had paid court the letter he wrote to Sally at about this time declaring his intentions was matter-of-fact and business-like. He told her that he had made the acquaintance of a woman in Paris who would have no objection to having him for a husband and who in all respects would be a proper match for him. He described her as a widow without children, never having had any, who enjoyed good health, was very pleasant in society, enjoyed a most respectable fortune, kept a good house and, what was more than all the rest, was goodness itself. She was, in short, another Lady Palmerston. She had been handsome in her day and even now was not bad-looking; of a middling size but *en-bon-point* rather than thin. She was vivacious and wrote incomparably well.

Blagden was wrong. An engagement took place between Rumford and Mme Lavoisier early in January 1804. They both seem to have been enthusiastic about their marriage but the arrangements were made carefully, as befitted two intelligent people in middle life and certainly as was appropriate to Rumford with his passion for order. Sally was provided for. She had her pension of 2000 florins a year from Bavaria and in addition her father settled on her a sum which would give her an additional income of £300 per year. The Elector of Bavaria increased Rumford's own pension by 4000 florins a year in view of his marriage. Mme Lavoisier, who had a large available fortune, settled on him for life a sum of about £5000 sterling. They decided to buy the large house in which Mme Lavoisier had been living and Rumford had great alterations made. It was, he said, 'a rather old-fashioned concern' but had a garden of two acres and was in the Rue d'Anjou, in 'the very centre and finest part of Paris . . .'. His house in Brompton was assigned by will to whomever was the survivor. When the marriage finally took place the *Literary Tablet* seized on the financial advantage to the Count and described the marriage as 'the most effective of all the Rumfordizing projects for keeping a house warm'.

There was some delay before the final arrangements could be made. Rumford found that French law made it necessary for him to produce a birth certificate and a certificate of the death of his first wife in order to legalize the settlements which were being proposed. He also had, rather oddly, to obtain the consent of his mother to his marriage. What the sturdy old lady said when he wrote to tell her of his plans is not recorded. He wrote to Sally in July to ask her to have the certificates made out and signed. His letter was seriously phrased as he knew she was not remarkable for her attention to matters of business. He went so far as to send the appropriate forms of words and asked for one set, duly signed, to be sent to him in Paris at 356 Rue de Clichy and a duplicate set to his London bankers. When his request reached Sally she characteristically asked Colonel Baldwin to obtain them. Rumford received them in December or thereabouts.

There had been some difference of opinion about Sally's mainten-ance which Rumford tried to settle at this time. Seven years earlier he had written to Baldwin to say that either he or his daughter had a legal claim on his wife's personal estate. It was obviously untrue that he had any claim as a proscribed citizen but Sally's might have been substantiated. He was willing to strike a bargain with Paul Rolfe, Sally's half-brother, to renounce all claims for himself or his daughter formally provided that no counter-claim was made by Rolfe for her education and maintenance. Baldwin was asked to be kind to Rolfe if he behaved reasonably but to say he would not benefit under Sally's will unless he came to terms. These affairs remained unsettled in 1804 and Sally was asked to negotiate with her half-brother and send a receipt to her father. She was given freedom to use as a bargaining counter the waste acres which he still possessed at Amariscoggin.

But the need to obtain the certificates was not the only cause of postponement. Rumford still paid his yearly visits to Bavaria in accordance with what seems to have been the bargain made with Charles Theodore and continued under Maximilian. He left Paris on 9 June but he could do little towards founding the long promised Academy of Arts and Sciences. He stayed for some time occupying himself with his experiments. The country at that time was again under pressure from both Austria and France. The Elector, in March 1805, had concluded an agreement with Napoleon which had angered Austria, and Austria presented her with an ultimatum in September, the gist of which was that either her armies fought alongside those of Austria or she would be treated as an enemy. After some hesitation Maximilian fled the country, seeking the protection of the French army. Rumford had left Munich a day earlier. Before leaving he closed his house and wound up his affairs. He was free afterwards to live where he chose though he would 'go from time to time to pay his respects to the Elector'.[17]

The letter just quoted shows how different Rumford's standing and influence in Bavaria were in 1805 from nine years earlier. Then he had been the strong man of the moment and he had met the demands upon him. In 1805 he was in the background, mainly because the exigences of war overrode his plans for social and scientific reform. When he loaded his carriage and took his valet Aichner and Aichner's family with him he was finished as a man of action. He himself said that he had the best-founded hopes of spending his days in peace and quiet in his new house with Mme Lavoisier, 'in this paradise of a place, made what it is by me,—my money, my skill and my direction'.

Benjamin Thompson and Marie Anne Pierrete Lavoisier, *née* Paulze, were married in Paris on 24 October 1805. The wedding was a quiet one. A friend of Blagden writing from Paris said of it: '*Ils ne donnent ni l'un ni l'autre aucun détail sur leur mariage ni sur l'époque; un jour ils l'ont dit à leurs amis, et il n'y a pas en plus de formalité que cela.*' They moved straight away into their house.

At fifty-two, after a life of struggle and activity, Rumford had arrived at a time when prolonged effort or anxiety left him weary or made him ill. His great need was for a quiet life with time to carry out his scientific experiments, surrounded by friends and servants who would acknowledge his importance and minister to his needs. So I shall interrupt my narrative of his personal affairs to look at his scientific and practical achievements.

9

Master of Fuel and Fire

Lo, ev'ry parlour, drawing room I see,
Boasts of thy stoves and talks of *nought* but *thee*
Yet not *alone* my Lady and young Misses,
The Cooks themselves could smother thee with kisses.

Long as thy chimneys shall thy praise endure;
Oblivion ne'er shall swallow Rumford's name,
Aloft ascending, lo, thy radiant Fame,
With thine own curling clouds of smoke shall rise
And sun-like give them lustre on the skies.
PETER PINDAR in Epistle to Count Rumford

A DRAWING by Gillray shows Rumford standing contentedly
with his back to one of his own fireplaces; two of his sauce-
pans are on the mantelshelf. Closer attention to the picture,
which is entitled 'The Comforts of a Rumford Stove', reveals that a
part of his person, formerly sometimes bared by schoolboys—but not
from choice—is exposed to the congenial warmth of the fire.

The depiction is a good-natured one and it was suggested to the
artist by one of Garnett's lectures. Rumford very probably approved
of it because he attached the highest importance to the improvements
he made in chimneys, fireplaces and cooking appliances. The pity was
that the influence of his work in this field depended so much upon his
reputation and so little upon the merit of his improvements. The
builders of the day and the manufacturerers were slow to change, and
when he left England his ideas lost much of the influence they had had.
Fifty years after his death, however, and from then on, many recognized
the importance of his work. In his lifetime he wrote in the most

practical way about his inventions, and personally supervised the construction of kitchens and the cure of smoking chimneys. At one time, he tells us, he had no less than 500 chimneys under his hands. This work was for him 'the sublime in science', but the inertia of the middle and upper classes, the failure of his plans at the Royal Institution and the inability of all to appreciate the influence that science could exert on everyday living, left him working in isolation.

From about 1860 onwards the tide of acknowledgement began to turn. In a book entitled *Our Domestic Fireplaces*, published in 1864, the author, F. Edwards, Jr, spoke of the little progress that had been made in warming rooms by open fires partly because Rumford's elementary principles had not been understood and applied. No one since his day, with his ability, had been sufficiently interested in the problem either to make a study of it or to make extensively known what had already been done. Edwards was so impressed by Rumford's contributions in this field of domestic heating that he made some study of his life and wrote a short biographical account of him which he included in one of his own books.[1]

T. Pridgin Teal, a Fellow of the Royal Society, when reading a paper on *Designs of Fireplaces* before the Architectural Society of London in 1886 dealt with Rumford's work, and his twelve rules of design followed Rumford's suggestions very closely. Recognition has happily continued into recent times[2] and his ideas still find wide application.

Many would describe this field as mundane but to Rumford it was sublime because in it science was used in the interest of philanthropy. Its appeal was thus twofold. Science was a life-long interest and he was genuinely moved by the sufferings of the poor. 'Those who have never been exposed to the inclemencies of the seasons—who have never been eye-witnesses to the sufferings of the poor in their miserable habitations pinched with cold and starving with hunger—can form no idea of the importance *to them* of the subject I propose to treat. . . .'[3]

He had been led to conclude that in many fireplaces seven-eighths of the heat generated by the burning of the fuel was carried away into the atmosphere and totally lost. He was concerned to reduce this waste. His early experiments were undertaken in the House of Industry in Munich and in the Military Academy he had established there. He saw that one fire could be made to heat a number of boilers. The hot air and gases should be made to give up as much of their heat as possible before they were allowed to escape. In an early installation in The House of Industry in 1790 there were two rows each of four boilers, set in brickwork and heated by one fireplace. The heat was distributed by flues with dampers, and the fire regulated by a register. The saving of fuel with such an arrangement was enormous. He calculated that when a thousand or more people were being fed the daily cost of the fuel was one-twentieth of a farthing per person. It was results such as these which created a demand for his help and advice. On the scientific side it is important to see that he had grasped the quantitative nature of heat, he regarded it as something which flowed and he understood the notion of calorific value of fuels.

He excused his own prolixity in description by saying that the subjects he had undertaken to investigate were connected with the comforts and enjoyments of mankind. As we should expect he was not afraid to praise his own work: he judged the kitchen at the Military Academy to be 'so perfect in all its parts' that he did not 'think it capable of any considerable improvement'. Before writing this essay, which was published in 1797, he had designed kitchens at Verona in Italy, in London at the Foundling Hospital, and at the house of his friend Sir John Sinclair, one of the founders of the Board of Agriculture. His large roaster installed at the Foundling Hospital roasted a hundredweight of beef at the cost of fourpence for coal. His *chef-d'œuvre*, described in a later essay, was constructed at the House of Baron de Lerchenfeld at Munich.

He was not always concerned with cooking at institutions or for large numbers of people. In the late eighteenth century the kitchen fireplace in a medium-sized or larger dwelling house usually consisted of a large coal-burning grate placed in the space under a wide and deep open chimney. There was commonly an oven at one end and, less often, a boiler at the other. A good deal of iron was used in its construction and it was inefficient; designed, according to Rumford, 'for the express purpose of devouring fuel'. If the inefficiency of the grate annoyed him the smoke jack infuriated him. 'No human invention that ever came to my knowledge appears to me to be so absurd as this.' Its inefficiency as a machine appalled him. 'Would to God', he cried, 'that I could contrive to fix the public attention on this subject. . . . Nothing surely is so disgraceful to society and individuals as unmeaning wastefulness.' Rumford's forcefulness can be excused; his essays were designed to reform abuses. He was speaking no more than the sober truth when he said that before his time neither science nor art had done much for the kitchen range. His own approach was scientific and practical, and, propaganda apart, his essays are most impressive, and his conclusions are based on experiments he carried out.

In medium-sized installations Rumford revised his earlier designs. In his Tenth Essay, *Of the Construction of Kitchen Fireplaces*, he recommends that each boiler, kettle and saucepan should have its own separate closed fireplace and each fireplace its separate grate, ashpit and flue with a damper.[4] All the fireplaces were connected by flues to the same chimney. The initial mass, so to speak, was a suitably shaped brick structure. Let into it vertically were the fireplaces which were connected by ducts, canals or flues with the chimney. As many as a dozen of these might be found in one installation, some small, others much bigger for heating large boilers. As each was separately controlled, if it was merely necessary to boil the kettle only one fireplace need be in use. Alternatively, fires could be kept in slow combustion in any or all the fireplaces by cutting down the draught. Provision was also made for an open fire on a hearth if desired, and for a cowl to ensure that the fumes produced by frying or broiling were led off into the chimney. Rumford saw very clearly in his work that heating and ventilation were often aspects of one problem. He had also seen that 'there is nothing so wasteful as the attempt to heat ovens and boilers by heat drawn off laterally from a fire in an open grate'. His designs were far in advance of the practice of his day and it is only in the last forty years that an approach has been made to his principles in the design of solid fuel cookers and heaters for small houses.

He attended to details, and considered the thickness of the metal for boilers, the design of lids and utensils and the planning of the kitchen. Often, he said, more heat was consumed in a kitchen range to boil a kettle than would be needed to cook a dinner for fifty men. He said that his designs even satisfied the cook and it was important to put her in a good humour, but he then remembered his mission and recovered himself to say:

'I don't know what opinion others may entertain of these amusements, but with regard to myself I own that I know nothing more interesting than the planning and executing of machinery by which the powers of Nature are made subservient to my views, by which the very elements are bound as it were in chains and made to obey my despotic commands.'

His roaster was famous in many parts of the world. It was a cylindrical oven, made of iron, about two feet long and eighteen inches in diameter. It was placed in brickwork over a small fireplace so designed that the fire gave quick and even heating. The meat was placed on a gridiron with a dripping pan underneath. Potatoes and Yorkshire pudding could be cooked at the same time as the beef. Its most ingenious feature was a pair of blowpipes. These were two tubes, two inches in diameter, which entered the roaster near the back. They ran forward parallel to each other under the roaster and terminated in the brickwork at the front. They were normally closed by two stoppers, but when the joint was ready for browning the stoppers were removed and very hot air entered the roaster, slightly drying and scorching the surface of the meat.

The improvements he made in the fireplaces of what house agents now call reception rooms were no less important and have proved more enduring than the rest (see Fig. 1). His services were called upon by many of his distinguished and noble friends, among them Lord Palmerston, the Marquis of Salisbury, the Earl of Bessborough and Sir Joseph Banks.

He saw that the great fault in most of the chimneys of his day was the great size and excessive height of the throat. He was also fully aware of the importance of increasing the radiation from a fire at the expense of the convection; that is to say he understood the need for achieving a steady bright red glow in the coals and for obtaining as large a glowing surface as possible from the even combustion of a given weight of fuel. The aims were to control the combustion, to avoid smoke in the room and to diminish the proportion of heat lost through the chimney into the atmosphere. His methods were simple. He diminished the size of the throat, which helped to prevent 'blowing back', restricting its width and reducing its depth from front to back to three to five inches. It was placed perpendicularly over the fire and was rounded off so that the smoke and air from the fire would gradually be led upwards when the fire was first lighted or burning low. The fireplace was much reduced in size and was brought forward; with the chimney it made an organic whole. Its width at the front was three times that at the back. The sides made an angle with the back of 135 degrees. The amount of iron was reduced to a minimum, the back of the fireplace and the covings were of stone or firebrick. To allow the sweep's boy to climb into the chimney his fireplace was furnished with a movable slab.

He gave very clear and detailed instructions so that workmen could

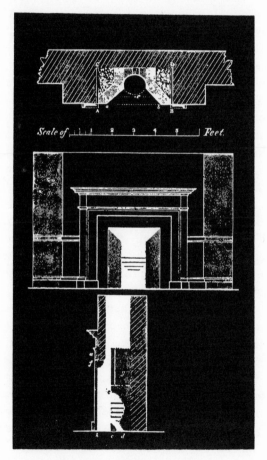

Fig. 1

Rumford's fireplace. (Reproduced by permission of the American Academy of Arts and Sciences from the American edition of the *Complete Works*)

fit his appliances, and also particulars of the costs. The excellence of his own motive was attested by the fact that he took out no patent to protect his designs but undertook to give information and instructions without charge. Speaking of the length of his writings, he laments the great disadvantage under which he labours, namely 'that those who might profit most from his labours will not read and others cannot'. He concluded that apathy rather than obstinacy prevented the introduction of his improvements and angrily denounced 'that *apathy* which follows a total corruption of taste and morals', an apathy which is 'an incurable evil' and which is followed by 'calamity and extermination'.

It is likely that some conservative people thought the Rumford fireplace rather small and the fire insignificant; its efficiency was not in question but the fireplace lost its baronial look. Lord Palmerston did not at first entirely accept Rumford's plan when he was trying to cure his smoky chimney in the inner drawing-room at his house in Hanover Square. Rumford had no qualms: he was 'even sanguine enough to expect' that the time would come when the open fire would disappear 'even in our dwelling rooms and most elegant apartments' though he was 'still child enough to be pleased with the brilliant appearance of burning fuel'. He could not help thinking that something equally attractive might be invented to fix the attention and please the eye; it would be less expensive and less connected with dirt, ashes and other unwholesome and disagreeable objects.

Rumford's passion for a practical approach to the common purposes of life is shown in the following experiment. Two legs of mutton taken from the same carcass were made equal in weight and roasted on the same day, one on a spit the other in a roaster. The cooks were not told of the design of the experiment. After being cooked the joints were again weighed carefully. It was found that the one from the roaster was six per cent heavier than the other; it was also pronounced to be much more juicy and to taste better. They were both 'fairly eaten up' leaving only the inedible fragments. There was a greater weight of these from the joint that had been spitted. Though Rumford had not got all the variable factors under control the evidence for the advantages of the roaster seems conclusive.

The *Annual Register* for 1798 gives an account of the kitchen fitted up at the Foundling Hospital under the direction of 'His Excellency Count Rumford'. Particulars are given of the roaster, steam-box and double boiler. The prices are quoted. The roaster with accessories cost 22 guineas, the large boiler £25, small boiler £11, steam-box £2 8s, incidentals £10. Altogether the 'iron work' cost more than £70 and the cost of installation 'near as much more'. These amounts are considerable, and the writer justifiably concludes that the greater the scale the greater the return. The article draws attention to the necessity for care in opening the doors to stoke the fires (especially 'where the cook wears muslin') lest the strong draught draw in and set fire to her clothes.

An experienced and clear-sighted man like Rumford was obviously aware of the industrial applications of his ideas. He understood how they were capable of producing better boilers for breweries, more efficient laundries and lime-kilns. In the burning of lime his objects were to ensure the complete combustion of the coal and gases, to bring the hot gases into contact with the limestone over a wide area, to make the burning process continuous in order to avoid the wasteful loss of heat suffered by a cooling kiln and to enable the cooling lime to give up its heat to the new charge of limestone. Such ideas are now commonplace, and have been widely used in brick-making, but at the time they were novel. His quantitative approach towards cost, efficient use of materials and labour involved mark him as a pioneer in technology.

It was a logical step from the efficient production of heat to its controlled conveyance. Rumford perceived the advantage of circulation by steam and hot water. His methods were applied in the heating of halls and large rooms. His great theatre at the Royal Institution was, as we should say, centrally heated. In the report he made to the managers on 26 April 1802 he gave some of the details:

'The theatre is warmed in cold weather by steam, which, coming in covered and concealed tubes from the lower part of the house circulates in a large semi-circular copper tube eight inches in diameter and about sixty feet long which is concealed under the rising seats of the pit.'

This heating apparatus had its flaws and came to a sad end. Webster said that 'the lecture room had been warmed by steam and satisfactorily'. When in the course of time the boiler was worn out the 'ironmonger' who was called in tore out Rumford's installation and substituted something of his own. This new apparatus was 'for years an annoyance to Mr Faraday' who did not know that steam had ever been employed till Webster informed him.

Years after he left the Royal Institution Rumford read a paper to the French *Institut National* in which he put forward the advantages of heating buildings by steam and suggested that the Hall of the *Institut* might be heated that way. Whether his proposal was adopted is not disclosed and in the *Éloge* Cuvier does not mention it.

One glimpse of the notions of elegance in the early nineteenth century is given by Rumford's suggestions for steam stoves for heating halls and corridors. 'They are', he writes, 'susceptible of a variety of beautiful forms. . . . A most elegant steam stove might be made in the form of a Doric temple, of eight or ten columns, standing on a pedestal. The fireplace might be situated in the pedestal, and the columns and dome of the temple of brass or bronze, and made hollow to admit the steam. In the centre of the temple a small statue might be placed as an ornamental decoration. . . .'[5] An appropriate addition would have been a door opened and closed by the steam in the manner employed by Hero of Alexandria. The temple would then have been worthy of a place in any science museum.

Among the enterprising manufacturers of the latter part of the eighteenth century was Benjamin Gott, a Yorkshireman. Needing to rebuild a factory, Gott, who manufactured woollen cloth, read Rumford's Seventh Essay and used the steam from one boiler to heat a number of dyeing vats instead of using a separate fire for each. He estimated that by so doing he reduced his fuel costs by nearly two-thirds. Other dyers quickly followed his example. Gott, who in 1800 was mayor of Leeds, received Count Rumford with warmth when he paid a visit to Leeds. Rumford was highly pleased and praised the initiative of such men in the essay from which these facts are taken:

'To the spirited exertions of such men who abound in no other country, we owe one of the proudest distinctions of our national character, that of being *an enlightened and enterprising people*.'[6]

The tone of this was different from that of the letter to Bernard in which he saw England as a great and powerful nation in decline.

But however much Rumford's judgement of national characteristics depended upon his mood, his objectivity in the scientific field is exemplified in this paper. His account of the arrangement of a boiler with steam tubes, safety-valves and vessels to be heated is thorough and

6–7. The English Garden, Munich.

8. Two of Rumford's portable illuminators.
(*From photographs of lamps in the collection at Old Sturbridge
Village, Mass.; by permission of the Curator*)

he incorporates the results of experiments he had carried out on the tensile strengths of materials and the methods of strengthening copper tubes. He also suggests the use of superheated steam for heating and manufacturing processes.

The range of his ideas was wide, and the arrangements for puttng his ideas into practice no less impressive. Fireplaces and cooking utensils for cottages as well as for mansions and institutions engaged his attention. The kitchen he designed for Sir John Sinclair at the premises of the Board of Agriculture was open for the public to see, and the place was chosen because it was visited by influential people from all parts of the country. In 1798 he asked Mr Summers, 'an ingenious tradesman . . . to put up a roaster in his own kitchen; to instruct his cook in the management of it; to make daily use of it; to show it in actual use to his customers and others who might desire to see it; and also to allow other cooks to be present, and assist when meat was roasted in it, in order to their being convinced of its utility and taught how to manage it'. Mr Summers was also persuaded to engage an intelligent brick-layer who would 'follow without deviation the instructions he received'.

In less than three years Summers had sold and erected no fewer than 260 roasters and was unable to meet the demand for them. Many other tradesmen were selling them at the same time including Hopkins, the King's Ironmonger, who had sold over 200.

Kitchen ranges, roasters and parlour grates of Rumford's design were constructed in America as early as they were in England. According to James Renwick, his essays on the use of fuel and allied topics reached New York 'at a time when the sudden and unexpected growth of that city threatened the speedy exhaustion of all the forests within reach of its existing communications; where firewood had risen to a price unexampled before or since; and where, in consequence, an active importation of bituminous coal from Liverpool began to take place'. Rumford's grate afforded the most efficient and clean method of using the new fuel. Both parlour grates and kitchen ranges had been set up before the end of the year 1798.

There are many passing references to Rumford stoves and grates. In Weld's book *A History of the Royal Society*, published in 1848, the writer says that 'Rumford's stove or fireplace is well known. One of the earliest is that set up under the Count's immediate superintendence in my office at the Royal Society. It is by far the best fireplace which I have seen. . . .' What Rumford's relations would have been with Banks and the other officers of the Royal Society had it been otherwise can easily be guessed.

In *Northanger Abbey*, written while Count Rumford was in England at the end of the eighteenth century, the drawing-room fireplace had been contracted from 'the ample and ponderous carving of former times' to a Rumford, 'with slabs of plain though handsome marble . . .' The eponym indicates the wide popularity of Rumford's grates within a few years of their introduction.

Cuvier is both witty and eulogistic in the *Éloge* when describing this aspect of Rumford's work. 'He has', he says, 'been able to extract part of the heat from smoke which he will not allow to emerge from his apparatus until it is almost cold. Someone justly renowned for his Attic wit said of him that he would soon be cooking his dinner with his neighbour's smoke.' But on the other hand, as Cuvier also said, it was not for himself that he sought economy; his experiments cost him a good deal and he spent his own money so that other people could save theirs.

Rumford was always happy in his laboratory exploring practical problems. He left his truculence, self-importance and irritability outside. It is a short step from heat to light and he was interested in efficient and economical lighting as well as heating. The photometer which bears his name and which, though based on a principle clearly enunciated by J. H. Lambert, he made into an instrument of precision, was of great help to him in designing lamps. In his essay *The Management of Light in Illumination* he points out that it is not only intensity of illumination that enables one to see clearly, but that also light and shade must be clearly defined; the facility with which we see objects distinctly depends on their shadows. Rumford stresses the importance of translucent shades in cutting down glare, a 'system of illumination practised by the Chinese for many ages; and so wise and so economical a nation could not have continued to practise it so long, had it not been found to be really advantageous'. However he appeals to experiment rather than to tradition and proves that a ground-glass shade cuts off very little more light than a clear one. Screens or shades not only diminish glare but conceal 'all that is ugly and disgusting in a lamp'.

The Argand lamp was already in use; its essential principle was the admission of air to the interior of the flame in order to give more complete combustion of the oil. Rumford's most important contribution was to introduce parallel wicks close together. In his own words: 'I lately caused a lamp to be constructed of a very simple form, which, with four flat ribbon wicks, each one inch and six-tenths English measure in width, placed vertically, one by the side of the other, at the distance of about two-tenths of an inch, and so separated as to let air come up between them, gives more light than six Argand lamps burning with their usual brilliancy.'[7] After dwelling on its merits he continues: 'The fundamental principle on which this lamp is constructed is so easy to understand that it will be sufficient merely to mention it. . . . The object to be had in view in all cases is to *preserve the heat of the flame as long as possible.*'

This was an advance for which Rumford had received little or no recognition. The same principle in a different setting was rediscovered by Langmuir when he invented the coiled filament to increase the efficiency of the electric lamp, causing it to emit more light for a given expenditure of electrical energy. The conduction losses of heat from the filament are diminished by winding it as a close coil. In Rumford's oil-lamp the several flat flames were placed close together, but not touching, so that they might 'mutually cover and defend each other against the powerful cooling influences of the surrounding cold bodies'. Early electric-lamp manufacturers might therefore have taken two hints from Rumford. They might have used a filament in the form of a thin close spiral and they might have used translucent instead of transparent glass.

He put his ideas into practice in 1800 at the Royal Institution, using Argand lamps with several burners, covered by large screens of white gauze. Later he made an elegant lamp for his Paris dining-room. He thought this and the other lamps he designed (see Plate 8, facing page 177) so much better than 'lamps in general' that he wanted a new and grander name for them, so he called them *illuminators*. As usual he gave details of sizes, prices and methods of construction, and compliments the English workman for whom 'a hint is sufficient, [for] their ingenuity and address are such that they seldom fail to succeed in what they undertake'.

He has something to say about the personal and social implications of his lamps. The kind of illumination which is most favourable to very distinct vision is not the most agreeable; 'nor is it the most favourable to the beauty of objects in general or to human beauty. . . . No decayed beauty ought ever to expose her face to the direct rays of an Argand lamp; nor should she ever look at herself with her spectacles on. The mysterious light which comes from bodies moderately illuminated is certainly most favourable to female beauty and ought on that account to be preferred by all persons who are wise.' He leaves 'these pleasing speculations', to give details of a portable lamp which well deserves the epithet *ingenious*, so often applied to him by his contemporaries. But his lamps illustrate not only his scientific acumen but also his fastidiousness and his regard for what was considered elegance at that time. They exemplify his industry too, for on one occasion when he changed houses there were over a hundred lamps to be moved.

He did not escape mild ridicule in France. His clothes, carriage, soups and lamps all provoked chaff and banter. For a time one of the stock anecdotes in Paris told of a man who constructed a lamp of Rumford's design to light him home. When he lit it he was so dazzled by its brilliance that he was unable to find his way and spent the night wandering, half blinded, in the Bois de Boulogne.[8]

Rumford's ideas on the advantages of warm rooms[9] and the salubrity of warm bathing are connected with his scientific work.[10] He had probably suffered discomfort when spending his winters in London after enjoying his thoroughly heated apartments in Munich and would have sympathized with those Americans of today who, when wintering in this country, walk out in order to keep warm. He inveighed against the draughts caused by large open fires, rightly saying that such fires instead of making a room uniformly warm do little more 'than increase the violence of those streams of cold air which come whistling in through every crevice of the doors and windows'. These 'cold blasts' chill the body on one side while the other is strongly heated by the fires. He then overstates his case by attributing to this unequal heating of the human body 'the severe colds and catarrhs which are so frequently gotten by persons in this country'.

Rumford very rightly points out the cooling effect of large windows 'which in open defiance of every principle of good taste' had lately come into fashion, and shudders at 'the perilous situation' of delicate young ladies in muslins or gauzes 'when exposed to these rigours. How many young persons of delicate habits', he laments, 'are carried off annually by consumptions.' He contrasts our practice with that of the Swedes and the Russians who keep their rooms very hot 'and yet no people are more strong and healthy than they are, nor are there any less liable to catarrhs and consumptions'.

Rumford suffered over many years with stomach ailments—possibly gastric ulcers. He overtaxed his strength by continuous work and was inclined to worry. From time to time he was obliged to rest and relax. He was at Harrogate in the summer of the year 1800 having been advised to take the waters there by his physician. There was no invalidish complacency about his treatment—he subjected himself to a systematic regimen. At first he drank the waters every morning and bathed in them at a temperature of 96°F every third evening at ten o'clock, getting straight into bed after his bath. This treatment induced feverishness and restlessness and, on the advice 'of an intelligent gentleman who happened to lodge in the house', he decided to bathe two hours before dinner, staying half an hour in the water. This was better. He was less sensitive to cold, less prone to fatigue, and appetite and digestion were improved. On the strength of this result he bathed at first every other day, and finally every day, though this was thought to be 'very hazardous and not much approved by the physician'. Nevertheless, feeling the benefit in health he continued the process for thirty-five days.

These experiments gave rise to much thought about baths and bathing and prompted the writing of his *Observations concerning the Salubrity of Warm Bathing. . . .* Not only is the bath wholesome but 'the luxury of bathing is so great, and the tranquil state of mind and body which follows it so exquisitely delightful that it is quite impossible to recommend it too strongly, if we consider it merely as a rational and elegant refinement'. He envies the poor Russian peasant who even amidst his snows, with his warm room and warm bath, may enjoy (who knows?) quite as much happiness as the inhabitants of more favoured countries. For ingenuity of construction he likens the vapour bath to the canoes and snow-shoes of the North American Indian. He describes its construction and use. If he were asked to design a bath he would apply the same principles. He goes on to give his plans for such a bathroom. He would have it built of brick, with double walls 'covered above by a Gothic or pointed dome', and lighted by three or four very small double windows so placed 'that a person from without should not be able to see any person in the bath even though they were to get a ladder and attempt to look in at the window'. The walls would be lined with Dutch tiles and the floor covered with matting. The entrance would be from below, through a pavement, by a flight of stairs.

The steam boiler would be placed under the tiled floor and the smoke from the fire would circulate in flues built into the floors and walls. A bath-tub with hot and cold water would be provided on a raised platform in the bathing chamber. Such a structure could be used as a warm-air bath and a warm-vapour bath as well as a warm-water bath.

To complete the appeal of this bathroom he recommended, for ornament, 'a figure of Vesta on a pedestal, holding an Argand's lamp and, for fragrance, a small chafing dish heated by live coals containing sweet-scented woods or aromatic gums and resins'.

He suspected this might sound effeminate but vigorously denied it. Would a statesman or a general going from the refreshing enjoyment of such a bath to the senate or to the field be less likely to do his duty than one whose head is filled and whose faculties are deranged by the fumes of wine? He could see 'no good reason for considering these grateful aromatic perfumes . . . as a less elegant or less rational luxury than smoking tobacco or stuffing the nose with snuff. Can a thing be effeminate if it has no tendency to diminish . . . the strength of the body, the dignity of sentiment or the energy of the mind?'

On a larger and more communal scale he suggested rebuilding some of the baths left to us by the Romans, though he was 'far from wishing to see the baths of Diocletian and Caracalla rise up in all their splendour in the neighbourhood of London'.

On a smaller scale, remembering as usual the needs of the less well-to-do, he described another bathroom 'on a less expensive and more modest plan'.

The essays described in this chapter show many of the characteristics of Rumford's writings. We find some self-justification, some overstatement arising from enthusiasm and an occasional lack of caution in the reasoning. On the other hand, they contain many sound ideas based upon scientific knowledge and much common sense, and they are fervent with a sense of mission. In treating the heating of rooms, for example, his main theories were right and in the last hundred years many have been put into practice. Though he was hampered in his discussion by ignorance of the part played by humidity in good ventilation, and though the experimental and factual evidence he adduced in support of his ideas was slender, this essay was a timely attack on the ignorance and inertia of his day. He was not 'without hope that at some future period houses in England' would become 'as celebrated for warmth and comfort' as they were then 'for neatness and for the richness and elegance of their furniture'.

Sometimes he was oversensitive to criticism and took his task too seriously, but he did not realize that much of the criticism he received was aroused by his own sense of self-importance. He said a great deal that was of importance to his age, and he was of a stature to make his message impressive, but he sometimes spoilt the effect because his readers were amused and exasperated as well as instructed and edified. He was inclined to put on his robes and talk from the high pulpit. 'I am', he says, 'not unacquainted with the manners of the age. I have lived long in the world and have studied mankind attentively and am fully aware of the difficulties in the pursuit of the great object to which I have devoted myself. I am even sensible, fully sensible, of the dangers to which I expose myself.' His self-importance giving way to anger he complains: 'In this selfish and suspicious age it is hardly possible that justice should be done to the purity of my motives; and in the present state of society, when so few who have leisure can bring themselves to take the trouble to read anything except it be for mere amusement I can hardly expect to engage attention.'[11]

Although he wished to engage the interest and secure the influence of the rich he castigated their blind indifference in pursuing useless pleasures.

'How might I exult could I but succeed so far as to make it fashionable for the rich to take the trouble to choose for themselves those enjoyments which their money can command instead of being the dupes of those tyrants who, in the garb of submissive fawning slaves, not only plunder them in the most disgraceful manner but render them at the same time perfectly ridiculous, and fit them for that distruction which is near at hand when good taste has been driven quite off the stage.

'When I see in the capital of a great country, in the midst of summer, a coachman sitting on a coach-box dressed in a thick heavy greatcoat with sixteen capes I am not surprised to find the coach door surrounded by a group of naked beggars.'

IO

Philanthropist and Reformer

'This was the triumph, and the first introduction
of public kitchens, Count Rumfords, and cooking
committees. "Chemistry strained itself to extract
nutriment from everything".'

LORD COCKBURN (*Memorials of his Time*)

RUMFORD's work among the poor of Great Britain was done as an expert rather than an inspirer. As early as the middle of the eighteenth century the old workhouse movement had failed. In 1760 Dean Tucker put forward a plan to eliminate the parish as the unit of relief and to set up 'Houses' in market towns to serve groups of parishes. In 1782 Thomas Gilbert, the Member of Parliament for Lichfield, succeeded after years of effort in piloting a Bill through Parliament which 'had for its main object the establishment by unions of parishes of reformed workhouses in which the aged, the sick and the infirm, together with their dependent children and all the orphans might be provided for'.[1] Gilbert's Act forbade admitting the able-bodied to hospital and asylum but allowed for providing work or, failing it, relief for the unemployed. In the years which followed, the need was so great that scores of union workhouses were built.

It was an age of unrest. There was a growing sense of responsibility among the upper classes, allied with kindly feeling and also fear. Among the labouring classes discontent was widespread because of low wages and high prices. The problem was twofold: to provide work for the able-bodied which would be adequate to support them and, at the same time, to help care for and maintain the sick and the infirm. Gilbert's aim was to solve this problem, and the degree of success depended on local enterprise. At Shrewsbury, for example, there was a quick and successful response which owed much to the insight and energy of Isaac Wood. In 1783 a body of Guardians was incorporated there which bought a conveniently situated, suitable building and 'adapted it to furnish employment for the poor and compel them to earn their own support'. The sick were cared for in an infirmary. Those fit to undertake light work were encouraged to spin and weave wool and other yarns, and there were workshops for skilled tradesmen.

There was no sentimentality in these plans or in their execution. In writing of the success of the Shrewsbury House of Industry Isaac Wood said it had arisen because of 'the rapid and alarming increase in the Poor's Rates' and because 'the Poor must not be supported in Idleness'; two of its aims were 'to prevent a waste of public money' and 'to introduce the effects of a good education among the poor'.[2] The similarities between the Shrewsbury House and those founded by Rumford in Munich a few years later are obvious.

The Shrewsbury institution and others like it, although very successful, did not fully meet the needs of the time. In 1795 a Bill for *The Better Relief and Maintenance of the Poor within the Several Hundreds and Districts in England* received Royal Assent, its purpose being to make provision for the poor where there were no suitable Houses of Industry. By this time Rumford's work in Bavaria was widely known and in 1796 William Pitt introduced another Bill for *The Better Support and Maintenance of the Poor* which sought to establish Schools of Industry in every district based on the Rumford Institutions in Munich.

There were many petitions against the Bill, with Shrewsbury first in the field.[3] The excellence of the Rumford model was admitted but it was objected that the establishment of such houses of industry in every district would double the rates and place too big a burden on the Wardens of the Poor. Furthermore, those establishments like Shrewsbury's which were already successful should be exempted from the Bill's provisions.

Wood, in his letter to Sir William Pulteney, wrote words which Rumford himself might have composed:

'I could, at this hour, entertain Mr Pitt with the pleasing spectacle of two hundred children and youth well fed, clothed and taught; the young ones attending the schools established in the House; those of five years old and upwards busy at the wheel, the jenny and the loom: all of them early inured to habits of cleanliness, decency and virtue and happily preserved from the misery of contagion and vice. I know that if this establishment had not taken place, these very children would have been strolling and begging in our streets, covered with filth and rags, without education or instruction, unless it were instruction in the arts of pilfering or education in the habits of debauchery.

'I could shew him the prostitute, snatched from the paths of infamy and rescued from the fangs of disease, labouring diligently for her support. . . .'

Isaac Wood did not question Rumford's ability or success. His objection was, on the contrary, that there were not enough Rumfords to go round:

'If indeed a Rumford . . . could be found to execute the office of "Manager of the Poor" in every District School of Industry to be established throughout the Kingdom much fewer objections would lie against the present measure.'

Whatever ideas Rumford may have taken to Bavaria the success of his work there during the years 1790 to 1795 had led him to think out his principles of philanthropy and to propagate them in several countries. His early essays, which dealt with establishments for the poor and foods, were published in London in 1796, in Weimar in 1797, in Boston, Massachusetts, in 1798 and in Geneva in 1799. As we have seen, action followed.

In England The Society for Bettering the Condition of the Poor was greatly influenced by the Second Essay. Its founders were the Bishop of Durham, Thomas Bernard, William Wilberforce and Edward James Eliot. The society held its first meeting in December 1796, and proposed to achieve its aims by correcting abuses in workhouses, establishing public kitchens, rousing the public conscience to the need for reform, by the personal example of its members and by encouraging industry. Shortly afterwards Rumford, though not in England at the time, was elected a life-member of the Society and of its Committee. It has already been shown how the

Royal Institution, which grew out of part of a wider plan, became a separate and major task under Rumford's direction.

Other writers, too, have given evidence of Rumford's standing. He is acknowledged as a scientific expert in Eden's comprehensive and contemporary work *The State of the Poor*.[4] Coleridge reviewed his Fifth Essay in *The Watchman*[5] and referred to him 'as the reincarnation of [John] Howard, his zeal the same, his genius superior, his sphere of action more enlarged'. His review was prefaced by the eulogistic sonnet reproduced at the beginning of this book.

In 1796 Thomas Pelham, the Secretary for Ireland, invited Rumford to go to Dublin. He was there for about two months and during this time even his versatility must have been stretched and his energies taxed. He enjoyed himself greatly. He was honoured by learned societies and after his visit was warmly thanked by the Viceroy and the Lord Mayor of Dublin. He found Ireland receptive of his ideas and anxious for his improvements and he was 'able to do more in two months' than he could have achieved in many years in some 'other older countries where the progress of wealth and of refinements had rendered it extremely difficult to get people to attend to useful improvements'. He gave advice on the flues for the principal boiler in the laundry of the Dublin Society, supervised the installation of a heating plant in a large church, agreed to be a consultant on the heating apparatus for the new building for the Irish House of Commons and carried out experiments in the workhouse.

His workhouse experiments sound more economical than appetizing. On 6 May under his direction a meal of calecannon was provided for 927 persons.

The recipe, paraphrased, reads:

Take 19 cwt of potatoes, 26 flaskets (300 lb) of greens, 98 lb of butter, 14 lb of chopped onions, 40 lb of salt, 1 lb of black pepper and ½ lb of ginger. Wash, boil and mash the potatoes. Wash greens and chop with sharp shovel, then boil. Mix potatoes and greens; add onions, butter and seasoning.

This *mélange* when completely cooked provided a ration of 2 lb for each person, serving him (or her) for dinner and supper.

The cost was £7 19s 11½d—every halfpenny counted—made up as follows:

		£	s.	d.
Potatoes:	19 cwt at 3s 6d per cwt ..	3	6	6
Greens:	26 flaskets at 10d per flasket..	1	1	10
Butter:	98 lb at 72s per cwt	3	3	0
Onions:	14 lb at 2s per stone		2	0
Ginger:	½ lb	1	3
Salt:	40 lb		1	1
Pepper:	1 lb		1	1
	Cost of ingredients	7	16	9
Fuel:	Whitehaven Coal 450½ lb at			
	at £1 3s 3d per ton ..		3	2½
	Total			
		7	19	11½

(13 Irish pence = 12 pence sterling)

Two meals were provided at a cost per person of a fraction over twopence. (There is no allowance for the cost of labour since presumably the inmates prepared their own meal.)

Rumford said he could have improved this performance. First by altering the boiler, flues and fireplaces he claimed he could provide a meal for 3210 persons in Ireland at a fuel cost of sixpence farthing. Secondly, he could have replaced most of the butter by salted herrings; and, thirdly, he could have made the ingredients into a soup instead of into calecannon.

Another experiment he carried out at the same place, and one which may have done little to endear him to the inmates, was to substitute oaten cakes for wheaten bread. This meant a considerable saving as the institution's yearly bread bill was more than £3800.

These particulars show clearly both the problems of feeding the poor at the time and Rumford's scientific, if unappetizing solution.

Having left various models in Dublin, including one of a perpetual lime-kiln, he returned to England to superintend the changes which were being made at the Foundling Hospital.

It is not surprising that Rumford was a figure in his day. An American loyalist, a soldier, a count, yet an expert in feeding and flues, and a man who carried his samples with him. Even in an age of eccentrics he stood out. More than anything else he was associated with soup. As the cigar is to Churchill and the pipe was to Baldwin, as the moustache was to Hitler and the nose to Wellington, so was soup to Rumford. It was his correlate in the public mind. In 1801, writing to his daughter, he says:

'I have the unspeakable satisfaction to find that my labors have not been in vain. In this moment of scarcity and general alarm the measures I have recommended in my writings for relieving the distresses of the poor are very generally adopted, and public kitchens have been erected in all the great towns in England and Scotland. Upwards of sixty thousand persons are fed daily from the different public kitchens in London.

'The plan has lately been adopted in France, and a very large kitchen for feeding the poor was opened in Paris three weeks since. A gentleman present tells me that the founders of the Institution did me the honour to put my name at the head of the Tickets given to the poor authorizing them to receive soup at the public kitchen.'

At Geneva they paid him even greater respect: the tickets were stamped with his name and portrait.

His recommendations had two great attractions for the organizers of relief in a time of scarcity. They were economical and they had scientific backing. Harassed caterers were comforted when they read in his Tenth Essay that 'Many persons in this country are of opinion that a good deal of meat is necessary in order to make a good and wholesome soup but this is far from being the case in fact'. They were reassured when they went on to learn that 'Some of the most savoury and most nourishing soups are made without any meat; and in providing food for the poor it is necessary, on many accounts, to be very sparing in the use of it'. One justification was that it was unwise to give the poor better food in the public kitchen than they would afterwards be able to provide for themselves in their own homes.

In his *Proposal for forming by Private Subscription an Establishment for Feeding the Poor and giving them Useful Employment* he recommended four grades of soup to cost, respectively, one penny, twopence, fourpence and sixpence per helping. The penny variety was made from barley, peas, potatoes and bread, seasoned with salt, pepper and herbs; for sixpence the soup contained boiled meat, potatoes and cabbage and was accompanied by a quarter of a pound of good rye bread.

His recipe for the cheapest possible food in England included samp, which was made by simmering maize kernels in boiling water for several hours. It read:

'Take of water eight gallons, and mixing with it 5 lbs of barley-meal, boil it to the consistency of a thick jelly. Season it with salt, pepper, vinegar, sweet herbs, and four red herrings pounded in a mortar. Instead of bread, add to it five lbs of Indian Corn made into samp and serve immediately.'

The cost of this concoction was one-third of a penny per portion of twenty ounces.

Rumford also recommended brown soup, 'the common breakfast of the peasants in Bavaria'. It was prepared by frying flour or rye meal in butter until brown and then boiling the roasted meal in water. After it had been seasoned it was, he said, 'infinitely preferable in all respects to that most pernicious wash, *tea*, with which the lower classes of the inhabitants of this island drench their stomachs and ruin their constitutions'.

If tea can be regarded as Chinese in origin it was one of the few Chinese things he disapproved of, for he was a convinced Sinophile. He preferred coffee and ale. Lord Palmerston recorded under the date 6 December 1798 that he had had a visit from Count Rumford who found 'very great benefit from Burton ale which he begins to take in the morning as people do asses milk and drinks little else through the day'. As Palmerston said, 'an odd plan for a feverish man'.[6]

Rumford's weakness was to overdo things, to let his enthusiasm cloud his reasoning and warp his judgement. The tendency is seen, for example, in his discussion of the nutritive value of water. It gave his critics an opportunity of which they readily took advantage. His argument was stronger when he dwelt on the importance of palatability and good mastication as aids to nutrition; though again he went too far when he recommended that hard and stale bread be eaten because *it prolongs the duration of the enjoyment of eating* and when he claimed that eating communally improves moral character.

Many people were ready either privately or publicly to poke fun at him. Samuel Galton, the head of a famous firm of gun-makers, Fellow of the Royal Society and a member of the Lunar Society of Birmingham, wrote to Matthew Boulton on Christmas Day in the year 1800 and said in a postscript to his letter:

'As you interest yourself so much for the poor, permit me to inform you that I have had some Soup made, into which some Barley scaled by a person in Deritend . . . was introduced and I find it very palatable and that it gives that Consistency wanting in the Metaphysical Soups of Count Rumford in which he seems to have mistaken Element for Aliment.'[7]

This was mild and private criticism. William Cobbett's was violent and public. He denounced both the soup-kitchens and the food served in them, reckoning that Englishmen deserved a better diet than bones and potatoes, whatever might suit the Irish. Both Renwick and Ellis speak of the unfortunate results of Cobbett's ridicule and strictures. Not only were the poor turned against the food offered to them, but doubts were raised in the minds of the charitable as to how far their efforts were worth while.

The ridicule continued for years after Rumford's death. As late as the year 1823 Rumford's proposals for feeding the poor were still a source of amusement. A writer in *Blackwood's Magazine*,[8] in an article, 'Panaceas for Poverty', deals satirically with the advice given to the poor upon feeding and other personal and domestic matters. Rumford's weaknesses are gleefully exposed. His essays 'afford some pleasant illustrations of the slashing style in which men construct theories when the practice is to fall upon their neighbours'. The writer goes on to say that 'after exhausting himself upon the smoky chimnies of the world, the Count strips to the next of its nuisances—the beggars'. The problem was how to feed the poor at the cheapest rate. ' "Water", then he begins—(the cunning rogue!) "Water, I am inclined to suspect, acts a much more important part *in nutrition* than has been generally supposed". This was a good active hobby to start upon; and truly his Countship, in the sequel, does outride all the field.'

The article continues in satirical vein, tilting at the low cost of Rumford's meals, the dry bread, the meatless soups and saying that 'those who can swallow the Count's dinners can swallow anything'. Much of this article degenerates into mere fooling, but it does draw attention to a truth which all philanthropists should bear in mind, namely that both benefactor and beneficiary belong to the same species; a fact which Rumford was sometimes inclined to overlook.

In Grabbe's *Scherz, Satire, Ironie und tiefore Bedeutung* the Devil attributes his old and wrinkled appearance to Rumford's soup.

Devil: You simpleton! As if my grandmother were old and ugly.
Don't you know that we immortals stay eternally young. If
in spite of that I have become old and wrinkled my particular
grief is to be attributed to the invention of Rumford's soup.

Rumford was ridiculed not only for his 'metaphysical soups' but
also for the detailed descriptions he indulged in. Lord Brougham
satirized him not for his manner of making Indian pudding but for the
instructions he gave for eating it from a plate. Even Ellis could not
forbear to point out an example of detail which Brougham might have
used with even greater justice; he refers to Rumford's elaborate description for making cooking vessels, at the end of which Rumford
pointed out that 'There should be a round hole about a quarter of an
inch in diameter near the end of the handle, by which the saucepan
may occasionally be hung upon a nail or peg when not in use. Also, the
cover belonging to the saucepan may be hung up on the same nail, or
peg, by means of the projection of its rim.'

Though Rumford was fair game for the satirist we must not forget
an essential characteristic of his work. He was concerned to observe
everyday objects, actions and processes very closely in order to discover
scientific principles and to improve living, and nothing was too trivial
to catch his attention. Once he was brought a bowl of rice soup, but as
he was busy he asked for it to be set on a stove. When he had leisure to
eat it he found the surface cold and thick but when he took a spoonful
from underneath he burnt his mouth. This led him to reflect on the
thermal conductivity of liquids; so did his observations on the temperature of the sand on the sea-shore near the hot springs at Baia in Italy.

But a discussion of his scientific work will come later. Here, while
we are concerned with food, I should mention his essay on coffee. It
was numerically the last of his essays and was numbered eighteen.
Characteristically it is compounded of careful observation, extreme
advocacy and references to social conditions. Because of 'its exhilar-
ating quality it [coffee] should, in some measure, supply the place of
spirituous liquors among the lower classes of the people. Those who
work hard stand in need of something to cheer and comfort them from
time to time. . . . Instead of irritating the mind, and exciting to acts of
violence, Coffee calms every turbulent and malevolent passion, and is
accompanied by a consciousness of ease, contentment and goodwill to

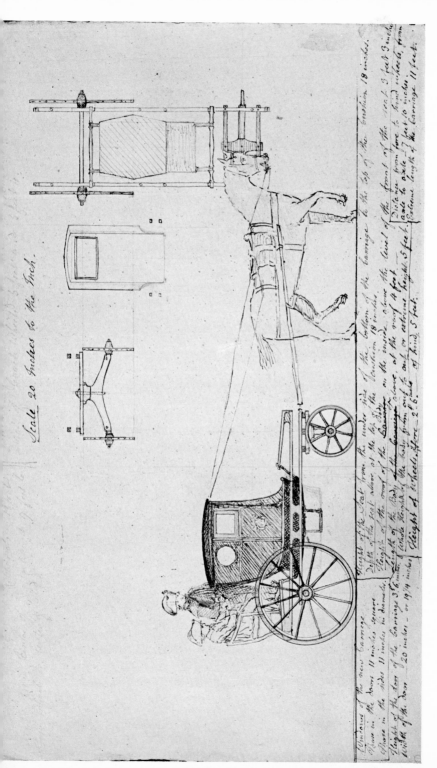

9. Rumford's French carriage before adaptation to wide wheel rims.
(*Rumford's own drawing reproduced by permission of Harvard University*)

10. An example of Rumford's later handwriting.

all men, which is very different from that wild joy and unbridled licentiousness which accompanies intoxication.' How different, in his opinion, from 'that miserable and unwholesome wash which the poor people in England drink under the name of tea. . . . There is more wit in Europe since the use of Coffee has become general among us. . . .' But with exaggeration and near justification come acute observation and sound advice. The essential aim is to prevent the coffee from los- ing its fragrance. Obviously the more it is exposed to the air either before or after infusion the more it loses its flavour. If after being prepared 'in the highest perfection and boiling hot' it is allowed to cool in an open room and is then warmed up its flavour will be impaired.

The powdered coffee should be 'well defended from the air' and after infusion the liquid should not be allowed to cool before it is served. 'This may be done by pouring boiling water on the Coffee in powder and surrounding the machine in which the coffee is made by boiling water or by the steam of boiling water. . . .'

For those who could not afford to buy a coffee-pot of full size he designed a simple percolator or drip-pot. It was the prototype of those drip-cups which have been used for a long time on the Continent, particularly in Belgium, to serve *café filtré*.

Rumford's coffee-pots had some renown. The philosopher Hegel used one. Rumford also experimented with a spirit-lamp for keeping coffee warm during breakfast. Characteristically, he worked out the cost of the fuel. It was one halfpenny per person.

Rumford incorporated many of his designs for household utensils and furnishing in his house[9] at 45 Brompton Row. It was described by Pictet for the readers of the *Bibliothèque Britannique* as the Elysium, and more soberly as a pleasing and ingenious structure. It had five storeys including the basement which was occupied by domestic staff. On each storey there were two rooms and a staircase. On the ground floor there was a parlour, where morning visitors were received, and a dining- room. On the first floor was a bedroom and a reception room, and on the second floor the same arrangement. On the third floor Rumford had his own bedroom and a workroom. The workroom was lighted by doubly glazed windows forming an arc of a circle through which a person standing in the middle of the room could see one-quarter of the horizon. There were window-boxes on the sills.

In the rooms there were built-in wardrobes and cupboards, and tables which fitted into the wall when not in use. The beds looked like elegant sofas, with the seat of the sofa formed by one of the mattresses, and the other mattress folded in two making the back. There were drawers underneath for sheets, blankets and night attire. The house was most efficiently heated and all the appliances for cooking were made to Rumford's own design. The furnishings were simple and elegant and the colour schemes based on his principles of harmony. Pictet also described the outbuildings which included a stable, coach-house, laboratory and rooms for coachman and carpenter. These outbuildings were joined to the house by a centrally heated corridor

Not everyone was as enthusiastic as Pictet about the house in Brompton Row. Sally found the care of it a trial after her father's death. Young acknowledged that it was 'fitted up with every contrivance for comfort and convenience that could render it fit for the abode of hospitality and luxury' but said that after all Rumford 'was never known to give a single entertainment in it'. It is quite true that while one often reads of Rumford's dining with friends, one never hears of friends dining with him, unless perhaps for experimental purposes.

Rumford had very complete plans for propagating his ideas. He took an important step when, in 1796, he placed funds at the disposal of the Royal Society for founding the Rumford Medal. He was in London during part of that year and on 12 July he wrote a formal letter to Sir Joseph Banks in which he said that being 'desirous of contributing efficaciously to the advancement of a branch of science' which had long employed his attention and which appeared to be of the 'highest importance to mankind', and also wishing to leave 'a lasting testimony of his respect for the Royal Society of London, he would ask the Society to do him the honour of accepting the sum of one thousand pounds'.

His aim was that the interest every second year, together with a medal, should 'be given as a premium to the author of the most important discovery, or useful improvement . . . in any part of Europe during the preceding two years, on Heat or on Light; the preference always being given to such discoveries' as should '. . . tend most to promote the good of mankind'.

The Royal Society gratefully acknowledged the gift and asked for further guidance about the kind of discovery or improvement which would qualify for the award. Writing from Munich in April of the following year, he made it quite clear that he hoped by founding the medal to stimulate the application of science for the benefit of the poorer classes, 'particularly in the generation and management of Heat and of Light'.[10]

A small committee of members of the Council including Banks, Rumford, Blagden and the secretary Dr Gray was set up to inaugurate the medal. The committee reported on the design in April 1799, and their report was accepted by the parent body.

In accordance with the conditions laid down there was no one more appropriate than Rumford himself to receive the medal, and in 1802 he was the first recipient. Ten years earlier he had been awarded the Copley Medal, the Royal Society's principal award. In 1804 Sir John Leslie followed Rumford, the award being made for his outstanding experiments in heat; and two years later William Murdock's experiments in using coal gas for illumination were recognized. In the course of time the medal has gone to many great men of science including Davy, Faraday, Pasteur, Maxwell and Kirchoff. On one occasion, in 1854, it was awarded for a new smoke-consuming and fuel-saving fireplace which was perhaps more in keeping with Rumford's intentions than some of the awards have been.

The Royal Society's Rumford Medal was to be awarded for discoveries or improvements in Europe. Far from wishing to exclude Americans from receiving such recognition, Rumford founded a similar medal in America. A letter he wrote on 12 July 1796 to the Hon. John Adams, the President of the American Academy of Arts and Sciences, is almost identical with the one he wrote on the same day to Banks. The history of the American medal, however, has been very different from that of its European counterpart. No move was made until 1829 and then a committee of the Academy was appointed to report on the state of the fund and the conditions of the award of the premium, and to make recommendations for its future administration. After a ruling in the Supreme Court of Massachusetts the original terms of the bequest were widened to enable the Academy to use the income of the accumulated funds to buy books, papers and apparatus, or to maintain lectureships and promote research if it so wished as well as to award the medal annually. The first award was made in 1839 to Dr Robert Hare of Philadelphia[11] mainly for the invention of a compound blowpipe, and the second not until 1862.

It is unlikely that the award of such medals as these appreciably stimulates men of science and inventors in their research and labours; motives lie deeper that that. On the other hand it is a sound principle, even in the field of science, that recognition and reward should be given to work of high importance no matter how much the modest and the altruistic might retire from accepting them. Rumford's generosity was therefore not misplaced and was all the more commendable because the amount he gave must have made a sizable hole in his savings.

It is possible that he changed his mind about the efficacy of premiums very shortly after these gifts to the Royal Society and the American Academy. In his *Proposals for Forming a Public Institution*, which led to the Royal Institution, he laid it down that the managers were never, on any pretext, to dispose of any money or property belonging to the Institution in *premiums*, as the intention was not to give rewards to the authors of ingenious inventions but *to diffuse the knowledge of such improvements as bid fair to be of general use*. On the other hand it is also possible that he looked upon the Royal Society and similar corporate bodies as serving the purpose of advancing science, and the Royal Institution as a means of diffusing scientific knowledge. From a practical point of view he would not wish to deplete the funds of the Royal Institution since he was most anxious for its financial transactions to be beyond reproach.

These benefactions should be considered together with Rumford's work for the Bavarian Academy of Arts and Sciences. His early efforts have been described; his later ones were frustrated by wars and rumours of wars. He was retained by Maximilian for some years and he paid regular visits, but the results were small. In 1805 he closed down his house in Munich and that was virtually the end. Five years later Maximilian, then advanced from Elector to King, invited him to spend some months in Bavaria, and the visit gave him great pleasure, but the Academy was still incomplete. Its great days were to come long after Rumford died. Munich was to be the place where Fraunhofer worked. His grave there bears the epitaph '*Approximavit sidera*'— he brought the stars nearer. It was also to see the birth of X-ray crystallography, with von Laue as the father; while the discovery of X-ray was made at Wurzburg, also in Bavaria.

When Rumford wrote his essays his purpose was to persuade as well as to instruct; rationalization followed action and practice preceded principle. Yet they are valuable in revealing the springs of his philanthropy. He eschewed pity but praised benevolence.

'However selfish pity may be, benevolence certainly springs from a more noble origin. It is a good-natured, generous sentiment, which does not require being put to the torture in order to be stimulated to action. And it is this sentiment, not pity, or compassion, which I would wish to excite.

'Pity is always attended with pain; and if our sufferings at being witnesses of the distresses of others force us to relieve them, we can neither have much merit nor lasting satisfaction from such involuntary acts of charity; but the enjoyments which result from acts of general benevolence are as lasting as they are exquisitely delightful; and the more they are analyzed and contemplated the more they contribute to that inward peace of mind and self-approbation which alone constitute real happiness. This is the "soul's calm sunshine and the heart-felt joy", which is virtue's prize!'[12]

This contrasting of pity and benevolence shows the working of his mind. His image of himself was that of a benevolent deity anxious for the ordered well-being of the humbler creation, remote himself from suffering and wishing to alleviate it at more than arm's length. His thinking was influenced by deism rather than by Christian teaching. He had little true charity. Contact with the blood or filth of the beggars was not for him. His role was not that of the Good Samaritan. One could not imagine him loving the poor and living among them as a Father Damien or a Schweitzer.

The tamers of wild horses which are bred in the Forest of Dusseldorf, he said, 'never use force in reclaiming that noble animal and making him docile and obedient. . . . It may be thought fanciful and trifling, but the fact really is, that an attention to the means used by these people to gain the confidence of those animals, and teach them to like their keepers, their stables and their managers, suggested to me many of the ideas I afterwards put into execution with great success, in reclaiming those abandoned and ferocious animals in human shape which I undertook to take and render gentle and docile.'

It gave him a glow of satisfaction to see the poor at work and to observe what a great change could be brought about in their habits.

'Would to God I were able to do justice to this subject. But no language can describe the affecting scenes to which I was a witness. . . . The exquisite delight which a sensible mind must feel upon seeing many hundreds of wretched beings awaking from a state of misery and inactivity and applying themselves with cheerfulness to the employments of useful industry, upon seeing the first dawn of placid contentment break upon a countenance covered with habitual gloom and furrowed and distorted by misery—this is easier to be conceived than described.'

When the poor were sufficiently regenerate to pray it was balm indeed, but he was not quite sure whether his pleasure was compatible with the enlightenment of the times.

Still talking of the House of Industry in Munich, he said:

'As soon as a company have taken their places at the table . . . upon a signal given by the officer who presides at the dinner, they all repeat together a short prayer. Perhaps I ought to ask pardon for mentioning so old-fashioned a custom; but I am old-fashioned enough myself to like such things. . . .'

His benevolence made him god-like. He was the microcosmic god bringing order into chaos and dispersing misery; he was identifying himself with the great God of the macrocosm whose instrument he was and who was ordering things well for mankind. Such was the *gestalt* which was vague and ill-defined when he began his work in Bavaria as an ambitious youngish man but which developed as he became the great international expert.

But such images belong only partly to consciousness and though they have some influence on action they are weak compared with the more fundamental urges such as self-assertion, which in Rumford was over-weening ambition. As ambition was satisfied, although his egocentricity was always strong, he pursued his practical aims, only rarely revealing his selfishness at one extreme and his benevolence at the other.

I shall end this chapter with a brief description of a few of his practical activities which are in line with those so far considered.

It is odd that Rumford is very seldom mentioned in histories of education. Yet as well as his part in the establishment of the Royal

Institution (which alone should ensure him an honoured place) he made several attempts to foster education. As we have already seen he founded schools for soldiers and their children, and employed a schoolmaster to give elementary instruction to children too young to work in the House of Industry. He was not, however, in favour of extended education for all children; he was concerned, no doubt with his own childhood in mind, to provide conditions for the bright child of humble parents to develop so that his talent and achievement should not be lost to public service.

His Military Academy[13] was primarily 'a nursery for genius'. It had 180 pupils of three types. The first group of thirty were orphans or children of the poorer class of military officers or civil servants. They entered the Academy between eleven and thirteen years of age, stayed for four years and paid no fees. The second group of sixty were fee-payers; they were the sons of the poorer nobility and less well-to-do merchants. For them the age of entry was from eleven to fifteen, and for a little less than twenty-five shillings a month they were fed, clothed and given instruction. The third and largest group consisted of older boys who went in at between fifteen and twenty. They were mostly boys from the lower classes of society who had shown 'evident signs of *uncommon talent*' and were of good physique and character; they were accepted on the recommendation of higher civil servants, magistrates and regimental commanders. When Rumford wrote about his Academy it had existed only six years; it was later dissolved.

Rumford describes this foundation in general terms and with little trace of the enthusiasm he had for the proved ventures of larger scale and greater popular appeal. This is a pity, for it sounds like a promising enterprise born only just out of due season. Though termed a Military Academy[14] it was designed not only to produce army officers but men of strength, character and accomplishment who would enter the higher professions and the civil service or 'adorn the station of a private gentleman'. With his lifelong attention to costs, which began with his expenditure as a boy on simple scientific apparatus, he says that the cost for one pupil for the four-year course was fourteen pounds, a figure which covered board, clothing, equipment and teachers' salaries, in fact everything but the rent of the building.

In addition to his influence through this academy Rumford encouraged and helped a number of young men of ability. The best example was Humphry Davy in England; but in Bavaria there were many others, including the distinguished soldier General von Wrede, the engineer Georg von Reichenbach (who was sent to England by Charles Theodore on Rumford's recommendation) and J. G. von Dillis, the painter.[15] As a cosmopolite, partly by necessity and partly from choice, Rumford had no sympathy with national exclusivism and he did all he could to spread ideas across the boundaries of countries. He held that neither personal gain nor national pride should act as a barrier to the flow of ideas.

A letter he wrote from Paris to Thomas Pelham on 28 July 1802 shows these beliefs. In it he introduced two well-known members of the Agricultural Section of the *Institut National* who wanted to attend the Sussex Agricultural Show at Lewes. He went on:

'I recommend these gentlemen to your Lordship in the full confidence that you agree with me in opinion respecting the Policy of encouraging that friendly intercourse between the two nations which by diffusing useful knowledge and promoting a liberal correspondence between the most enlightened and most respectable members of Society will tend to remove national prejudices and contribute very powerfully to the preservation of Peace and the formation of Commercial connections which may become beneficial to both Countries.'[16]

The letter which Rumford wrote to his housekeeper in Brompton Row giving instructions for the care of these same two 'french Gentlemen' shows the more homely arrangements he made:

'If they should invite you to breakfast with them you should thank them for their politeness, but you should not accept their offer. . . .

'One blanket on each bed with the white coverlid will be enough. . . .

'I hope my dear Bessey you will take great care of these friends of mine and let them want for nothing.'[17]

II

Man of Science

HIS EARLIER WORK

> It is certain that there is nothing more dangerous
> in philosophical investigations, than to take anything
> for granted, however unquestionable it may appear,
> till it has been proved by direct and decisive ex-
> periment.
>
> RUMFORD

UMFORD'S scientific work is easy to understand. He worked
in the kitchen of science rather than in the study or among
the brass instruments. His researches were almost entirely
concerned with heat and light and the simple properties of matter.
He was ahead of his time in his advocacy of 'the application of science
to the common purposes of life' however conservative he was in the
political and social field. He was pre-eminent as an apostle of applied
science and outstanding as an experimentalist, and has received less
than his deserved recognition in both fields.

The reasons are not obscure. Histories of science pay greatest
attention to those men of disciplined imagination who produce the
grand generalizations; men such as Newton with his theory of gravitation, Clerk Maxwell with his electro-magnetic theory of light and
Einstein in the field of relativity; to those who open new fields, like
Lavoisier who gave the modern explanation of combustion, Faraday
with his work in electrostatics and Planck who introduced the quantum
theory; and to those who re-orientate systems of ideas as did Coper-
nicus with his explanation of planetary movements, Galileo with his

ideas about inertia and motion and Darwin with his concept of natural evolution. Rumford did none of these things. His chief concern was not to add to the structure of scientific theory but to use science to improve the lot of man, particularly the life of the humbler classes.

Rumford's strongest motive was not a compelling curiosity but a passion for order. He started therefore from practical problems concerned with heating, lighting and firing guns. Scientific investigation was nearly always for him a secondary activity arising from more urgent needs or indulged in as a relaxation. Yet he had great skill in devising apparatus, and a flair for designing experiments, though not always a patient detachment in the interpretation of results. Both his insight and his results are all the more remarkable when it is remembered that for much of his lifetime he was continuously occupied with exacting military and administrative duties. Sometimes he showed the secondary nature of his scientific interests by his ignorance of the work of contemporary and earlier men of science; he failed, for example, to apply the ideas of molecular diffusion. But he was ready to modify his conclusions, and in its accuracy his best work matches that of Regnault and in its importance compares with that of Joule. Though he was never a theorist, he fired an explosive charge under the caloric theory of heat which—though it did not do so—should have brought it down immediately. Its foundations, however, were so badly cracked that, though its façade appeared undamaged to many of his contemporaries, its collapse was assured. It is for these experiments on the production of heat by friction, his shadow photometer and a simple calorimetric correction that he is chiefly remembered.

Rumford's interest in firearms and gunpowder was of long standing when in July 1778 as a young man of twenty-five he undertook a series of experiments 'to determine the most advantageous situation for the vent in firearms and to measure the velocities of bullets, and the recoil, under various circumstances'.[1] He was a guest of Germain's at the time, staying at Stoneland Lodge, and he was assisted by the Reverend Mr Ball, the Rector of Withyham.

His method was to suspend a gun horizontally by two parallel rods free to move in a vertical plane. The gun fired bullets into a target suspended like a pendulum. Arrangements were made to measure the movement of the pendulum and the recoil of the gun. The target was similar to one used by Robins with whose work in this field Rumford was well acquainted.

The care and thoroughness with which Rumford conducted the experiments are seen from the long series of readings given in his paper in the *Philosophical Transactions of the Royal Society*. For calculating the velocity of the bullet he first used formulae proposed by Robins and C. Hutton which gave the velocity in terms of the mass of the bullet, the mass of the pendulum, the chord of the ascending arc of the pendulum and certain other quantities dependent on the geometry of the pendulum. But he broke new ground by calculating the velocity of the bullet from the velocity of the recoil of the gun. This enabled him to compare the muzzle velocity with the bullet's velocity on striking the target. The discrepancies between the two sets of results were rather high in some experiments (of the order of 10 to 20 per cent) and low in others. After correcting for air resistance, since the velocity of impact is necessarily lower than the muzzle velocity, Rumford said that he could not account fully for the remaining differences but suspected that the cause was the breaking of the bullet in the barrel, which is plausible.

Rumford recommended applying his method to larger guns and in his paper, ninety-seven pages long, gave much valuable information to his contemporaries. He also tried to make a flame-thrower but could not manage it.

An observation which astonished him, and which is of greater significance to us than his failure to invent a flame-thrower, was the fact that the barrel of the gun felt hotter after a charge had been exploded without a bullet than it did when the same weight of powder had been used to fire a bullet. In a long and historically interesting discussion he rejected the view that a gun when fired is appreciably heated by the flame of the powder and went on to say that 'the heat generated in a piece by firing is, therefore, as the force by which the particles of the metal are strained and compressed, the suddenness with which this force is exerted and the shortness of the time of its action'. The action, he said, is retarded when a bullet is fired because of the time taken by the bullet to leave the barrel, and therefore the shock or impact on the barrel is less than when the powder is fired with no bullet. He argued from the effect of the conversion of mechanical energy into heat when a bullet strikes a target, but while he was groping towards a correct view of the nature of heat he was, of course, unaware of the principle of conservation of energy. He had inadequate ideas about the energy released by chemical action and he made no allowance for the kinetic energy given to the bullet or the gun. As Tyndall pointed out,[2] Mayer, sixty years later, 'was the first to discern the meaning of the observation'.

In 1797 Rumford had second thoughts about his explanation, though it was only to acknowledge his ignorance. He had carried out experiments which attempted to measure directly the pressure produced when a given quantity of gunpowder is exploded in a closed space.[3] The results gave, under the conditions in which he worked, a value of over 800,000 lb to the square inch which was a great deal more than suggested by the experts of his day and certainly an improvement on their estimates. But this paper is most interesting for the incidental information it affords and the discussion it contains. He asked questions about the nature of heat and avoided answering them (although later he was able to throw more light on the subject) and he rejected his previous explanation of the heating of the gun barrel by the blow it receives from the explosion of the powder.

In a third paper[4] in this field he described his efforts to improve field artillery and his establishment of the cannon foundry at Munich: 'neither pains nor expence were spared to make it as perfect as possible'. He had good workmen as well as workshops and 'a most excellent machine for boring cannon'. His main contributions were designing a six-pounder and advocating iron instead of brass as the material for cannon. His six-pounder has already been mentioned in connection with his proposed employment in America. It was for horse artillery and provision was made for carrying the crew upon the limber and the ammunition waggon where seats were provided. It seems to have been simple in design, easily moved and quick and effective in action.

His iron guns were of various sizes from one-pounders to eighteen-pounders. They were cast solid and bored horizontally; the trunnions were turned by a special machine. The smallest was based on the design of a British gun which Rumford had been given by Desaguliers twenty years earlier. He thought that Great Britain could with advantage use iron artillery instead of brass because of the cheapness and availability of iron in good quality as against the high cost of and demand for copper. He believed that in this respect the army might well follow the navy's example.

Rumford's work on guns derived from his boyhood interests, his experiences as a soldier and his voyage on the *Victory*. The next experiments I shall describe were an attempt to investigate 'the warmth of natural and artificial clothing'. He gave an account of them in his Eighth Essay[5] which contains the substance of two papers contributed to the *Philosophical Transactions of the Royal Society* in 1786 and 1792 respectively. It was for the second of these papers that the Royal Society awarded him the Copley Medal.

At the beginning of the essay Rumford remarked that in general good conductors of heat are good conductors of electricity and bodies which 'are bad conductors of the electric fluid are likewise bad conductors of Heat'. He was therefore 'led to imagine that the Torricellian vacuum which is known to afford so ready a passage to the electric fluid would also have afforded a ready passage to Heat'.

This preliminary statement is both interesting and misleading. Its early reference to the supposed conducting power of the Torricellian vacuum was no doubt based upon the important but imperfectly understood experiments of Grummert of Dresden, Lord Charles Cavendish and Watson, all of whom had observed the passage of a spark discharge through a partially exhausted tube. As this work was carried out in about 1750 Rumford might well have seen a repetition of parts of it when he attended the lectures at Harvard College. The mechanism of the discharge was at the time quite inexplicable and it was not known that a high vacuum was an insulator. The statement that good conductors of heat are good conductors of electricity has received confirmation for pure metals through the later work of Forbes and of Wiedemann and Franz.[6] The statement is interesting because it shows that Rumford in the 1780s was familiar with the discoveries in the field of electricity though he himself contributed nothing to it, perhaps because he could see no useful applications of such experiments.

His main concern was with the conduction of heat and for his experiments he constructed jacketed thermometers. The bulb and stem of a thermometer were surrounded by a larger vessel of the same general shape but with a much larger bulb. The space between the thermometer and the jacket could be evacuated or filled with various substances including air. The thermometer thus served as a body to be heated and as an indicator of the temperature rise. A similar device was used some years later by Dulong and Petit in an important series of experiments. Rumford's procedure, however, was as follows: he evacuated the space surrounding the thermometer and plunged jacket and thermometer into boiling water noting the time it took the thermometer to rise through a certain number of degrees. He then let the jacketed thermometer cool, allowed air to enter the jacket and repeated the experiment. The thermometer rose much more quickly, showing that the air was a better conductor than the evacuated space. He devised other tubes and found that if the conducting power of air were taken as 1000 the conducting power of the Torricellian vacuum was 602. He tried without success to investigate the effect of the size of the bulb, but he did show that moist air was a better conductor than dry air.

These experiments were by present standards both qualitative and crude. He made no distinction between conduction, convection and radiation, all of which processes were involved in the transference of heat from the boiling water to the thermometer. Not understanding the concealed difficulties he tried to determine the variation of conducting power with the pressure of the air in the jacket. He found only slight variation although the lowest pressure he used was only just over an inch of mercury.

The results surprised him but, as he says, not having any favourite theory to defend and since the sole object of his inquiries was to discover truth they did not disappoint him. He did, however, comment on the greater conductivity of moist air than cold air. He saw as an example of the infinite wisdom and goodness of Divine Providence the fact that cold air cannot contain as much water vapour as warm air, so that in winter the conductivity of the air is less and our bodies lose heat less readily. Had it been otherwise 'its conducting power, and consequently its apparent coldness when applied to our bodies would be so much increased, by such an additional degree of moisture, that it would become quite intolerable'.

Having carried out these experiments with air Rumford turned to his more practical aims. He used the same kind of instrument, which he called a passage thermometer, and filled the space in turn with equal weights of silk, eider down, hare's fur and other substances. He modified the procedure slightly by heating the passage thermometer in boiling water, then plunging it into an ice bath and noting the rate of fall of temperature. He found the relative conducting powers of these substances and, further, he was led to distinguish between the ease with which air allows heat to pass by convection currents or mass movements and its apparent inability to conduct heat in the way a solid substance allows heat to pass. This was an advance of thought though he assumed that the true conductivity of air was zero. He rightly saw that the low conductivity of many substances, for example, wool, arises from the ease with which they imprison air between their fibres.

It should be said that Ingen-Hausz, a Dutch engineer, was comparing the thermal conductivities of metals at about the same time as Rumford was experimenting, and his results were also qualitative. The absolute measurement of thermal conductivity had to await the brilliant mathematical treatment of heat flow by Fourier, given in his book *Théorie Analytique de la Chaleur* which was published in 1822. Rumford was not a mathematician and sometimes his scientific work suffered because of his practical approach: often what appears a simple practical problem is scientifically complex; rapid progress depends upon isolating the scientific problem and keeping all variables but one under control. The experiments just described illustrate this point. When Dulong and Petit in 1817 investigated the cooling of a thermometer surrounded by air at different pressures they isolated a scientific problem and dealt systematically with the variables concerned.[7]

The experimental work of Rumford's Seventh Essay was carried out after these experiments, which belonged to the Eighth Essay. It will be sufficient to indicate in general terms the purposes Rumford had in mind in his Seventh Essay and to discuss some of his main methods and conclusions. The essay begins with the well-known sentence which introduces the present chapter, and is followed by the confession that in the course of his philosophical researches he had very often 'to lament the consequences of . . . this most elementary precaution'.

The rueful admission was prompted by Rumford's realizing the error of presupposing that heat could pass *freely* through liquids in all directions. He went too far in his reaction, however, and concluded that water was a non-conductor of heat rather than a weak conductor.[8]

Having seen his major error he recounts some of his observations of everyday processes, such as the cooling of rice soup which led him to these experiments on the propagation of heat in liquids. He goes on to describe his observation of convection currents in the stem of a very large alcohol thermometer. The thermometer was cooling in a window illuminated by sunlight and so the convection currents could be clearly seen. Fine dust particles showed the circulatory movement of the alcohol; the direction of motion was vertically up the axis and down the sides of the tube.

For this new series of experiments he designed another 'passage thermometer'. This had a cylindrical bulb of sheet copper five inches long and just under two inches in diameter. The stem was a glass capillary tube twenty-four inches long. The thermometer contained linseed oil—a liquid Newton had used—and was surrounded by a copper cylinder a foot long and just over two inches in diameter.

As before, the substance under test was put in the space between the jacket and the thermometer. He first experimented with stewed apples, which he chose because their power of retaining heat had been impressed upon him when he had burnt his mouth. The simple procedure he adopted was to put the instrument containing the substance in a freezing mixture until it had cooled to 32°F and then to transfer it quickly to a water bath at 212°F, noting the rate of the thermometer's rise of temperature. He repeated the experiment with various substances including water containing starch, and water containing eider down. He rightly concluded that anything which diminishes the fluidity of water by restricting its internal motions diminishes its power to propagate heat. Incidentally he was incorrect in attributing the retention of heat by hot apples entirely to their conducting power. He argued that apples are nearly all water (he had found by experiment that water accounts for 98 per cent of their weight), and that they lose their heat slowly because the fibrous part impedes the heat of flow through their substance. His experiment showed that the rate of heat transfer was twice as fast with water as with stewed apples, thus bearing out his contention about conducting power. It is true that a dish of stewed apples left in a room will cool more slowly than a similar dish containing the same weight of pure water. But the mouth-burning property of apples compared with, say, pastry, depends on the high specific heat and high density of water. Volume for volume, foods which contain much water have much more heat to lose than others and so the mouth has to absorb much more.

Impressed by his results Rumford characteristically looked for their significance in the 'economy of Nature' and there found examples of the principles he had discovered. Some of his speculations are understandably wide of the mark through lack of knowledge; for instance, he takes no account of supercooling when he treats the frost-resisting properties of fruits containing water. Others seem naive, because the revolution of thought brought about by Darwin, Lamarck and others was yet to come. But there can be no doubt that these speculations were important in their day in directing the attention of the many readers of his essays to the manifold implications of scientific knowledge and research. They also reveal very clearly Rumford's keen eye for natural phenomena and his grasp of causal relations.

In the second chapter of the Seventh Essay[9] Rumford first addressed himself to methods.of showing convection in liquids. The methods show increased insight and much ingenuity. To exhibit the movement of the currents he used a suspension of amber particles in a solution of salt and found that the liquid at the top of a tube could be made to boil without much effect on the liquid at the bottom. This naturally led him to study the passage of heat vertically downwards in a column of water. A piece of ice was kept in place at the bottom of a large gas jar and hot water was poured into the jar, the ice being shielded while the water was poured. He then proceeded to find how the temperature of the water in the jar varied with the distance from the top at intervals of 20, 35, 60, 90 and 120 minutes. Finally, he calculated the total heat lost by the water and the heat used in melting the ice (he knew the latent heat of fusion), and concluded that seven-eighths of the heat lost had been given to the surrounding air and only one-eighth had been absorbed by the ice. In another experiment where the same weight of ice had been allowed to float on the water the ice had melted in under three minutes, a rate of melting eighty times more rapid than when the ice was at the bottom. These experiments will be recognized as the prototype of a simple experiment now conducted in elementary classes to show the low thermal conductivity of water.

But some ice was in fact melted by the downward passage of heat and Rumford had to reconcile this fact with his belief that water was a perfect non-conductor of heat—convection having been eliminated.

He tried to do this by bringing in the anomalous expansion of water near its freezing point: when heated from 32°F to 40°F it contracts and afterwards begins to expand when the temperature is further raised. There was something in this but not much, and he was using the peculiar behaviour of water to support an inaccurate contention. He proceeded to get out of his depth in performing experiments which he believed justified his arbitrary assumption.

We need not follow in detail Rumford's discussion in Chapter III of the essay on the important effects in nature which follow from the thermal properties of water. But because he was so impressed by the property of water of expanding when cooled from 40°F to 32°F, and as his discussion at this point throws light on his beliefs we should pay some attention to it.

'Those who are acquainted', he writes, 'with the law of condensation of water on parting with its Heat have already anticipated me in these speculations; and it does not appear to me that there is anything which human sagacity can fathom, within the wide-extended bounds of the visible creation, which affords a more striking proof of the wisdom of the Creator, and of the special care he has taken in the general arrangement of the universe to preserve animal life, than this wonderful contrivance; for though the extensiveness and immutability of the general laws of Nature impress our minds with awe and reverence for the Creator of the Universe, *yet exceptions to those laws* afford still more striking proofs of contrivance, and ought certainly to awaken in us the most lively sentiments of love, admiration and gratitude.'

Rumford was wrong in implying that water is the only substance to show anomalous expansion with a fall of temperature. Water also shares with other substances its property of expansion, or diminution in density, on freezing. Hence, as Tyndall pointed out, the teleological argument based on its expansion is 'found to be a mere quicksand'.[10] Of course, it is true that the most common of liquids—water—has the most remarkable properties of any. It has great powers of dissolving other substances and a very high dielectric constant—to name only two. Hence, if we are going to argue in teleological terms, the entire set of properties of water provides a firmer foundation. But the whole argument now has an ancient ring about it. The sort of life which has appeared on our planet has been contingent upon pre-existing physical conditions. 'Legitimate grounds for wonder exist everywhere around us' and our belief in the beneficence of God rests on other foundations. We no longer look to science as such to fortify our faith, not even to the Principle of Indeterminacy—at least not many do so. Equally we find in science nothing which need undermine it.

We are not directly concerned here with the validity or the falsity of the teleological argument, but it is clear that Rumford's religious beliefs, such as he had, at the time he wrote this essay were expressible in terms of his understanding of natural processes. Religion, he believed, was essential not only to simple and ignorant people but also to the civilized and refined. It was not something that people grew out of.

He dwelt on his speculations 'with satisfaction and complacency' because 'they might be of real use in an age of *refinement* and *scepticism*'. 'If among barbarous nations, the *fear of a God*, and the practice of religious duties tend to soften savage dispositions and to prepare the mind for all those sweet enjoyments which result from peace, order, industry and friendly intercourse—a *belief in the existence of a Supreme Intelligence* who rules and governs the universe with wisdom and goodness is not less essential to the happiness of those who, by cultivating their mental powers, HAVE LEARNED TO KNOW HOW LITTLE CAN BE KNOWN.'[11]

Rumford's Seventh Essay originally ended at this point, but when the second edition was brought out in 1798 he added new chapters. They opened with a rather curious statement. His friend Pictet in editing the Swiss edition published at Geneva had added a personal letter which Rumford had written to him. In this letter he had said that he had 'suppressed a whole chapter of interesting speculation'. Rumford felt that such an assertion needed justification and (reading between the lines) he was slightly annoyed at Pictet's quoting a private letter. The publication of the assertion might have two effects: it might damp the spirit of inquiry by discouraging others from venturing into a field already investigated; and it might look as though he was lying in wait to 'seize on the fair fruits of the labour of others' when they published their results. His justification was that having 'laid open a new and most enticing prospect to those who are fond of philosophical pursuits' he was afraid if he advanced too far that others might merely copy him instead of striking out for themselves. In other words he had, as it were, conducted other investigators to the gate, opened it for them, saying, 'this is all yours, go ahead'. He explained this altruism by saying that 'with regard to the reputation of being a *discoverer*' though he rejoiced—he might say he exulted and triumphed—in the progress of human knowledge yet he 'set no very high value on being the first to stumble on those treasures which everywhere lay so lightly covered'.[12]

After this rather egotistical introduction he described more experiments which, he held, were final proof that liquids were non-conductors of heat. It is very easy to criticize them in the light of knowledge gained in the last 160 years but nevertheless it is arguable that Rumford showed less than his usual acumen in designing them. It is also probable that it required an unusual effort of intellect in his day to regard as definite and precisely measurable small numerical values like that of the thermal conductivity of water, though a lead had been given by Smeaton, Ramsden and others in the determination of the coefficient of expansion of metals. In any case his statement that water was a non-conductor of heat was criticized by Dalton and he reopened the subject in 1805, a circumstance which I shall refer to later.

His speculations about the influence of heat on chemical combination are more interesting. He rightly preferred a crude theory in accordance with known facts to the metaphysical idea of chemical affinity. He showed insight in his statement that 'perhaps it will be found that . . . every change from a solid to a liquid form is a real fusion . . . and that no metal is ever dissolved till it has *first been melted*'. Interesting too was his essay into the diffusion of two liquids kept at a uniform temperature. These experiments must be the earliest systematic, recorded investigation in the field; fifty years elapsed before Graham's classical work appeared. They were unfortunately negative and are a greater tribute to his experimental skill than to his patience. He kept in contact at a constant temperature a layer of coloured water and a salt solution. After four days he observed no diffusion and brought the experiment to an end, treating it as decisive, and drawing the quite erroneous conclusion that 'a particle of water saturated with salt, and another perfectly free from salt, *may be* in contact with each other for any length of time without showing any appearance of a disposition to equalize the salt between them'. This shows the headstrong quality of his reasoning. If he had been more interested in the phenomenon of diffusion he might well have anticipated Graham's work though he could scarcely have gone further because progress had to wait upon mathematical analysis.

However, he appeared to think, perhaps in view of his negative result, that molecular motions are the result of minute temperature differences. Fluidity is *the life of inanimate bodies* and congelation is *the sleep of death*. Then he had a flight of fancy. Does not the life of animals depend upon the internal motions in their fluids, occasioned by an *unequal* distribution of heat? And is not *stimulation*, in all cases, the mere mechanical effect of the communication of heat? Would not any liquid in which heat was *equally distributed* be a *fatal poison* if injected into the veins of a living animal? Does not the *dram of brandy* at St Petersburgh produce the same effects as the *draught of iced lemonade* at Naples, and by the same mechanical operation but acting in opposite directions?

Having by these and other questions entered alien territory, he beat a hasty retreat by ending the chapter.

12

Man of Science

THE NATURE OF HEAT

I think I shall live to drive Caloric off the
stage, as the late Monsieur Lavoisier (the
author of Caloric) drove away Phlogiston.

RUMFORD (1804)

THE scientific work for which Rumford is most often remembered was described in a short paper read before the Royal Society in January 1798.[1]

'Being engaged lately in superintending the boring of cannon in the workshops of the military arsenal at Munich I was struck[2] with the very considerable degree of heat which a brass cannon acquires in a short time in being bored, and with the still more intense heat of the metallic chips separated from it by the borer.'

But although this observation was the beginning of Rumford's experiments it was not the beginning of the quest to discover the nature of heat. Speculation had continued from the time of Pythagoras with fire as one of the classical elements and hotness as one of the four primary qualities. Thus fire was hot and dry and earth was cold and dry; water was cold and wet and air was hot and wet. Although distinctions became blurred with time—for example, the distinction between heat and fire—the early thinking in modern science was profoundly influenced by ideas inherited from Greece.

Was heat a substance? And, if so, was it continuous or was it discrete? Some held the view that both heat and cold consisted of atoms of a special kind—the atoms of cold being termed *spiculae* or little

214

darts. But many came to regard heat as a fluid to which the properties of intensity and quantity could be applied. This fluid theory was strongly developed by Black and a group of French chemists who followed Lavoisier and it was Lavoisier who gave the name *caloric* to the fluid. I shall refer to this theory as the caloric theory even when describing its development before Lavoisier took it over.

The alternative to the caloric theory was one which regarded heat as a form of motion, generally a motion of the particles of a body. Such a view was consonant with the atomic theory of Democritus for whom, in the words of Lucretius:

> 'All nature, then, as self-sustained, consists
> Of twain of things: of bodies and of void
> In which they're set, and where they're moved around.'[3]

Francis Bacon, who reacted vigorously against the scholastic philosophy of the middle ages, turned to a study of nature based on observation and induction. His method which he called *Novum Organum* was designed to discover truth about the physical world, and to give an example of its working in practice he applied it to determine the nature of heat. It must be understood that he carried out no experiments, his examination was theoretical or mental, rather than practical and concrete. Nevertheless, he felt able to conclude that heat was motion: 'heat itself, its essence and quiddity is Motion and nothing else'. But motion of what? 'Heat is a motion of expansion, not uniformly of the whole body together, but in the smaller parts of it, and at the same time checked, repelled, and beaten back, so that the body acquires a motion alternative, perpetually quivering, striving, and irritated by repercussion. . . .'[4]

Both Boyle and Hooke held similar views. Boyle carried out a number of experiments and made shrewd observations in support of his views. He was impressed by the heat produced by friction and by hammering. In order to find out whether the ambient air was the source of heat he set up a device whereby two pieces of brass were rubbed together under the exhausted receiver of an air pump. The pieces of brass were heated as though air were present.

When a smith hastily hammered a nail it became hot, according to Boyle, because the motion of the hammer was destroyed by impact and communicated to the particles of the nail. He understood that if the hammer were small it too would get hot if the blows were often and nimbly repeated.

Like many others Boyle did not understand that coldness meant absence of heat. There was a tendency to think that cold was a positive quality and that the earth was its primary source as the sun was the source of heat. He and others could not understand the expansion of water on freezing. At first sight it looked as if the water gained something when it froze. The obvious test was to weigh a sample, and this Boyle did. He could detect no change in weight on freezing and he considered this evidence against atoms of cold.

Robert Hooke, Boyle's contemporary and assistant, was more definite in his statements. He discussed *fluidity* quite brilliantly.

'This I conceive', he writes, 'to be nothing else but a certain pulse or shake of heat; for heat being nothing else but a brisk and vehement agitation of the parts of a body (as I have elsewhere made probable), the parts of a body are thereby made so loose from one another, that they may easily move any way and become fluid. That I may explain this a little by a gross similitude, let us suppose a dish of sand set upon some body that is very much agitated, and shaken with some quick and strong vibrating motion, as on a millstone turn'd round upon the understone very violently whilst it is empty; or on a very stiff drumhead which is vehemently or very nimbly beaten with the drumsticks. By this means the sand in the dish, which before lay like a dull and inactive body, becomes a perfect fluid; and ye can no sooner make a hole in it with your finger, but it is immediately filled up again, and the upper surface of it levell'd. Nor can you bury a light body, as a piece of cork, under it but it presently emerges and swims as 'twere on the top; nor can you lay a heavier on the top of it, as a piece of lead, but it is immediately buried in sand, and (as 'twere) sinks to the bottom. Nor can you make a hole in the side of the dish, but the sand shall run out of it to a level.'[5]

This apt analogy should not suggest that Hooke thought the particles of a solid were at rest. He compared the vibrations of the particles with the vibrations which set up sound waves. Everything had some heat in it; nothing was perfectly cold.

John Locke was in the same tradition:

'Heat is a very brisk agitation of the insensible parts of the object, which produces in us that sensation from whence we denominate the body hot; so what in our sensation is heat, in the object is nothing but motion.'

He based his statement on the availability of great heat from friction. Locke was also definite about cold, for he said: 'On the other side the utmost degree of cold is the cessation of that motion of the insensible particles which to our touch is heat'.[6]

These opinions of Boyle, Hooke and Locke belong to the seventeenth century. There was a reaction against them which started in the eighteenth century and lasted for over a hundred years. It would be inaccurate to describe the change as a retrogression. In the eighteenth century the concept of quantity of heat became clear and measurable as did the idea of temperature. Chemists, and others to a smaller degree, found the notion of heat as a fluid much easier to grasp than the more abstract concept of heat as a molecular vibration. Many of the properties of heat were appropriate to the fluid theory. A fluid had weight and volume; it could impregnate objects; it could be squeezed out or absorbed, and, above all, it flowed. These ideas led Joseph Black, who laid the foundations of calorimetry, to prefer the fluid or caloric theory of heat. He regarded heat as a fluid 'subtile and highly elastic' which was contained among the particles of bodies, and which was all-pervading and self-repellent. He examined Bacon's theory and rejected it, saying:

'I confess I cannot form to myself a conception of this tremor that has any tendency to explain even the more simple effects of heat . . . and I think Lord Verulam and his followers have been contented with very slight resemblances indeed between those most simple effects of heat and the legitimate consequences of tremulous motion.'[7]

Cleghorn, a contemporary of Black, had added another property of caloric to explain the different specific heats of substances. He suggested that although caloric was self-repellent, that is, it tended to spread of its own accord, it attracted matter and did so to varying degrees.

The theory was thus powerful in explanation of simple phenomena. When heat was produced by hammering, the caloric was squeezed out. The expansion produced by heat was caused by its self-repellent nature; as a body took in more heat, pressure was exerted on the particles of the body, increasing the distance between them. When a piece of metal was filed or sawn the heat produced was that which was lost by the particles of the metal abraded; these had, so it was supposed, a smaller specific heat than the parent body.

When Black discovered and measured latent heats he suggested that water is a combination of ice and caloric and that the formation of steam is due to a further addition of caloric at the boiling point. By a simple extension the cooling produced by an evaporating liquid could be accounted for.

In the late eighteenth century, therefore, the caloric theory was firmly established. It had the backing of Black, Lavoisier, Dalton and Leslie (who referred to the dynamical theory as a shapeless hypothesis which will not bear examination), and it was in keeping with the prevalent scientific notions.

After meditating on the excitation of heat by friction Rumford realized that it might throw light upon 'the existence, or non-existence of an igneous fluid. From whence', he asks, 'comes the Heat actually produced in the mechanical operation above mentioned?' The caloric theory suggested that it came from chips produced by the borer. Rumford for the first time challenged the theory quantitatively on this contention. By experiment he showed that the chips had the same specific heat as the parent block and so eliminated one source of caloric. This was an important step, but he saw that it was not conclusive and he set about the task of generating as much heat as possible with as little abrasion of metal as he could contrive.

He used the waste head of a cannon for his experiments (see Fig. 2). The waste head was a solid mass of metal, about two feet long, left on the muzzle during casting so that the extra weight would prevent the honeycombing of the gun by the escaping gases.[8] Having turned the cannon he removed the metal between the muzzle and the waste head until the two were connected by a neck four inches long and two inches in diameter. Then he bored the cylindrical waste head with a horizontal borer to a depth of seven inches, the diameter of the hole being just under four inches. The whole piece was then set up in a lathe turned by two horses, and by means of a screw a blunt borer was held against the bottom of the hole with a force of about four tons.

A small transverse hole had been drilled in the cylinder so that the rise in temperature of the mass of metal could be measured. A flannel covering diminished loss of heat to the atmosphere. After half an hour of turning the horses were stopped and the temperature of the cylinder had risen by 70°F. Only 837 grains of metal, Troy weight, had been abraded.

As the next step Rumford surrounded the cylinder with water by

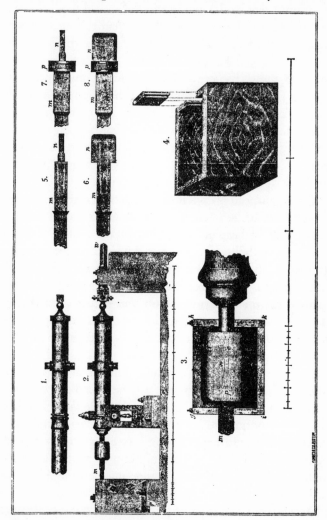

Fig. 2

The apparatus of the cannon boring experiment—after Rumford's original engraving. (*Reproduced by permission of the American Academy of Arts and Sciences*)

enclosing it in a wooden box. The neck passed through the box at one end; the borer passed through it at the other, see Fig. 2 (3). Well-oiled leather collars prevented water leakage. This time, after two and a half hours of turning, enough heat had been generated to boil the water in the box. This astonished the lookers-on and delighted him. Then he examined the implications.

He calculated that more than sufficient heat had been generated to raise twenty-six pounds of water from freezing point to boiling point and that it was equivalent to the combustion of nearly five ounces of wax. The rate of heat production was greater than that of nine wax candles, three-quarters of an inch in diameter, all burning steadily together.

In an important passage he pointed out how much heat is produced by the active strength of a horse and suggested that the heat might be used for cooking victuals. But, as he said, it would be more efficient to burn the fodder directly under the cooking pot than to have the horse as a link in the chain of energy changes. Such an argument as this is a stage in a quantitative grasp of energy changes which he might well have developed.

His statement that instead of two horses one could easily have done the work, has frequently been used as the basis for calculating the mechanical equivalent of heat using the rest of the figures he gives. The value works out at about 1000 ft.lb per B.Th.U., a value which is 30 per cent too high. But Rumford was mainly concerned not with the wider implications of quantitative energy change but with the light thrown by the experiments on the nature of heat. He realized that the most important consideration was the apparently inexhaustible supply of heat which could be produced by mechanical means.

'What is Heat?' he asks. 'Is there any such thing as an *igneous fluid*? Is there anything which with propriety can be called caloric? It is hardly necessary to add that anything which any *insulated* body, or system of bodies, can continue to furnish *without limitation* cannot possibly be a *material substance*; and it appears to me to be extremely difficult, if not quite impossible, to form any distinct idea of anything capable of being excited and communicated in the manner the Heat was communicated in these experiments unless it be MOTION.'

It is well known that these experiments failed to convince the men of science of Rumford's day. The caloric theory was firmly held and all his arguments could be met, save his claim that the supply of heat was inexhaustible—a claim which was contested. Berthollet in France, Dalton and others in England represented orthodoxy. But Rumford clung to his view and later elaborated his concept of motion, which in his first paper he left unexplained.

Writing in 1804, he likened caloric to phlogiston, a pseudo-stance which had been driven off the stage by Lavoisier. He explained his conjectures in a paper presented to the Royal Society.[9] It seemed probable that motion was an essential quality of matter and that no-where in the universe were bodies completely at rest. There were also, he said, many appearances indicating that the constituent particles of bodies were in motion and that it was the motion of these particles that 'constituted the heat or temperature of sensible bodies'.

In fact, though this made his own view clearer it added nothing to the general argument. He made a similar statement in a paper he read before the *Institut National*,[10] speaking deferentially but firmly in the stronghold of the supporters of the caloric theory. Also in 1804 he published his paper *Mémoire sur la Chaleur*,[11] in which, after opening in the grand style, he discussed the whole question.

One of the points at issue was whether caloric had weight. Experiments to decide whether a body changed in weight when heated or cooled were not easy to carry out with accuracy. Black, after examining the evidence, had come to a negative conclusion and admitted that the imponderability of heat was contrary to any theory that held it to be a fluid. In Rumford's time, however, it could not be said to have been established beyond doubt that heat was weightless. It was argued that even if caloric had weight it would be difficult to detect the fact by ordinary weighing, and moreover weight was not an essential quality of caloric. Rumford took the view that if it could be established that heat was weightless then the plausibility of the caloric theory was greatly diminished. He himself investigated this question in what was probably his most brilliant series of experiments.[12] But of course more than this was needed to convince his opponents.

He referred to these experiments in another paper[13] and went on to describe one which appears to be an idealized form of his cannon-boring experiment, stressing the inexhaustibility of the supply of heat and repeating his former arguments. He answered Berthollet who 'in his admirable *Essai de Statique Chimique*' had tried to reconcile Rumford's original experiments with the accepted theory. What Berthollet had said was that the great pressure of the borer had prevented an expansion of the metal and in so doing had caused an evolution of heat equal to what would have been absorbed had the metal been heated normally through the same range of temperature.

This, of course, was the old argument with an ingenious addition which was probably suggested by the fact that when a gas is suddenly compressed a considerable rise of temperature occurs.[14] Rumford replied patiently with the familiar argument and computed that if the experiment had continued for twenty days all the metal would have been reduced to powder and enough heat evolved to melt a mass of metal sixteen times heavier than the piece used in the experiment.[15]

'Is it conceivable', he asks, 'that such an enormous quantity of caloric could really be present in this body?'

The answer should have been no, but by this time the discussion was based not so much on experiment as upon preconceived ideas, and was almost sterile. Dalton, in 1808, repeated the old assumptions when he said, succinctly:

'The most probable opinion concerning the nature of heat is that of its being an elastic fluid of great subtility, the particles of which repel one another, but are attracted by other bodies.

'The heat produced by percussion and friction arises from one and the same cause, namely a condensation in volume and a consequent diminution of the capacity of the body just as condensation of air produces heat.'[16]

He wrote later, with a deplorable lack of scientific caution, 'if a diminution of capacity has not been observed it is because it is small and has not been investigated with sufficient accuracy'. He said of the cannon-boring experiment: 'The heat excited does not arise from the scales merely, the whole mass of metal is more or less condensed by the violence used in the boring.'

There was no lack of ingenuity in the arguments of the caloricists. In 1816 a correspondent to the *Philosophical Magazine* described how he had successfully set up a device with which he had demonstrated analogically, using water instead of heat, how the caloric was evolved in Rumford's original experiment. The main aim at this time was to show that simple attempts to demonstrate that heat has no weight were necessarily fruitless and that Rumford had not proved that the supply of heat was inexhaustible.[17]

Meanwhile Humphry Davy had made a contribution which, though it attracted Rumford's attention, had small influence on the trend of opinion. Davy's biographer says: 'He was not more than seventeen when he formed a strong opinion adverse to the general belief in the existence of caloric, or the materiality of heat.'[18] In 1799 one of his essays, *On Heat, Light, and the Combinations of Light*, was published in a collection of tracts, edited by Dr Beddoes. It contained an account of an experiment which may have been suggested by the work of Boyle.

Davy set up a piece of clockwork arranged so that it would rub two pieces of ice together, each six inches long, two inches wide, and two-thirds of an inch thick. The experiment was carried out with the surrounding atmosphere at 29°F. After some minutes the two pieces 'were almost entirely converted into water, which water was collected and its temperature ascertained to be 35°. . . .' This experiment would seem very damaging to the caloric theory. It was known since Black's experiments that a good deal of heat is necessary to melt ice; it was also known that the specific heat of ice is much less than that of water. From the second fact it could be inferred that the density of caloric in water was greater than it was in the ice and so the water had gained caloric. From the first fact it followed that caloric had to be supplied to melt the ice. Hence the system must have gained caloric and the only feasible source was from the energy in the clockwork.[19]

Davy concluded that heat 'may be defined as a peculiar motion, probably a vibration of the corpuscles, of a body, tending to separate them'. But it was not until he published his book, *Elements of Chemical Philosophy*, in 1812, that he clearly stated his conviction that 'the immediate cause of the phenomena . . . of heat is motion, and the laws of its communication are precisely the same as the laws of communication of motion'.[20] It must be remembered, however, that Davy carried out his experiments in this field as a young man working in Bristol and that subsequently other interests absorbed his time and energy.

As Tyndall points out in *Heat, A Mode of Motion*, both Cavendish and Young accepted the dynamical theory in its undeveloped form. Young in particular was convinced by the experiments of Rumford and Davy, and Cavendish on more general grounds.

What a division this debate caused. On one side Bacon, Newton, Boyle, Hooke, Locke, Cavendish, Rumford, Davy, Young; on the other Black, Lavoisier, Dalton, Berthollet, Leslie. There is no doubt that the acutest minds, and particularly those most at home in the realm of mathematics, were proved right in the long run.

It was indeed a long run. To clinch the matter two contributions were needed. They were provided by Julius Robert Mayer and James Prescott Joule. Mayer was a German physician who, in 1842, published a paper in Liebig's *Annalen* in which he stated the principle that there is a numerical equivalence between mechanical work done and the heat it produces. Three years later he developed his views, discussing the five main forms of energy, putting forward the principle of the conservation of energy and calculating the mechanical equivalent of heat. His was a noble and comprehensive contribution to science which should have made the debate on the caloric theory look like mere small talk, or perhaps one scene in a three-act drama. In fact, it was received as the idle speculation of a quack, dabbling in fields he did not understand. He was derided and cold-shouldered. As a result he was driven to attempt suicide and he recovered only slowly from the effects. This is a dark episode in the history of science, but one who emerges creditably is Tyndall of the Royal Institution who did his utmost to support Mayer's views.

Mayer's opponents stressed the importance of accurate, quantitative experimental work and deplored the introduction of metaphysical speculation, which as a general rule is a rewarding attitude to take, but many men of science had too little vision to encompass the great and fruitful generalization Mayer attempted.

Little need be added to end this account of the development of the mechanical theory of heat. Joule, a brewer who was a gifted experimenter, began by investigating the heat generated by the passage of an electric current through a conductor. His aim was not unconnected with Rumford's experiment for he was concerned with the source of heat in the circuit. He found that the cells providing the current did not cool but were heated according to the same law that applied to the rest of the circuit. He next replaced the cells by a primitive dynamo —Faraday had discovered the principle of electromagnetic induction ten years earlier—and concluded that the source of the heat was the mechanical work necessary to drive the dynamo. In his first series of experiments heat had been provided by chemical change; in the second by mechanical work, and it was not fruitful to explain the changes in terms of caloric. These experiments were described in papers published in 1840 and 1841. The next logical step was determining whether there was in all circumstances an equivalence between work done and heat produced. With the publication of Mayer's work Joule's experiments took on added importance and interest and he found a value for the mechanical equivalent of heat which supported Mayer's quite different calculation.

The scientific world was not electrified by these results, though they ended one scientific epoch and began another. After some hesitation Joule continued his work with ever increasing accuracy, using various methods of producing heat. His main principle was established and his value of the mechanical equivalent, since then known as J, was found with considerable precision. The caloric theory was dead.

The years from 1840 to 1880 brought about great unification in science. The fields of heat and mechanics were linked, not only by the work just described but by the calculation of the pressure exerted by a gas in terms of its density and the velocity of its molecules. Electrical, chemical and physiological changes were brought within the scope of quantitative energy calculations. The second half of the nineteenth century was the heyday of classical physics, a period which profitably took over and developed the contributions of Mayer and Joule and led to the great work of Planck in quantum theory and Einstein in relativity theory.

What was the value of Rumford's contribution? In one way not very great, for it could be argued that the ideas for which he stood did not gain acceptance until fifty years after his death. But the superficial view is very misleading. His main paper published in 1798, and his subsequent advocacy of the dynamical theory, influenced many of the greater minds. He experimented on the nature of heat far more than anyone had before. His discussion too was in scientific terms and free from some of the metaphysical notions which, in retrospect at any rate, have irritated men of science. Joule in his papers frequently acknowledged Rumford's insight, and he calculated a value for the mechanical equivalent from the particulars in Rumford's paper.

One cannot help regretting that Rumford did not design a dynamometer to measure the mechanical work done by the horses which turned the lathe. He could measure the heat produced with fair precision. If his measurements on the mechanical side had been comparable, his results would have been conclusive. Furthermore, since his experiments were on a large scale they might have carried conviction where Joule's early work failed. However, when he left Munich he lost the opportunity of further experiment of this kind and contented himself with verbal argument. It must also be said that he did not realize the problem to be a pressing one until he became involved in controversy.

It is evidence of the merit of Rumford's work that he has for the last hundred years received high praise both by historians of science and men of science. Some have made exaggerated claims,[21] but Tyndall's judgement can be accepted: 'When the history of the dynamical theory of heat is completely written . . . Rumford . . . may count on a foremost place.'

13

Man of Science

FURTHER IMPORTANT RESEARCHES

... I think we may very safely conclude, that
all attempts to discover any effect of heat on
the apparent weights of bodies will be fruitless.
RUMFORD

IN THE words which introduce this chapter Rumford summed up
his conclusions after making a series of experiments,[1] brilliantly
conceived and scrupulously carried out, to determine the change
in weight, if any, which accompanies the heating or cooling of a body.
Others had worked in the same field, among them Boerhaave, the
celebrated physician of Leiden, whose writings had fired Rumford's
early ambitions, the Comte de Buffon, the great French naturalist, and
John Roebuck, the Birmingham physician and chemist. Although
Black had concluded that heat was weightless the evidence did not
convince everybody.

The practical difficulties when weighing hot bodies are considerable. Convection currents may be set up which disturb the balance
and cause unequal expansion of the arms; a cooling body may oxidize
and so increase in weight. Rumford began by following the methods
of his predecessors fairly closely. He weighed a small ball at different
temperatures and found a slight change in weight. He then weighed
a cooling bullet at intervals starting at white heat, and again found a
small increase. Because of the uncertainty associated with these and
similar experiments, he devised greatly improved methods in

which, at the same time, larger quantities of heat and smaller temperature differences were involved. He also eliminated the risk of oxidation.

In the first experiment of his major series he used two thin flasks as nearly alike as possible. In one (A) he put nearly 1 lb of pure distilled water weighed with great accuracy, and in the other (B) an equal weight of spirits of wine. The flasks were sealed, wiped and suspended from the arms of a sensitive balance. A rider was used to secure an exact counterpoise. For twelve hours they were left in a room at 61°F and no change was observed. The apparatus was then wholly transferred to a room where the temperature was below freezing point and left for two days. By that time the water in A was completely frozen and the balance was no longer in equilibrium; A and its contents appeared to weigh more than B and its contents by slightly more than one part in 40,000. The apparatus was then returned to the warmer room and when it had regained the temperature of the surroundings A and B balanced each other as before.

Rumford suspected that the balance might be at fault, so he prepared two equal gilt, polished brass spheres and suspended them from the balance by gold wires. He repeated the procedure of his first experiment and found that the spheres exactly counterpoised each other after removal to the cold room. This suggested that the balance was not the cause of the apparent increase in weight. So again he took two flasks, as similar as possible, and repeated his first experiment but this time using mercury instead of spirits of wine and taking his second weighing in a room at 34°F. He found no difference in the weights although the water in cooling, on account of its much higher specific heat, had obviously given out much more heat than the mercury. He now believed that the small difference observed the first time was due to some accidental cause. Accordingly he took three bottles and put into them, respectively, equal weights of water, spirits of wine and mercury. He left them for twenty-four hours in the warm room and brought them exactly to the same weight by adding silver wire to the necks of the lighter flasks. All were then removed to a room below freezing point and left for two days when they each weighed the same as before. After returning to the warmer room there was still no observable change. The whole procedure was then repeated, again with a null result. Rumford concluded among other things that 'water does not acquire or lose any weight, upon being changed from a state of *fluidity* to that of *ice*, and *vice versa*'. He continued:

'I shall now take my final leave of a subject which has long occupied me, and which has cost me much pains and trouble; being fully convinced . . . that if heat be in fact *a substance* or matter—a fluid *sui generis*, as has been supposed . . . it must be something so infinitely rare, even in its most condensed state, as to baffle all our attempts to discover its gravity.'

Rumford can often be justly accused of preaching and prolixity but not here; these experiments reveal his skill at its highest. As Tyndall truly said:

'When he ceases to think of the exquisite delight of his philanthropic labours—ceases to think of himself—and permits his personality to be effaced by his subject, we see Rumford at his best; and his best was excellent. Suggestion follows suggestion, experiment succeeds experiment, until he has finally exhausted his subject or is pulled up by inability to proceed further.'[2]

The radiation of heat was a field in which Rumford carried out important experiments. He covered a good deal of ground being worked over at about the same time by Sir John Leslie and this caused him later to write in support of the independence of his work. He was led to these experiments by his investigation of the ability of different kinds of woven fabrics to retain heat. He suspended a long thermometer with a large cylindrical bulb inside a brass cylinder filled with water. With the vessel jacketed by the material under experiment he took readings to determine the rate of the water's cooling. As a standard of comparison he used a similar vessel polished and uncovered.[3] Continuing, he found that a blackened surface was a better radiator than a polished one. By using silvered, gilt and brass surfaces he discovered that the important factor was the nature of the surface and not the metal of which the vessel was made.

At this stage he became involved in the controversy about the radiation of 'cold'. If a piece of ice is put near a sensitive thermometer in a room at normal temperature the temperature of the thermometer falls. A similar effect can be produced when two concave mirrors are placed facing each other, having a common axis. If a thermometer is placed with its bulb at one focus, and a piece of ice at the other, the thermometer shows a fall in temperature. This effect was ascribed to the emission and reflection of frigorific rays. Like his friend Pictet, Rumford carried out experiments of this kind. He did not fully understand his observations although the way had been shown by Prévost of Geneva. It was difficult to discard the notion that cold was a positive quality and to regard coldness as a relative term. Prévost did this and more, however, in his theory of exchanges.[4] He suggested that all bodies are radiating heat. When they are in thermal equilibrium the exchange still goes on. When one body is colder than its surroundings it receives more than it gives and its temperature will tend to rise until equilibrium is restored. The idea of a dynamical equilibrium was important but difficult to grasp at the time when it was put forward.[5]

Rumford, writing after 1792, knew of Prévost's theory but did not comprehend its full significance. In his experiments he found that dull black surfaces radiate strongly and absorb strongly. He therefore said 'we may conclude that those circumstances which are favourable to the copious emission of calorific rays from the surfaces of hot bodies are equally favourable to a copious emission of frigorific rays from similar bodies when they are cold'. He then arrived halfway to the truth when he asked the question: 'Are not the same rays either calorific or frigorific according as the body at whose surface they arrive is colder or hotter than that from which they proceed?' The idea of a body emitting and receiving radiation at the same time was missing. Prévost had this idea, Rumford had not. It is tantalizing to see him groping in semi-darkness when he used the analogy of a bell setting in vibration the surrounding medium and bodies nearby. 'Supposing', he said, 'that heat be nothing more than the motions of constituent particles of bodies among themselves (an hypothesis of ancient date and which always appeared to me very probable) if for the bell we substitute a hot body, the cooling of it will be attended by a series of actions and reactions similar to those described.' But then he continued: 'According to this hypothesis cold can with no more propriety be considered as the absence of heat than a low or grave sound can be considered as the absence of a higher or more acute note; and the admission of rays which generate cold involves no absurdity and creates no confusion of ideas.'

In discussing the radiation from a hot body he showed greater insight, though he might have been acquainted with the discovery of infra-red radiation by Sir William Herschel in 1800 and with J. W.

Ritter's discovery of ultra-violet rays. He concluded that rays of light and heat rays were regulated by the same laws and said: 'Perhaps there may be no other difference between them than exists between those vibrations in the air which are audible and those which make no sensible impressions on our organs of hearing.'

He concluded his long paper with examples of the application of his ideas to cooking utensils, the lagging of pipes and clothing. Finally, he reverted to his belief in frigorific rays, and in speaking of wearing a fur coat with the fur (which he calls the polished surface!) outwards, his question seems perverse: 'Is not this a proof that we are kept warm by our clothing, not so much by confining our heat as by keeping off the frigorific rays which tend to cool us?'

In a paper, *Reflections on Heat*,[6] which he read before the *Institut* in 1804 he described (for the second time) his differential thermometer or thermoscope. This was a simple device consisting of two spherical glass bulbs each one and a half inches in diameter joined by a glass tube bent twice at right-angles. In the horizontal part of the tube was a bead of spirit to serve as an indicator. Rumford used this instrument for many of his experiments in radiation, and because of it he was involved in a controversy over priority after he had been attacked in the *Edinburgh Review*[7]—a brilliant but waspish journalistic venture then two years old.

The writer of the article, probably Brougham, paid a grudging tribute to the value of Rumford's experimental work in science and to the assistance his researches had rendered 'to the useful arts of common life'. He could not, however, accept his theories.

'We profess', he wrote, 'to be of the daily increasing number of those who do not think very highly of Count Rumford's talents as a philosopher, and if our former prepossession required any confirmation (which it certainly did not), he has taken very great pains, in the elaborate performance now before us,[8] to supply a variety of new proofs. . . . The merits of Count Rumford, too, have been so much a theme of conversation, and have had such an active influence on the world of science, that it is proper his intentions should at length be sifted. But, above all, a paper filled with theoretical matter, abounding in pulses, vibrations, internal motions and ethereal fluids deserves to be exposed.'

Rumford's theory was objectionable to the writer on several

counts. He seized on Rumford's inconsistency in assuming the existence of both frigorific and calorific rays and at the same time using
the analogy of sound waves in explanation.[9] Moreover his introduction
of an ether seemed, he thought, merely a confusion. If an ether had to
be assumed why not stick to the accepted idea of caloric and thus be
'spared the labour of all his prolix and useless argumentation'. This was
the core of the dispute over theory. The writer of the article was of
the tradition, and in the environment, of Black whose influence was
still paramount in Edinburgh though he had been dead five years.
More pertinent is the controversy over priority.

It seems necessary to distinguish between the claims for the introduction of what Leslie called a *differential thermometer* and Rumford a
thermoscope, and on the other hand the experimental work carried out
with the instrument. The writer accuses Rumford of borrowing the
idea and calling it his own:

'We have described it sufficiently to prove that the *thermoscope* is
exactly Mr Leslie's elegant instrument, denominated by him, not a
hygrometer, as Count Rumford is pleased to say, but a *differential
thermometer*. According to the Count's own statement, he borrows the
whole idea from that gentleman; yet with an ardour for discoveries
not quite scientific, he talks of it as his own contrivance, and with his
accustomed love of nomenclature he gives it a new appellation.'

Rumford's words were, 'This instrument which I shall take the
liberty to call a thermoscope is very simple in its operation. Like the
hygrometer of Mr Leslie, it is composed of . . .'[10] He did therefore
acknowledge Leslie's priority and he had a reason for calling Leslie's
instrument a hygrometer. He had read, no doubt, in *Nicholson's Journal*
a description of the instrument (some of his own papers were in the
same number), and how Leslie had shown that by wetting one of the
bulbs the humidity of the atmosphere could be inferred from the
difference in temperature of the two bulbs.[11] Furthermore Rumford
did not say that he invented the instrument but that he contrived, that
is to say, fashioned or constructed it.[12] We need not argue the merits
of the name Rumford gave it or whether he should have been content
with Leslie's—though how true it is that he loved nomenclature! The
experimental work carried out with it is more important. Here the
caustic reviewer let himself go:

'. . . if we were asked to state the opinion with which a review of the whole work has impressed us, we should say that Count Rumford has borrowed Mr Leslie's leading discovery, without completely understanding its nature and extent; that he had pursued it imperfectly, and so mixed it up with error and fanciful theory as to disfigure it, and almost prevent one from recognizing the property.'

There was more to come. In the concluding sentences invective and sarcasm follow. The writer alludes to 'want of arrangement; the prolixity and the repetition; the perpetual digressions and deviations . . . which form the distinguishing features of the author's style of writing . . .', and goes on:

'he is rather too fond of self-gratulation; of bestowing epithets on himself and his experiments; of indulging in well-turned compliments to his success and dexterity. . . . He never mentions or refers to one of his experiments, without calling it *most interesting* or *highly instructive* —or *singularly beautiful*—or at once *simple* and *decisive*. . . . The simplest experiment or remark, when touched by the finger of Count Rumford, is covered with brilliancy, swelled into grandeur, and branched into fruitful consequences.'

Rumford was a sitting bird when it came to this kind of shooting. It was the particular skill in which Brougham excelled; he was less able to judge scientific questions. Rumford was sensitive about his own reputation. He was in France at the time and Leslie's work was known there. He replied in the paper read before the *Institut* in the same year and proved the substantial originality of his experiments in radiation. He described his movements over the previous four years. When he was in Edinburgh in the summer of the year 1800 he had carried out experiments in the university in the company of Hope, Playfair and others. Together they had repeated Pictet's experiments on the apparent radiation of cold. When he returned to London he had told Banks and Cavendish of his intention to establish beyond doubt the existence of the cooling emanations from cold bodies. This he had not been able to do. He had been fully occupied with other affairs before leaving England in 1802. Since then he had been in Munich and Paris and all he had been able to do was to repeat certain experiments with his thermoscope in Geneva. He finished his memoir in 1803 and it was read before the Royal Society early in 1804. Leslie's book[13] was published later in the same year.

This in outline was Rumford's own account. The writer in the

Edinburgh Review was wide of the mark when he said that 'the Count only began to operate in 1803'. He had no justification for implying as he did that Rumford had seen the early chapters of Leslie's book. The two men were not personally acquainted with each other and there is little doubt that, apart from Rumford's access to the paper in *Nicholson's Journal*, they worked independently. There is no evidence at all that Leslie (in Largo, Fifeshire) paid or was able to pay any attention to Rumford's work on radiation. In fact he thought Rumford was dead. Speaking of pots and pans evidently reminded him of Rumford,[14] and in a note he referred to 'a late ingenious experimenter who by the perspicuity and useful tendency of his writings is deservedly a favourite of the public. . . .'[15]

Leslie's experimental researches in this field have had greater recognition than those of his supposed rival and this is probably fair, though on the theoretical side, Rumford was nearer the mark. As we have seen he approached acceptance of the theory of exchanges while Leslie concluded that radiation was propagated by pulsations or vibrations *of the atmosphere.* In closing this episode, lest the *Edinburgh Review* be thought too partisan let me say that Leslie's literary style and his theoretical conclusions did not escape strong criticism.[16]

It is tempting to linger over Leslie's book which has some delightful passages[17] and contains sound advice on scientific matters. It was a happy decision of the Royal Society to award Leslie the Rumford medal in 1804.

For convenience I have left Rumford's researches in optics until now. His photometer was first described in 1794.[18] Here again there is a question of priority to answer. It was not the first photometer to be used—Bouguer described and used one as early as 1725.[19] Moreover the principle of Rumford's instrument was clearly and conclusively stated by Lambert in 1760.[20] There is doubt, however, whether Lambert invented or used a serviceable instrument.[21] On balance it seems not, and that Rumford's instrument was the first shadow photometer. It was probably designed quite independently of the work of Bouguer and Lambert, for Rumford records in a footnote that Laplace gave him a copy of Bouguer's *Traité d'Optique pour la Gradation de la Lumière* in November 1801, long after he had designed the instrument.[22] It was in character for him when faced with a practical problem to solve it there and then without referring to the work of others; as

Philipp Lenard said, his mind was not 'loaded with the ballast of learning'. The practical problem in this case was 'the most economical method of lighting up a very large workhouse or public manufactory', and a method occurred to him, he said, 'for measuring the relative quantities of light emitted by lamps of different construction, candles, etc.'

The principle (see Fig. 3) is to set up an opaque object O in front of and close to a screen. The two sources of light to be compared, say S_1 and S_2, are situated almost on a line at right-angles to the screen passing through the opaque object. The part $b\,c$ of the screen is illuminated only by one source, S_1; the part $c\,d$ only by the other, S_2; and the rest by both. There will therefore be two shadows on the screen, a shadow being the relative absence of light. When the distances of the sources are adjusted so that the shadows are of equal intensity then the intensity of light falling on the screen from each source is the same. If d_1 is the distance of S_1 from the screen and d_2 of S_2, remembering that light intensity from a point source diminishes as the square of the distance, it follows that

$$\frac{S_1}{S_2} = \frac{d_1{}^2}{d_2{}^2}$$

Rumford's instrument (see Fig. 4) consisted of a wooden box B painted black on the inside with a white screen on the rear interior surface. The box was open at the front and contained two black cylinders set up perpendicularly, three inches from each other and just over two inches from the screen. The use of two cylinders does not materially affect, though it slightly complicates, the theory given above. Rumford's reason for using two objects was a practical and structural one. The sources of light were so placed that a line drawn from the centre of the vertical screen, and perpendicular to it, bisected the angle formed by joining the sources to the point from which this line arose. This arrangement gave equal angles of illumination. The cylinders were placed so that they were, respectively, in the direct lines of illumination, one for each source. The two main shadows (there were of course four with this arrangement) made contact along a line drawn vertically down the centre of the screen. There were various minor refinements to make adjustment sensitive.

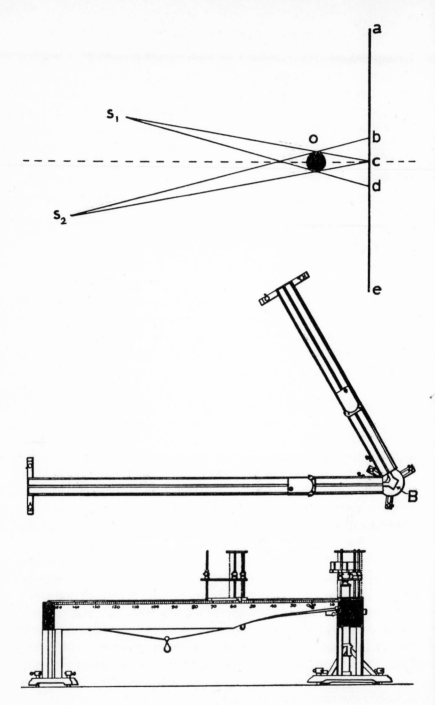

Figs. 3 & 4
Rumford's photometer

The sources under experiment were moved on carriages along grooves in strong tables, one twelve feet and the other twenty feet long. The movement was effected by winches so that adjustments could be made by the observer without having to move his vision from the screen. Rumford's photometer was a precision instrument very different from its description in most books on light.

He used it not only for his main practical purpose of comparing sources to ensure adequate intensity of light for the various activities which went on in the House of Industry, but also to measure absorption of light by glass plates, loss of intensity due to reflection from mirrors, and the fluctuation in the luminosity of candles. He also attempted to measure the absorption of light by air. His results in this were negative, but nevertheless a tribute to his experimental skill. An assistant wrote down the distances from the screen because he did not want his readings to be influenced by his 'predilections for any favourite theory'; he was 'glad to find means to avoid being *led into temptation*'.

While he was engaged in these experiments he noticed that the shadow illuminated by a candle was yellow and that illuminated by daylight was blue. This observation led him to a series of beautiful experiments conducted in orderly precision using different lamps, daylight and glasses of various colours. He concluded that the colours of shadows were subjective and the result of the contrast of one light with the other in the field of view. He left further inferences to be drawn by 'philosophers, opticians and painters', saying: 'In the meantime I believe it is a new discovery—at least it is undoubtedly a very extraordinary fact—that our eyes are not always to be believed even in respect to the presence or absence of colours.'

It was obviously an exaggeration to call this a new discovery. Quite simple observations illustrate the same fact. Anyone who looks at a neutral background after having gazed fixedly at a bright blue or a bright red object will be aware of it. Exaggerations like this warranted the Edinburgh reviewer's jibe that he was fond of 'indulging in well-turned compliments to his success'. This paper also illustrates again Rumford's ignorance of others' work related to his own experiments. It was not until he was writing his paper that he recalled what he had read in Priestley's *History of Optics*.[23] The progression of his work was often like this: the pressure of a practical problem led to observations which aroused his scientific curiosity; he continued by investigating the phenomenon revealed, using careful methods and ingenious apparatus; and then, either before or after publishing the results, he examined previous or contemporary work in the same field. But until quite late in his life he continually returned to his administrative and practical problems, so that his scientific work lacked continuity. His work was never amateurish, yet he was a scientific amateur—even at the time when he was advanced in years, and living in Paris as a pensioner.

Having remembered Priestley's writings he did not alter his own paper. The footnote giving his reasons is yet another example of Rumford's self-esteem. 'When the glow of the sudden blush which I felt on discovering my danger of being thought ignorant or worse had passed off . . . I concluded that it might be *useful* to permit my paper to go into the world in its original state.' Trying to present forgetfulness as a virtue he continued:

'I conceived that it would show in a very striking manner, if not the advantages which sometimes result from forgetting what we have read, at least of preserving the mind totally unbiassed by the speculative opinion of others when we are in search of truth. An ardent lover of science will not hesitate to expose himself to personal danger when he perceives that by so doing he has a chance of promoting useful investigation.'

I have already remarked that Rumford carried out experiments with colours when he was staying in Italy with the Palmerstons. In the paper we are discussing he allowed his imagination to toy with the idea of a knowledge of the real harmony of colours and the construction of instruments 'for producing that harmony for the entertainment of the eyes in a manner similar to that in which the ears are entertained by musical sounds . . . where the flowing tide, the varying swell, the *crescendo* is wanting, colours must ever remain hard, cold and inanimate masses'. This is a pleasing if not altogether original fancy which still awaits its Bach.

One of the problems occupying the attention of many scientists at the end of the eighteenth century was the relation between heat and light. Although Huyghens, as early as 1678, had clearly proposed a wave theory of light, and had later made use of his theory to explain reflection, refraction and double refraction in crystals, it had not held its ground. The corpuscular theory which Newton held and developed was accepted as orthodox. It is often said that Newton's prestige greatly delayed the development of a study of optics, but there is more to it than that. A corpuscular theory of light as a sort of substance conformed to the pattern of eighteenth-century thought much better than a wave theory. As the caloric theory of heat has illustrated, the idea of materiality was influential in the thought of the time.

Although in general the eighteenth century consolidated and moved forward from the scheme of concepts of the seventeenth century—the century of genius—it was farther from the truth in its theories of light and heat; this is true in spite of the recent discoveries of the relation between energy and mass, and the quantum theory of the emission and absorption of light. For example, Leslie held that *heat is only light in a state of combination*[24] and though there were obvious objections to that view, for him at any rate they were 'not formidable'. The objections he saw were concerned with the chemical effects of light; his explanation was that 'the force of impulsion' of light acts as a blow when it detonates an explosive substance. Rumford was interested in the same problem; he doubted the existence of the chemical properties in light which had been attributed to it, and concluded that all the visible changes which are produced in bodies by exposure to the action of the sun's rays are effected not by any chemical combination of the matter of light with such bodies but merely by the heat which is generated or excited by the light which is absorbed by them.

To support his belief he made a series of experiments 'concerning the Chemical Properties which have been attributed to Light'.[25] They were inconclusive, and when some of them appeared contrary to his opinions he hoped and trusted that he would never be so weak as to feel pain at discovering truth.

14

Man of Science

LATER RESEARCHES

The sublime in science consists in employing
it to extend the powers and increase the innocent
enjoyments of the human race.

RUMFORD

THOUGH much of Rumford's most fruitful scientific work was
achieved before he settled in Paris, he was by no means a spent
force in his later years. He reflected on his earlier publications
and made experiments to test his conclusions, but he also had the urge
and ability to undertake new researches.

An investigation in the main tradition was one he entitled *Experiments and Observations on the Advantage of Employing Wheels with Broad Felloes for Travelling and Pleasure Carriages*.[1] Wide felloes or rims had
been introduced on large vehicles for carrying heavy loads because
they reduced wear and rutting, but opinion differed over whether they
made the load easier to draw. On lighter carriages broad rims had not
been tried because they would have looked inelegant. But Rumford,
having talked to several waggoners about the advantages, decided 'to
brave the ridicule which is always encountered by those who dare to
be the first to deviate from customs which are consecrated by fashion'.

He experimented with wheels of three widths; just under two
inches, two and a quarter inches and four inches. To measure the
tractive force required he constructed a simple dynamometer reading
up to 600 lb. With his carriage containing a coachman, a footman and
himself, he measured the pull required to keep it going at different

speeds from a slow walk to a fast trot. On good roads he found with the horses moving at a slow walk that the average forces were 54 lb, 46 lb and 42 lb for wheels in ascending order of size. At the highest speed the corresponding figures were 145 lb, 135 lb and 125 lb. So the broadest wheels were the best.

Rumford continued his experiments on different kinds of surfaces and obtained a similar result. One important conclusion was that on unpaved and sandy roads the tractive force varied little with the speed. He discussed the importance of this result for husbanding the horses' strength on long journeys, and said that the Italian postillions were perhaps right in trying to pass rapidly over a disagreeable stretch of road they could not avoid. After describing further the setting of the wheels, he said that his carriage was on view in the Court of the *Palais de l'Institut* 'for members to examine if they wished'. For posterity he left a lively sketch of his carriage with horse, footman and coachman and with a full set of dimensions (see Plate 9, facing page 192). This has been reproduced by Professor Sanborn C. Brown together with certain other of Rumford's drawings which have recently been acquired by the Harvard College Library.[2]

Some of Rumford's later experiments were prompted by criticisms of his earlier results and the explanations he had given of natural phenomena. In his Seventh Essay he had argued widely about the formation and the influence of winds and ocean currents on the foundation of De Luc's experiments on the density of water. He decided to investigate for himself convection currents in water near its freezing point. His experiments were carried out in 1805, at about the same time as the better-known ones of T. C. Hope in Scotland. Hope set up a cylinder of water at about 8°C, and surrounding the cylinder about halfway up was an annular trough containing ice. He studied the change in temperature of the water in the cylinder at the bottom and near the surface. He found that the lower thermometer at first fell rapidly, but the top one slowly. When the lower thermometer registered 4°C it remained constant. Meanwhile the top thermometer fell at an increasing rate to the freezing point. The explanation is that with such an apparatus the water near the middle of the trough is cooled by the ice. At first as it is cooled below 8°C its density increases and it sinks to the bottom, the water in the upper half of the vessel remaining relatively undisturbed. When the water near the bottom has reached its maximum density further loss of heat through the annular trough diminishes the density of the water at the middle which rises to the top until the water there is near freezing point. Steady conditions are not reached, but roughly there is a temperature gradient from 0°C at the top to 4°C at the bottom. The experiment shows that water has its greatest density near 4°C and also throws light on the freezing of pools, the penetration into a glacier of a small pool of water on its surface, and other natural phenomena.

When Rumford had second thoughts, he tackled the problem rather differently from Hope. Essentially his apparatus consisted of an almost hemispherical cup containing water. The cup was of cork, waxed on the inside; the temperature of the water it contained could be measured directly by a thermometer; to begin with it was at 0°C. The cup was placed in a larger vessel also containing ice-cold water. This water was heated from the top by an iron ball, with a projecting point which could be placed just under the surface of the water. Rumford found that the convection currents set up raised the temperature of the water below the heated ball to about 4°C but no higher. The result was similar to that of the independent experiments carried out by Hope. The account I give does less than justice to the care Rumford exercised in designing and conducting these experiments.[3]

One problem to which Rumford returned again and again was the thermal conductivity of liquids. When he had distinguished conduction from convection he concluded that water was a perfect nonconductor. This inference, based insecurely on experiment, was criticized by Dalton and other men of science. In 1805 Rumford reconsidered his statement which he admitted had been too hasty. He devised further elaborate experiments to detect thermal conductivity in liquids but still obtained negative results. He was, however, much more cautious this time in reaching a conclusion, carefully stating that his experiments did not prove that all direct communication of heat in a liquid 'from particle to particle, *de proche en proche*, is impossible'. This statement, negative as it was, shows a gain in his scientific thinking.

Thirty-three years later C. Despretz succeeded where Rumford failed, probably largely because he used a number of thermometers to measure the temperature along the slowly heated column of water.

Rumford had relied on one and that one at the greatest distance from the supply of heat.

The diffusion of liquids had been superficially investigated by Rumford and here too he had drawn hasty conclusions. In a new attempt he was more successful. He poured salt solution, which of course is denser than water, into a tall jar and added a layer of water. At the interface of the water and the solution there was a drop of oil of cloves to act as a 'sentinel' or index. He found that the index rose by about one-quarter of an inch each day for six days after which he put an end to the experiment. This showed that there was slow diffusion where the liquids met. He experimented with other solutions and speculated on the causes of diffusion. Does it, he asked, 'depend on a peculiar force of attraction different from the attraction of universal gravitation, a force which has been designated by the name of chemical affinity; or is it simply a result of the motions of liquids in contact caused by changes in their temperatures? Or is it, perhaps, the result of a peculiar and continual motion common to all liquids caused by the instability of the equilibrium existing among their molecules?'[4]

I will end this review of Rumford's researches with an account of his measurements of the heats of combustion of various substances.[5] The determination of calorific values was for him a major problem because it was so closely linked with the economical use of fuels. He attempted measurements over a period of twenty years before he published his results in 1812. They were not the first in the field but they were without doubt better than any previously made. This was mainly because he paid careful attention to the details of procedure. He arranged for the products of combustion of a known weight of fuel to pass into a flattened copper worm contained in a calorimeter of rectangular section, eight inches long, four inches wide and five inches high. The rise in temperature was observed, and to avoid a cooling correction the experiment started with the calorimeter at a few degrees below room temperature and finished a few degrees above.[6] His criteria for the completion of combustion were a clear flame, no smell and no residue. He devised lamps for burning alcohol and ether; when he used candles he saw to it that there was no smoke; with wood he used shavings of a given thickness.

In experiments with white wax he burned a weight of the order of two grammes and obtained a rise of temperature of his calorimeter of from 10° to 15°F. The consistency of his results was within one per cent. His value for wax, expressed in the modern way, was $1·71 \times 10^4$ B.Th.U. per lb; for olive oil, $1·69 \times 10^4$ B.Th.U. per lb.

He compared his results with those obtained by that 'excellent man' Lavoisier. He found wide differences, Lavoisier's being generally higher and less accurate. He also compared his values with those of A. Crawford who worked extensively in this field.

By no means all of Rumford's scientific work has been examined in these chapters. He also made experiments on surface tension, the rate of absorption of moisture by different kinds of clothing materials, and the chemical properties attributed to light. He measured specific heats and latent heats. He investigated the heat excited by the rays of the sun and the mode of formation of deep holes in the 'glaciers of Chamouny'. But I have discussed his major works and they were in bulk by far the greater part.

In assessing what he did it is worth repeating that Rumford learned a good deal of science as he went along, apart from the knowledge he gained immediately from his own discoveries. He was often hampered by a lack of background. This is particularly true of the experiments which impinge on molecular motion. It is certain that his ideas about the kinetic theory of matter developed with the years. It is a pity that he did not study the work of D. Bernoulli of Basle more fully, but others, as well as Rumford, failed to take the hint.

In a paper which described some of his experiments on surface tension he put forward the view that the phenomena suggested a kind of pellicle or skin on the surface of a liquid. This was not original and the fact was pointed out. Later when Laplace put before the *Institut* his theory of capillarity Rumford, a fellow member, attempted to reconcile, in principle, the new theory with his own ideas on adhesion and the pellicle. The incident illustrates not only Rumford's ignorance of the scientific work of others but also the fact that his knowledge of mathematics was elementary. Beside Laplace, Lagrange and other French mathematicians, he was a star of the seventh magnitude. He admitted that Laplace's methods were a little beyond him. This is an understatement for his own methods of calculation were arithmetical rather than algebraical; there is no evidence of his knowing calculus and he made no contribution to the theory of mathematics or to mathematical physics.

In case the reader is thinking 'What *do* you expect?', let me hasten to add that I make this estimate of Rumford as a mathematician mainly because one of Rumford's biographers, J. A. Thompson,[7] referred to him not very long ago as a brilliant mathematician. One can only conclude that the judgement was made on the strength of Rumford's having, as a boy, 'calculated an eclipse', which sounds very impressive.

Yet a lack of great mathematical ability was not crippling to a man of science. Faraday, two generations after Rumford, provides an outstanding example of a man of genius who thought in shape and made great contributions in his field, but left his successors to put his ideas in mathematical terms.

Scientifically, Rumford was more of an amateur than most men of science in an age of amateurs. Banks, Cavendish and Joule were men of substance who could devote all their time and energies to science; Pictet and Black held university appointments. But Rumford was for many years a paid employee, to an extent that has always been underestimated, of the Bavarian electors. Particularly in his days of young manhood (so important for scientific output), he was gripped by many aims which relegated science to a subsidiary place.

His papers give a clear impression of his ability to isolate a problem and design an experiment to solve it. In his most fruitful researches his experiments had a clear progression designed to meet objections and overcome difficulties. At all times his scientific skill was of a high order and his attention to detail exemplary. The virtues of his methods, however, were sometimes obscured by impatient and enthusiastic inferences, and by his posturing. He was not of the stature of Davy and Young. He lacked the imagination and the mathematical skill of the great theorists, and the compelling curiosity of the greatest experimenters. But though not in the first rank his work ensures him a place not far behind the great leaders.

15

Clouded Evening

Marriage with peace, is this world's paradise;
with strife, this life's purgatory.
ANON.
Not heav'n itself upon the past has pow'r;
But what has been has been, and I have had my hour.
DRYDEN

WHEN Rumford married Mme Lavoisier she insisted on
retaining the name Lavoisier and was known as Mme
Lavoisier de Rumford. It was a sign that she also intended
to retain her personality and way of life. She had agreed to marry
after a long courtship which Rumford conducted with persistence. The
preliminaries were carefully settled. He closed his house in Munich,
wound up his affairs and brought his servant Aichner to Paris. Aichner
had his wife and four of their six children with him, the two oldest
boys being in the Bavarian army. The Aichner family acted as
Rumford's servants; Mme de Rumford had her own.

After two months of married life he wrote to his daughter Sally,
who wanted to join him in Paris, to say that although he wanted her
with him she must wait patiently, as he and his wife were to start in
the spring of 1806 on a long tour of Italy and the South of France.
His style of living was 'magnificent'. Madame was exceedingly fond
of company and was herself a splendid figure in company. Her house
was open to 'all the great and worthy, such as the philosophers, members of the *Institut*, ladies of celebrity, &c'. On Mondays they received
to dinner eight or ten of the most noted of their associates—and 'lived
on bits for the rest of the week'. On Thursdays they entertained after

246

dinner, regardless of numbers, serving tea and fruit till midnight or later.

This entertaining was irksome to Rumford who was better as a diner out than a host. He had never given dinner parties at Brompton Row. Moreover he liked to be the centre of attraction, and in this establishment he took second place and was quipped by the guests. His tendency to pontificate and even his store of experience made him vulnerable to the quick sallies of the brilliant company they entertained. It was not long before he questioned the wisdom of marrying. After three months of married life he told Sally of his doubts. Already he had had to send the Aichner family home except for one girl, Mary Sarah, whom Mme de Rumford had taken a fancy to. Because of his gastritis he had to live on a spare and carefully chosen diet which set him apart at the Monday dinners.

It is probable, too, that he found himself out of sympathy with the *weltanschauung* of Laplace, Lagrange and others. They had a mathematical and mechanistic approach to science which was very different from Rumford's. As we have seen he usually started with a simple, concrete problem and attempted to solve it by a sequence of well-designed experiments. Often, having come upon a principle, law, or example of unusual behaviour in the physical world, he would search for its wider applications or its climatic and geographical significance and then admire the intelligence of the deity in so ordaining events—and as likely as not his own in disclosing them. The French mathematicians, on the other hand, took the individual discoveries which had been made and developed mathematical equations of great power and generality to cover them. It is arguable that disagreement between Rumford and some members of his wife's circle may have helped to give rise to his repeated statement that he was the victim of persecution by French *savants*.

Rumford adopted the curious practice of writing to Sally on the anniversaries of his wedding day to say how unhappy he was. By 1806 he had come to see that there was deep incompatibility between himself and his wife. They were both set in their ways, both having enjoyed freedom and independence for many years. He had seen that his wife would not change and he had no intention of doing so himself. Even if they had been able to make the proposed tour of Italy, which renewed war had prevented, it would only, he felt, have delayed difficulties; a cure was impossible.

He was very unhappy at this time. Added to his marital dis-appointment was uncertainty over the continuation of his allowance from Bavaria and his isolation from England. He had decided on a separation from his wife but the following October he was still in the Rue d'Anjou. He wrote to Sally on the twenty-fourth of the month,[1] saying that 'things were becoming worse every day'. The quarrels were more violent and open. They were in fact both behaving like children. Wishing to confide in someone he recounted the details of the latest squabble. His wife had arranged one of her dinner parties and had included guests of whom he disapproved—to spite him, he thought. He determined to take firm action, went to the porter's lodge, gave orders that no one was to be admitted, locked the gates and took possession of the keys. When the guests arrived and were unable to enter, their hostess was obliged to talk to them over the garden wall, giving her apologies and explaining the situation as best she could. Her husband's action made her so angry that she poured boiling water on some of his prize blooms.

Six months later his language was violent. For a long time he had thought of her as a female dragon, and now he had 'the misfortune to be married to one of the most imperious, tyrannical, unfeeling women that ever existed, and whose perseverance in pursuing an object was equal to her profound cunning and wickedness in fram-ing it'.

His delay in separating from his wife was due to his determination to have his rights as well as his freedom. They could not agree on the financial arrangements. The house was the difficulty. Mme de Rumford had provided the greater share of the purchase price but he had spent 'an immensity of money in repairs and maintenance'.

The unhappy haggling, the nagging and the tribulation went on until June 1809. For a long time he lived a separate life in the house, taking his meals alone unless he had the company of Aichner's daughter. He told Sally that he had shown unexampled patience in waiting so long for a return to reason on the part of his wife but she had met him with 'implacable hatred and malice'. The worry and anxiety brought on illness, and for three months before he left his wife he was confined to his bed. At length it was decided that their affairs should be put to arbitration and chosen friends acted as judges. When they separated Rumford kept most of the money settled on him in return for what he had spent on the improvement of their joint property. His wife kept the house.

The Count moved to a pleasant and imposing house at Auteuil a few miles away, a house whose lease he had acquired some months before. He began to recover his health and spirits and to realize as never before 'the sweets of quiet, liberty and independence'. But his unhappy experiences and his dependence upon a pension that was never quite safe had affected and continued to affect his outlook. He withdrew from society and sought seclusion in his new house, relying for comradeship on a few close friends. He was now anxious for Sally to join him as soon as she could.

The separation though formal was outwardly friendly. Mme de Rumford occasionally visited her husband and behaved well towards Sally who thought her 'in every respect a very superior person'. For twenty-seven years longer she maintained her way of life. Her programme of entertaining was dinner for the distinguished on Mondays, at home to all on Tuesdays, musical concerts or large assemblies on Fridays. We have a glimpse of her unfailing zest in a letter written by the Hon. W. H. Lyttelton to Sarah, Lady Lyttelton, dated from Paris, 26 November 1817:

'Last night I was introduced by Lord [Lansdowne] at Countess Rumford's and we passed a good hour and a half there with a dozen other people. The evening went off pleasantly enough and finished with ice and cakes and tea made in the room with a great monster of an urn by Mme la Comtesse herself. She talked a great deal to me and concluded by asking me to dine with her on Monday and to come to another soirée on Friday both of which summons I shall duly attend to. To quiet your apprehensions I will just add that Mme de Rumford is like Sydney Smith, French Simpson and Lady de Grey.'[2]

The French writer Guizot wrote elegantly and appreciatively of Mme de Rumford and her salons. He spoke of the range and distinction of those who visited her because of the attraction of good company, polite behaviour and amusing conversation. At her house opponents forgot their differences and men of different races their nationality, the old found common ground with the young, and the man of action shared his experiences with the philosopher. It was not a house for the display of patronage, the award of honours or the scheming of politicians but one where easy fellowship could be found and opinions frankly expressed.

The Comtesse de Bassanville also wrote sympathetically about Rumford's second wife, saying that she was gracious to all and the most amiable woman in the world.[3] She was biting in her description of Rumford the 'theoretical liberal' who was 'in practice a domestic tyrant'.

Sally tried to be fair to both and saw clearly how her father's desires and interests clashed with those of his wife. He wanted quiet, she loved company; he resented spending money on entertainments and wanted to see *improvements* for his expenditure. Moreover he would go on and on talking, so that his wife was forced to say kindly 'My Rumford would make me happy could he but keep quiet.'

When two intelligent and strong-minded people disagree violently over trifles, or fail to compromise and adapt their habits and ways of living to each other's needs or desires, it is probable that deeply rooted sentiments are in opposition. It was so with Rumford and his wife. Almost certainly her salons were to her more than social occasions. Through them she was keeping alive the world of her youth, the secure world that had vanished, and also the memories of her father and her husband. She reproduced in her own home something of *la douceur de la vie* (in Talleyrand's phrase) of the days before the Revolution as a girl in her father's house. When she clung to the name Lavoisier she was clinging to the deep attachment she had to her first husband in the early days of her married life.

It was therefore not a superficial obstacle that Rumford broke his foot against; only a small part of it, so to speak, appeared above ground, the rest had become deeply buried over the years. If he had been a man of humble spirit and quiet mind all might have been well. But he was not. He had to be 'the hero of his own panegyric' and so his conversation was about himself, his knowledge and his experiences. While the rest of the party were enjoying their food he, having barely touched his plate, discoursed on the virtues of the potato or the bread-fruit. His disquisitions led his wife, even in the early days, to remark kindly but *sotto voce* to her companions at table that he was 'a veritable sample-card'. He was not likely to be accorded in the salon, except perhaps out of polite condescension, the dutiful respect given to a form master in the schoolroom or the deference to which he had become accustomed in Bavaria. Moreover, Anne Lavoisier was very different in intellectual background and attainment from both Mary Palmerston and Mary Nogarola and met him on level terms.

We can imagine that after a dinner party he would retire uneasy and hurt, feeling that far from having carried the day he had been belittled. He would surely decide to assert himself and be master in his own house (for as his treatment of Sally had shown he must dominate) only to be met by his wife's mild but unshakable determination to retain her habits and run her salons in her own way.

He did not recognize how self-centred he was. His letters continually revealed the extent of this failing. They abound with such phrases as 'I am not vain, my dear Sally, but . . .', 'I mention this circumstance to show your Lordship that I am treated with *marked* attention and civility. . . .' He could even squeeze a little 'self-gratulation' out of his quarrel with his wife by using it as a warning to his 'good child'. For a long time his desire to have his own way in personal matters was unconsciously justified by the success of his public schemes. When success forsook him and he began to lose dominance he had to admit failure. He turned in on himself and sought relief in seclusion.

But not all the blame for the failure of the marriage should be laid to the charge of the two most concerned. It is not unlikely that by suggestion and assertion some of Mme de Rumford's relatives attempted to influence her against the Count. Her fortune, reputed to be three million francs, was not a negligible factor in the quarrel and reserving it for her own family was the aim of more than one of those who surrounded her. Rumford's wife, however, was too strong a character to be greatly influenced by those whose motives were suspect.

It had promised to be such a 'fine match', as Sally said, and 'although the first flush of youth was past' it was looked upon by both friend and foe 'as decidedly a love match'. Sally was proud of the fact that her father was 'very playful in his character, even lovely at times, and much handsomer for a man than she was for a woman and certainly quite as much a celebrity in the world'.

When the separation took place Rumford had been seven years in France and only half the time a married man, so that his conjugal misery must not blind us to the scientific fruitfulness of the seven years. Nearly twenty papers of his were read either before the Royal Society or the *Institut*, and more essays were published in France and

Germany. His travels in Switzerland with Anne Lavoisier gave rise to the paper *An Account of a Curious Phenomenon observed on the Glaciers of Chamouny*, and one is reminded that Joule, when he visited the same country for his honeymoon, took a thermometer with him to measure the difference of temperature at the top and the bottom of waterfalls.

As early as 1801 Rumford was elected a member of the *Institut* in the Second Class, having been proposed by the Section of Political Economy in recognition of his work as a philanthropist. Two years later he was moved to the First Class, which was a recognition of, and more in keeping with, his outstanding contributions to physics. It is a measure of his ability and fame that he received this honour earlier than his renowned contemporary, Volta.

The King of Bavaria was in Paris in 1810 and he invited Rumford to spend some months in Munich. Rumford accepted the invitation, and after the trials of his years of married life the visit gave him great pleasure. He was kindly received by the people and he had a letter from Maximilian's son, the Prince Royal, then holding Court at Salzburg, signed *Votre devoué, Louis*. He wrote to Sally: 'It is flattering to me to have acquired the confidence of the Princes of Bavaria to the third generation.' The English Garden was beautiful, no expense was spared on it. He dined with the King 'pretty much as often' as he wished. He was called on for advice in forming the long delayed Academy of Arts and Sciences and he planned an extended tour in search of a fine climate before returning to Paris. But there was sadness too. The Countess of Nogarola was dead and her more beautiful but less worthy sister, the mother of Sally's illegitimate half-sister, was very ill. His aides-de-camp had all died on military service.

He returned to Auteuil and laid out his new garden. Although he knew little about flowers he was extremely fond of them (see Plate 10, facing page 193) and employed two gardeners. He returned to his scientific experiments, writing essays and playing billiards. Some time previously he had made arrangements for his daughter to join him. He had wanted to receive her in England but war prevented this. His letters to her showed a return of warmth during his attack of self-pity, but he said she would have to quit the world if she came. He had written: 'Will you, my dear, quit it with me if you come? I cannot retire publicly, and cannot stay.'[4] When he wrote that he was almost beside himself; on top of his other worries his pension from Bavaria and his half pay from England had been temporarily cut off. After his visit to Bavaria he was calmer though he still looked back with horror on the 'purgatory' he had endured in the Rue d'Anjou.

For her part Sally was glad to be able to join her father in Europe; for years she had wished to escape from her aimless life. Her friend and protector Colonel Loammi Baldwin had died in 1807. The Rumfords owed much to this noble and generous man. He had never wavered in his friendship and in a busy and successful life as a civil engineer he always found time to watch the interests of Sally and her father and to act as their agent in financial affairs. Loammi's son James took over the responsibility when his father died and acted as Sally's adviser and later as her executor.

She joined her father in Paris in December 1811, after an exciting journey from America. She had sailed from New York on 24 July in the *Drummond*, which had been captured off Bordeaux by a British ship, on suspicion of its running the blockade, and taken to Plymouth. Sally unexpectedly finding herself in England sought the help of her old friend, Sir Charles Blagden. He was too ill to visit her but he gave her sound advice on how to conduct herself and with whom to associate. She needed a steadying influence and made the most of her enforced stay, only chafing at the delay while her ship waited at Plymouth for a favourable wind.

At Auteuil she found her father much changed but proud of his garden, his singing birds and his fiery horses. Before many days had passed Rumford's 'separated lady' paid them the first of several visits and charmed Sally by her graciousness. She also found her father regarded as an oddity by the people of Paris. How could he be thought normal—an American by birth, a British subject, a Bavarian pensioner separated from his wife, a man who rode in a carriage with very wide wheel-rims and, in winter, dressed in white from head to foot in order (on strictly scientific principles) to keep warm? Then there were his aloofness, the jokes about his soups, his lamps and his unusual diet.

Rumford was not entirely friendless however. There was an internee named Underwood who helped him with his experiments. This was the same man, now a great friend of Sir Humphry Davy, who had first recommended Davy as a likely candidate for a post as assistant lecturer at the Royal Institution. There were also Daniel Parker, a rich, cultured, hospitable American who had made Paris his home; Baron Delessert, Rumford's banker; and M. Leconteux Caneleux, a neighbour.

This was his circle of friends during the last three or four years of his life. Yet it is not quite complete. There was in the house, or perhaps established in the porter's lodge, a woman who, as Ellis delicately says, 'was not a servant, but who seemed to take charge of the flowers, the illuminations and the singing birds of the drawing-room'. In short, she was Rumford's mistress. It is not necessary to describe Sally's relationship with this person, or even to dwell upon her presence, though it must be recorded that in Rumford's house in the year of his death a male child was born 'who became a man of great excellence of character, and as an officer of the French army was killed at Sebastopol. To a son of this officer . . . the Countess left in her will a large legacy.'[5]

Towards the end of his life Rumford no longer attended meetings of the *Institut* and his presence is not recorded there even on the very special occasions of Davy's visits in 1813. There is a strange but interesting passage in the obituary notice in the *Gentleman's Magazine*, which is almost certainly from Underwood's pen and reads:

'The Count met with considerable plague in his pursuits from the malignant disposition and jealousies of his fellow-members of the National Institute in consequence of his having differed in opinion on capillary attraction from their despotic leader, Laplace. He often used to exclaim that no one who had not lived a considerable time in France could imagine how contemptible a nation they were and how void of honour and even honesty. Whenever he ordered any instrument at a mathematical instrument maker's, a similar one was instantly made for someone of the Great Nation, though of the intended use they were at the moment ignorant; but the hope of supplanting a foreigner and of arrogating to themselves a discovery (a common practice with them) incited them to adopt this dishonourable practice. I was one day with the Count at a sitting of the first class of the Institute when we heard one of the leading members declare that they would set their faces against any discovery which did not originate among themselves.'

There is no doubt at all that national feelings entered into scientific discussions at the *Institut* though what is remarkable to us who have experienced total war is the freedom allowed at that time to English men of science in France, a country deeply involved in war. The year was 1813, and although the battle for France was upon him, Napoleon issued a passport to Sir Humphry and Lady Davy, to Lady Davy's maid and to Michael Faraday to visit France to study volcanoes. They were allowed to pass through Paris and meet men of science. Davy was not even tactful on his visit. There was a play at the Théâtre de la Porte Saint Martin which was, as we should now say, a piece of anti-British propaganda in that it represented Lord Cornwallis as the assassin of the children of Tippoo Sahib. Davy went to see the play, was very angry and, according to his biographer, 'quitted the theatre in a state of great indignation'.[6]

The French men of science could acknowledge the supranationality of science at some personal risk; this was shown by their omitting the toast of the Emperor at the anniversary dinner of the Societé Philomatique when toasts were drunk to the Royal Society and to the *Institut*, the last on Davy's proposal.

But it is true that nationalism impinged on science in France at the time. I have already mentioned Napoleon's interest in the *Institut*, and in the discoveries published there. Once, on hearing of the decomposition of the alkalies, he asked impetuously why these discoveries had not been made in France. He was told that no battery of sufficient power had been constructed. 'Then', he exclaimed, 'let one be instantly formed without any regard to cost or labour.'[7] Both on general grounds and as a result of Napoleon's lead it is not surprising that some members of the *Institut*, including Laplace, allowed their patriotic fervour to enter their scientific discourses and warp their judgement of the priority of discovery. But what Underwood meant by the phrase 'set their faces against' is not clear. It could not imply a refusal to take note of other discoveries because that would argue a degree of blind foolishness greater than could be attributed to the *Institut*, or even to its more partisan members. It could conceivably imply a tendency to repeat seminal experiments which had been made elsewhere and then to claim them for France, but this again is unlikely, at any rate as any sort of policy. It is more likely that Underwood's inferences from what he heard were coloured, and understandably so, by his own position as an internee and by his patriotism.

But the passage on which these comments are made illustrates yet again Rumford's invective in referring to the French. He seldom spoke publicly in violent terms and because of this Ellis refers to his dignified restraint when opposed, but in his letters and his conversation he was often harshly outspoken in his condemnation. In his last years his vituperation was unabated: he could speak of his second wife as a 'tyrannical, avaricious, unfeeling woman'. The contrast between his public restraint and his private condemnation is indeed aptly shown in the very matter that Underwood refers to, namely, the supposed difference between the ideas of Rumford and Laplace in explaining the surface tension of liquids. Rumford, as a result of reflection on his experimental results, spoke of the *adhesion* of the molecules of a liquid to each other and of the existence of a *pellicle* at the surface of a liquid. Laplace began with the assumption that the molecules of a liquid attract each other with a force that is intense when they are close together but which rapidly falls off with increasing separation. Laplace's calculations suggest a *cohesive* force among the molecules of a liquid and lead to the idea that the surface of a liquid behaves *as if* it possessed a thin skin or membrane. Thus there was not much essential difference between their ideas, though they were developed from very different starting points and by different methods.

In view of the implication in Underwood's article that it was Rumford's opinion that Laplace was a despotic leader who, through jealousy, prevailed upon his followers to vex and annoy him it is instructive to re-read Rumford's words in the original paper:

'I must, however, confess that I am not sufficiently well versed in the higher geometry to understand fully the calculations of M. La Place on this subject . . . but I have such a high opinion of the talents of this man, learned and worthy of esteem both as a geometrician and as a natural-philosopher that I am always inclined to receive his opinions in matters of science (as well as on every other subject) with the greatest deference.'[8]

Towards the end of his life in addition to his scientific work on the calorific values of fuels and related topics he wrote about lamps and coffee. An essay on *Shoes*, which was planned much earlier, was not published although it may have been finished, and what he regarded as his greatest work was certainly unfinished. This was an essay entitled *On the Nature and Effects of Order*. We can only guess the nature of this essay since the manuscript was almost certainly destroyed by his daughter with many of his letters. It is certain, however, that the topic is one which attracted Rumford throughout his life, for the concept of order was fundamental to his being and philosophy.

He was much alone in his last year. Sally was travelling in Switzerland, apparently sent away because of the approaching birth of an illegitimate child to Rumford's housekeeper. But when Davy was in Paris on the extraordinary visit already mentioned he found time, along with Underwood, to dine with Rumford at Auteuil. After dinner they inspected the laboratory. Here was Davy at the height of his fame, a man of the highest ability and international renown with, in the words of Davy's biographer, 'the poor broken-hearted Count'. What a reversal in thirteen years from the time when Davy, the uncouth lad from the west country, had been given his chance by Rumford to embark on the career at the Royal Institution which had taken him to the very summit of his profession.

Soon afterwards Rumford died suddenly. His health had seemed good and he had been actively supervising some additions to his buildings, but he was taken ill and died 'of a nervous fever' within a few hours. He died on 21 August 1814, and was buried at Auteuil three days later. Even his few close friends were taken by surprise and there was not enough time to recall Sally from Le Havre where she was staying with friends.

It was an insignificant death and funeral for so famous a man. It happened so quickly that Sally thought for a few days that the Count had played a macabre joke on his acquaintances by disappearing and leaving a corpse in his bed to be buried in his name. But this was based only on idle gossip set going by the woman in the lodge.

He bequeathed his plain gold watch to Davy, his 'gold enamelled watch with the gold chain and the seals attached', and his gold-headed cane to Daniel Parker, one of his executors. To his other executor, Benjamin, Baron Delessert, he left his 'gold enamelled snuff box set round with diamonds; being the same which was given me by His Majesty Francis II, Emperor of Austria'.

To Sally who was already comfortably provided for he left a further annuity of four hundred dollars with other funds in trust in case she lost her pension from Bavaria.

Harvard College was, however, the principal beneficiary under the terms of his will. It received an annuity of one thousand dollars with the reversion of Sally's annuity and the reversion of the major part of his estate. The executors acted quickly and as a result Harvard established the Rumford professorship just over two years after the publication of the will. The terms of the bequest were in keeping with his lifelong aims in science:

'. . . to teach by regular courses of academical and public Lectures, accompanied with proper experiments, the utility of the physical and mathematical sciences for the improvement of the useful arts, and for the extension of the industry, prosperity, happiness, and well being of Society.'

Many judgements have been passed upon the Count and his work. During his life and for some time after his death he was most renowned for his philanthropy. In 1835 the Reverend Timothy Flint wrote in the *London Athenaeum*:[9]

'It is as unnecessary to enter into details of his attainments and discoveries as of Franklin's. Everyone knows that he was the philosopher of the poor, and that his philosophical experiments upon the economy of food and fuel would alone have rendered his name immortal.'

It is no cliché to say that his name before and after he died was a household word. His fire-grates, lamps, soups and coffee-pots ensured this. But fashions change and the household words of one generation are the rarities of the next.

His reputation as a man of science has grown though it has never been as high as it deserves. Because he initiated little and brought still less to completion his ability as an experimenter was obscured. He seldom stood on the shoulders of others even when it was possible, thus finding not infrequently that he had climbed where others had already made footholds. But it is in the fields of scientific education and technology that his work and ideas have been least recognized. His aims were frustrated and often forgotten, and later developments in technological and technical education in England arose from other sources. In America it is true there was more continuity and it was highly appropriate that the first Rumford professor at Harvard gave the opening address at the inauguration of the Massachusetts Institute of Technology. Rumford stands in much the same relation to the technological revolution as Wycliffe did to the Reformation.

As a man he has been variously assessed. Many have judged his character from the results of his work. This is a great mistake. Others have taken his letters as representing his true sentiments and have glossed over the inconsistencies. In recent times, since the discovery of the famous 'spy' letter among the Germain papers, one or two writers have been led by his equivocation and dissimulation into sweeping and facile condemnation.

Ellis was a gentlemanly and charitable biographer who tried to overlook or explain away his subject's faults without always succeeding. His portrait therefore seems sometimes almost perversely inconsistent and diffuse. Young spoke of Rumford's mild manner and tone of voice, yet Cuvier complained of the lack of amenity in his manners. Hale said he 'always had a kick for the underdog', and J. A. Thompson that he was 'unbelievably cold-blooded, inherently egotistic and a snob'. The loyal Renwick, angered by Cuvier's disparagement, was ready with a delicious explanation—not having heard of Rumford's illegitimate children—'It is possible and even probable', he says, 'that he may have rebuked the principles of infidelity, then so prevalent in France, with a sternness worthy of his pilgrim ancestors.'

The two essential clues to his character are his passion for order and his egotism. The first inspired much of his work; it was also influential in his daily life and the treatment of his servants. The second was more important, and a dominating influence throughout his life.

Looking down, he could be pleasant, playful and even generous, for instance with his subordinates and servants, and with his daughter. But he had to order their affairs and act as a minor deity dispensing favours. This gave him great satisfaction and a sense of power, and in such circumstances he was benignity itself. But if he were thwarted, the source of his benevolence was revealed as unmitigated self-esteem. These qualities made it difficult for him to work with equals. He was incapable of friendly give and take with them in conducting the ordinary affairs of life. He was driven always to establish some form of ascendancy either of rank, power, experience or intellect. Some of the friction at the Royal Institution, as well as his troubles with Anne Lavoisier, was the result of this. And so at the end he was suspicious and unhappy and unable to enjoy in retrospect his very great achievements, nor did he have the serenity of mind for calm enjoyment of his material possessions and his friends.

A treatise might be written on the funerals of great men. Sheridan's funeral was magnificent; Banks was buried, as he wished, in the parish where he died; Sackville was laid to rest in the family vault surrounded by his sorrowing tenants. Rumford would surely have wanted a ceremony on the grand scale, an international gathering attended, perhaps, by suitably dressed children from Houses of Industry in Munich and London, by representative paupers from Geneva and Paris, and the American Ambassador in London. He would undoubtedly have liked Davy, Laplace, Pictet and Banks (gout permitting) to act as pall-bearers, with the Kings of Bavaria, Sweden and Prussia as well as the Emperor Napoleon walking gravely in procession to see his coffin placed in an imposing mausoleum. But no! he was buried privately and hastily in an insignificant grave in a little suburban cemetery, and not even wife and daughter were present.

References and Notes

CHAPTER I

1. M. A. Pictet of Geneva, who wrote extensively of Rumford in the *Bibliothèque Britannique, Science et Arts* (Geneva, 1801 and after).

Many letters written by Rumford to M. A. Pictet are now in the possession of M. A. Rilliet of Geneva, a descendant of Pictet's.

2. Baron Cuvier in *Recueil des Éloges Historiques*, Tome Deuxième (Paris, 1861).

3. *The Autobiography of Benjamin Franklin* (Everyman Edition, 1937), p. 11.

4. Ibid., p. 236.

5. Carl Becker gives an urbane and illuminating account of the events leading to the American Revolution in *The Eve of the Revolution* (Newhaven, 1918).

6. *Complete Works*, Vol. III, p. 188.

7. Ellis, *Memoir of Sir Benjamin Thompson, Count Rumford* (Boston, 1870, and London, 1876).

8. I am indebted to Professor Sanborn Brown, of the Massachusetts Institute of Technology, for a copy of the authorization certificate given over the signature of John Wentworth, Captain-General, Governor and Commander-in-Chief in and over His Majesty's Province of New Hampshire, etc.

9. *Chalmers's Biographical Dictionary*, XXIX, p. 298. The account is based on Pictet's Memoir; given in *The Gentleman's Magazine*, LXXXIV.

CHAPTER 2

1. For an inspired treatment of these events see Becker, loc. cit., Ch. V.

2. *Benjamin Thompson, Graf von Rumford* (München, 1915), p. 6.

Thompson's statement of his position is quoted by K. Th. von Heigel in the address he delivered to mark the centenary of Rumford's death. The relevant passage is taken by von Heigel from Rumford's *Memorandum on the Alleged High Treason of the Munich Town Council*. In translation it reads:

'From principle I supported the King because I considered this to be the lawful attitude. I recognized these principles with the sword. I recognized these principles and I have never denied them. My reason has led me to come down on the side of a limited monarchy equally far removed from an Asiatic despotism and a dictatorship of the people.'

3. *Calendar of Home Office Papers of the Reign of George III*, H.M.S.O. (1899), No. 1020.

4. Ibid., No. 735. Letter from Admiral Graves.

5. Ibid., No. 735.

6. Ibid., No. 1037. Letter from H. Finlay, off Sandy Hook on board the *King Fisher*, to his brother.

7. I am greatly indebted to the William L. Clements Library for copies of these letters.

8. The minute men were organized groups ready to go into action at a minute's notice.

9. French, *General Gage's Informers* (Ann Arbor, 1932). The Lexington expedition is thoroughly described in this scholarly and interesting book.

10. Brown and Stein, *American Journal of Police Science*, Vol. 40, No. 5, p. 627.

11. Thompson varied his handwriting. For formal documents, for certain letters and at least one scientific paper he used a regular round hand with flourishes. Elsewhere his chirography, though clear, is less stylized and regular. To vary his hand would present no difficulty to him as he was a skilled engraver. It is possible to see his formal style in his later handwriting, e.g. in some letters written to his publishers, now preserved in the British Museum.

12. *Memoir*, p. 83.

13. The reference is to the story in Joshua vii. Achan, at the destruction of Jericho, concealed part of the spoil. For this crime he and his family were driven from the city and stoned to death.

14. I Kings iv, 25.

15. *Miscellanius Observations upon the state of the Rebel Army*. This is reproduced as an Appendix. See p. 277.

16. French, op. cit., Ch. V, et seq.

CHAPTER 3

1. General Clinton, who was present, wrote: 'A few more such victories would have shortly put an end to British dominion in America.' Clinton, *The American Rebellion* (New Haven, 1954).

2. *A Short Account of the King's American Dragoons, with authentic copies of all the Papers relative to the raising of that Regiment*. In the Public Record Office, Ref. HO 42/2.

3. Ibid.

4. Francis Bickley (ed.), *The Diaries of Sylvester Douglas (Lord Glenbervie)* (London, 1928), Vol. 1. Entry of 6 September 1801. A further accusation of paederasty is to be found in *the Diary and Letters of Thomas Hutchinson* (Boston, 1883 and 1886), Vol. II, p. 289. Entry of 18 October 1779.

5. *Complete Works*, Vol. II, p. 1.

6. Ibid., Vol. II, p. 111.

7. Thompson's letters from the *Victory* are reproduced in *The Naval Miscellany*, Vol. III, ed. W. G. Perrin. The ship's log-books for the period are in the Public Record Office. Thompson's own log is in the William L. Clements Library, University of Michigan.

8. *Royal Institution (Amer.) MSS.*, Vol. II, p. 297.

9. *Memoirs of Richard Cumberland* (London, 1807), Vol. II, p. 174.

10. For example, Curwen's friend S. H. Sparhawk had been given an equal allowance and gratuity. 'Let Mr. Rowe pay him £100 and also an Allowance of £100 a year from 5 Jany 1777'. Entry in *Treasury Minutes* P.R.O. T.79,97A.

11. P. O. Hutchinson (comp.), *The Diary and Letters of Thomas Hutchinson* (Boston, 1883 and 1886), Vol. 2, p. 337. Copies of the correspondence are to be found in the William L. Clements Library and in the British Museum. The original letters are also in the British Museum.

12. *The Annual Register* 1781, p. 239.

13. Termed Governor Johnstone's Squadron. Johnstone was a former governor of West Florida. He was one of the King's Commissioners appointed to negotiate with Congress. Earlier he had fought a harmless duel with Lord George Germain. See Marlow, *Sackville of Drayton* (London, 1948).

14. G. A. Ward (ed.), *Journal and Letters of Samuel Curwen* (London, 1844), p. 320.

15. Sanborn Brown and Kenneth Scott, 'Count Rumford: International Informer', *The New England Quarterly*, Vol. XXI, I, p. 1.

16. W. J. Sparrow, 'Count Rumford as a Spy', *Annals of Science*, Vol. II, 4, p. 325.

17. Quoted with permission from a letter in the William L. Clements Library.

CHAPTER 4

1. Richard Cumberland, writing to Germain, 'begs to be remembered to Mr Thompson, now in execution of Mr De Grey's place, and to congratulate him'. He had had 'the distant expectation that Lord North would have found a seat for him'. *Stopford-Sackville MSS*, Vol. I, 1904 (13 December 1780).

2. *A Short Account of the King's American Dragoons, with authentic copies of all the Papers relative to the raising of that Regiment.* P.R.O.: Ref. HO 42/2. The document was probably written in June 1783.

3. *Hist. MSS Comm., Royal Institution MSS,* Vol. II, p. 248.

4. Wraxall, *Historical Memoirs of my own Time* (London, 1815), Vol. II, p. 102.

5. Ibid., p. 108.

6. Major-General the Hon. Alexander Leslie was a son of the Earl of Leven and Melville.

7. From an unpublished letter written on 24 January 1782. In this chapter I have drawn upon the letters to Germain which are in the William L. Clements Library and for the help I acknowledge my indebtedness. Extracts from many letters are in the *Stopford-Sackville MSS.*

8. John Murray, fourth Earl of Dunmore, Governor of Virginia.

9. He was succeeded on 8 May 1782 by Sir Guy Carleton.

10. *R. I. Amer. MSS.,* Vol. II, p. 335.

11. *Stopford-Sackville MSS.,* Vol. II, p. 253.

12. Ellis, *Memoir,* p. 137.

13. Lieutenant-General James Robertson, one of the senior generals in America and a member of the 'Council of War'.

14. George M. Wrong, *Washington and his Comrades in Arms* (Yale, 1921).

15. *Journals of the House of Commons,* for 30 June 1783. 'Granted £15,000, Half-pay to certain Provincial Corps who served with His Majesty's Troops during the late war in America.'

16. Public Records Office, Ref. *H.O.* 42/2.

17. Ibid.

18. Sir John Fortescue (ed.), *The Correspondence of King George III* (London, 1928), Nos. 4411, 4412, pp. 414, 415.

CHAPTER 5

1. Letter to Sir Robert Murray Keith dated 6 February 1784. *B. M. Add. MSS.* 35530, *Hardwicke Papers.*

2. *B. M. Add. MSS.* 35530.

3. *The Autobiography and Correspondence of Edward Gibbon* (London, 1869).

4. J. Renwick, 'The Life of Count Rumford', *The Library of American Biography* (Boston, 1845), Vol. XV, p. 63.

5. *Memoir,* p. 160.

6. *Memoirs of Richard Cumberland* (London, 1807), Vol. I, p. 223.

7. Letter from Thompson to Keith, 20 December 1783.

8. Brown and Scott, *New England Quarterly*, Vol. XXI, p. 12.

9. It is just possible that this letter did give, in an apparently innocuous form, some of the information Keith wanted, namely that the visit was to take place. If so, and it was Thompson's intention that it should, then the rest of the letter was a sickly smokescreen. On the whole, judging from the style, the construction put on the letter in the text is the more likely one.

10. E.g. Walpole to Keith 18 January 1785: 'I believe the Comte de Seffeld will be very soon appointed President des Finances by the influence of his daughter in law, who is now the reigning favourite of the Elector.' *B. M. Add. MSS.* 35530, *Hardwicke Papers.*

11. Walpole to Keith, 4 November 1784 and 7 July 1784, loc. cit.

12. Quotations taken, with permission, from a letter in the Archives of the Royal Society. The Elector was duly admitted and his health drunk at a Royal Society banquet.

13. Quoted with permission from a copy on microfilm of the original letter which is in the William L. Clements Library.

14. See the article on Count Rumford by von Bauernfeind in *Deutsche Allgemeine Biographie*, Vol. 29, p. 643, et seq. Also von Heigel *Benjamin Thompson, Graf von Rumford* (München, 1915). Rumford was himself a Freemason but what influence his membership had upon his conduct has not been determined. Many of his political and diplomatic activities remain undisclosed.

15. von Heigel, op. cit., p. 22. I acknowledge with thanks the help I have received from this address.

16. See, e.g., Anne Cary Morris (ed.), *The Diary and Letters of Gouverneur Morris* (London, 1889), Vol. II. Gouverneur Morris (1752–1816) of Philadelphia was a member of the second American Congress. He helped to write the American Constitution and later succeeded Franklin as American Minister in Paris.

17. Op. cit.

18. *Complete Works*, Vol. V, p. 502.

19. I am greatly indebted to the Master of the Birmingham Assay Office for allowing me access to the letters and for permission to use them. Reichenbach, whilst at the Soho works, secretly sketched Watt's double-acting steam engine and later wrote an account of his visit. See *A History of Western Technology* (London, 1959). Dr Friedrich Klemm, the author of this fine work, is Librarian at the Deutsches Museum at Munich.

20. Brian Connell, *Portrait of a Whig Peer* (London, 1957), p. 286.

21. *Complete Works*, Vol. IV, p. 126, and Vol. V, p. 325.

22. Brian Connell, ibid., p. 297.

23. Ibid., p. 328.

24. *Complete Works*, Vol. II, p. 132.

25. Ibid., Vol. IV, p. 64.

26. Sanborn Brown and Kenneth Scott, *New England Quarterly*, XXI, No. 1, pp. 15, 16.

27. *Memoir*, p. 209.

28. Ibid., p. 228.

29. Brian Connell, ibid., p. 341.

30. C. T. Atkinson, *A History of Germany, 1715–1815* (London, 1908), p. 406.

31. In saying that he *asked* to be appointed ambassador I am accepting the authority of K. Th. von Heigel.

32. Brian Connell, ibid., p. 400. But this was not quite true.

33. The objections raised to Rumford's appointment may be taken at their face value though added to them there may have been some personal dislike on the part of the King. Rumford seems never to have been received at Court unless it was to deliver his credentials and a private letter.

A similar case arose soon afterwards. General Acton, after serving as Prime Minister of Naples, planned to retire to this country. In a letter to Lord Grenville, Arthur Paget wrote from Palermo on 13 May 1800:

'I have heard a good deal lately about General Acton's retiring to England . . . I should be disposed to do anything in my power to prevail upon him to remain here . . . as there appears to me to be a great deal of analogy between General Acton's and Count Rumford's situations. I should feel it my duty not to let the former leave this country with the idea of appearing in England in a public character from this Court.'—*H.M.Comm. Rep. Fortescue MSS.*, Vol. 6 (1908), p. 233.

It is very probable that Rumford had brought with him private proposals from Bavaria for an agreement between that country and Britain. Policy had changed and the pendulum had swung against the French. In return for a British subsidy the Bavarians agreed to put 20,000 men in the field. This agreement, slightly modified, was confirmed in 1799 by Maximilian Joseph who had succeeded Charles Theodore.

34. K. Th. von Heigel, *Benjamin Thompson—Graf von Rumford* (München, 1915), p. 13.

35. As a sidelight on Rumford's eminence, and as some slight evidence for the continuance of his reforms, the following note is of interest:

'There are no poor laws in operation at Munich, no mendicity societies, no tract and soup and blanket charities; yet pauperism, mendicity and starvation are nearly unknown. For the system of regulations by which these evils have been repressed or altogether remedied, I believe Bavaria is indebted to the celebrated American, Count Rumford, who was in the service of the late king, Max-Joseph [sic] from 1790 to 1799.' Mrs Jameson, *Visits and Sketches at Home and Abroad* (London, 1834), Vol. II, p. 61.

CHAPTER 6

1. H. Bence Jones, *The Royal Institution, its Founder and its First Professors* (London, 1871), p. 46.

2. Ibid., p. 48.

3. Ibid., p. 138.

4. Much of the information in this chapter is taken from the Minute Books of the Royal Institution by the very kind permission of the managers who generously allowed me access to their records.

5. From a letter written by the Earl of Aylesford to Matthew Boulton, 11 February 1800. The original is in the Birmingham Assay Office.

6. H. Bence Jones, ibid., p. 194.

7. From a letter in the Library of the Royal Institution.

8. Today the argument sounds hollow.

9. From a photographic copy of a letter in the Library of the Royal Institution.

10. H. Bence Jones, ibid., p. 171.

11. Ellis, *Memoir*, p. 535.

12. J. A. Paris, *The Life of Sir Humphry Davy*, Vol. I, p. 138.

13. Minute of 15 February 1802. The appointing Minute gives his salary as 100 guineas, not pounds, though Rumford referred to it in a letter as £100 which is probably what it was.

14. Alexander Wood and Frank Oldham, *Thomas Young, Natural Philosopher* (Cambridge, 1954), p. 119.

15. This striking phrase is older than the R.I. It was used by Thomas Barnes of Manchester. See D. S. L. Cardwell, *The Organization of Science in England* (London, 1957), p. 17.

It is instructive to compare Rumford's aims for the Royal Institution with those of the Conservatoire des Arts et des Métiers in Paris. Rumford, as his Paris Journal shows, was not without influence upon French advance in the technological field. Blagden records in his diary (6 June 1802)—he was in Paris with Rumford at the time: 'Went to the Abbaye St Martin aux Champs to see the Conservatoire des Arts et des Métiers which is a favourite object with the Ministry of the Interior. The plan is really a very fine one, to have models, even machines of full size where practicable of everything useful in the various trades and manufactures with liberty to study them, to get drawings or imitations of them made: a library of all the connected subjects: persons fit to give answers to artists consulting them and capable of telling those artists whether a project they have be new or not. There is also to be a Professor for elementary instruction. . . .'

This approving comment seems, in principle at least, to put Blagden on Rumford's side in the latter's aims for a Repository at the Royal Institution. More important, it implies that Rumford's influence and prestige had carried the day with M Molard who had been placed in charge of the Conservatoire des Arts et des Métiers—*Archives Internationales d'Histoire des Sciences*, 42 (Janvier–Mars, 1958), p. 18.

CHAPTER 7

1. Brian Connell, *Portrait of a Whig Peer*, p. 446.
2. The letter is in the Archives of the Royal Society.
3. The italics are mine.
4. Reprinted in Thomas Young's *Miscellaneous Works* (London, 1855), pp. 474–84.
5. *Memoir*, p. 434.
6. From an original letter in Birmingham Assay Office. There is no evidence of sarcasm, and courtesy did not demand 'our friend'.
7. Brian Connell, ibid., p. 462.
8. The letters are quoted by Bence Jones.

CHAPTER 8

1. The letter is quoted with permission from a copy on micro-film of the original letter which is in the William L. Clements Library. See also p. 77.
2. *Memoir*, p. 224.
3. This chapter owes a great deal to Ellis's *Memoir* in which is reproduced much of Sally's *Memoirs*.
4. *Memoir*, p. 288.
5. Ibid., p. 292.
6. Blagden's unpublished diaries throw much light on the characters of both men—Blagden and Rumford. The former hoped by his visit to France to help to re-establish friendly contact between the Royal Society and French *savants*—the Treaty of Amiens was signed on 25 March 1802. In fact Blagden was subsequently accused by Napoleon of being a spy; the incident is referred to in Sir Gavin de Beer's scholarly book, *The Sciences were never at War* (London, 1960).
7. Sally was by no means the only woman in Blagden's life. Rumford, whose influence on his friend was not highly moral, advised him when in Paris to live at 'the same place with Mrs L and form connexion'. Blagden

thought that in R's conversation there was 'so much of crooked intrigue' that he was alarmed (Blagden's Diary).

It is obvious from Blagden's Diary that at this time he (Blagden) paid constant attention to Mme Lavoisier.

In somewhat different vein Palmerston had written to his wife much earlier (6 March 1795): 'I suppose Emma (Godfrey) has told you that there is a report of her former lover Sir Charles B. marrying Caroline Grote. I think she is a bold girl. . . . I should fear after a short period she may find him a very worthy man, a man of strict honour, a man of learning and science and a man of the truest principals, a most unpleasant husband. I wish I may be mistaken but as I know we should fight in less than a week I own I am sorry for Caroline. . . .' Connell, *Portrait of a Whig Peer*, p. 310.

It was good both for Sally and Blagden that *their* proposed marriage never took place.

8. *Memoir*, p. 351. It was brought to light, like so much more, by Ellis.

9. The letter is in the British Museum. *B. M. Add. MSS.*, 34045.

10. The Pelhams were great friends of the Palmerstons.

11. From a letter in the British Museum. *Pelham Papers*, 33108.

12. See my article 'Count Rumford's Journal' in *Archives Internationales d'Histoire des Sciences*, Onzième Année, No. 42, 1958. It is hoped that later the Journal will be published in full.

13. Bladgen's diary has a curious entry for 17 August 1802 which throws light on his relationship with Rumford as well as on Rumford's character: 'Mad. de Kalb desired me to engage Count Rumford not to meddle much in affairs at Munich; they are all afraid of the present Elector's character and that Count Rumford would come to ill with him. Took affectionate leave of her. . . . I am the more struck with Count R's conduct in not having introduced me to her before. When in carriage an accession of vanity led him to tell me her history: married to a man she disliked, remains a virgin: loved much a brother who died—then placed affections on Count R who has been with her in all situations, seen her naked but out of principle and at her earnest desire would not enjoy her.'

14. Reproduced with permission from the original which is in the Library of the Royal Institution.

15. The substance of two letters in the Library of the Royal Institution.

16. *Memoir*, p. 522.

17. Letter to Sally, *Memoir*, p. 548.

CHAPTER 9

1. F. Edwards, Junior, *On the Extravagent Use of Fuel* (London, 1869). Chapter I is a biographical sketch based on the article in the *Biographie*

Universelle, Chalmers's Biographical Dictionary, and Rumford's own *Essays.* Edwards revealed far less insight into his subject's character than into his work.

See also *Our Domestic Fireplaces* (London, 1864), and *A Treatise on Smoky Chimneys* (London, 1868), both by the same author.

2. e.g. Margaret Fishenden, *House Heating* (London, 1925), and Thomas Bedford, *Basic Principles of Ventilation and Heating* (London, 1948).

3. *Of the Management of Fire and the Economy of Fuel* (Essay VI), *Complete Works,* Vol. IV, p. 1.

4. *Complete Works,* Vol. IV.

5. *Complete Works,* Vol. IV, p. 384.

6. 'Of the Use of Steam as a Vehicle for transporting Heat', *Journal of the Royal Institution,* No. 1, and *Complete Works,* Vol. III, p. 324.

7. *Complete Works,* Vol. V, p. 225. Although Rumford did not take out patents he protected his interests by going to law. He was involved in successful litigation in France during his last years. The action concerned priority in the improvements in the Argand Lamp. It seems as though Rumford while not taking out patent rights himself was jealous lest others should benefit financially from his ideas or receive the credit which was his by right.

8. The story is told by the Count's daughter and by Cuvier. *Complete Works,* Vol. I, p. 563, and *Éloge,* p. 46.

9. Essay XII, *Complete Works,* Vol. V, pp. 567–81.

10. Essay XIII, *Complete Works,* Vol. V, pp. 583–613.

11. *Complete Works,* Vol. IV, p. 331.

CHAPTER 10

1. Sidney and Beatrice Webb, *English Local Government: English Poor Law History: Part 1,* '*The Old Poor Law*' (London, 1927), p. 170.

2. Isaac Wood, *Some Account of the Shrewsbury House of Industry* (1791), pp. 1, 3, 35.

3. Isaac Wood, Letter to Sir William Pulteney [Member of Parliament for Shrewsbury]. *Observations on the Bill for the better Support and Maintenance of the Poor* (1797), p. 6.

4. Sir Frederic Norton Eden, Bart., *The State of the Poor* (London, 1797). See, e.g., p. 496.

5. *The Watchman* (Bristol, 1796), No. 5, p. 140.

6. Brian Connell, *Portrait of a Whig Peer,* p. 405.

7. The letter is in the Boulton and Watt Collection at the Birmingham Assay Office.

8. Vol. XIV, December 1823.

9. Rumford's house is now numbered 168 Brompton Road: it is a carpet store. Some account of it is given in Walford, *Old and New London*, Vol. V, p. 26. Sally disposed of the lease in 1837.

10. The original letters are in the possession of the Royal Society.

11. *Memoir*, p. 268.

12. *Complete Works*, Vol. V, p. 308. It is probable that Rumford's thoughts about benevolence were influenced by Adam Smith's *Wealth of Nations*, published in 1776.

13. *Complete Works*, Vol. V, p. 493.

14. In 1799 its Commandant was Major Baron von Schwecheim. Rumford seems to have taken a personal interest in its pupils judging by a letter he wrote to the guardian of one of them.

15. Particulars are given in Bauernfeind's article in *Allgemeine Deutsche Biographie*.

16. From a letter in the British Museum. Pelham Papers, Ref. 33108.

17. From a letter in the Library of the Royal Institution.

CHAPTER II

1. *Complete Works*, Vol. II, p. 1, and *Phil. Trans. Roy. Soc.* for 1781. The Royal Society keeps in its archives this and many other papers of Rumford's. It is beautifully set out and exhibits first-class draughtsmanship.

Hutton's formula was published in 1778, the year of these experiments.

2. *Heat, a Mode of Motion* (London, 1880), p. 47.

3. *Complete Works*, Vol. II, p. 98.

4. Ibid., p. 173.

5. *Complete Works*, Vol. II, p. 401.

6. Wiedemann and Franz showed in about 1850 that for many metals the ratio, thermal conductivity to electrical conductivity, was a constant. More recently Lorenz suggested that the ratio depends upon the temperature according to the formula: $\dfrac{k}{\sigma.T}$ = a constant, where k = thermal conductivity, σ = electrical conductivity and T = absolute temperature.

7. The rate of heat loss by convection was found by Dulong and Petit to be given by the formula:

$$h = m.p.^{0\cdot45}\theta^{1\cdot233}$$

where m is a factor depending on the shape and position of the cooling body, p the pressure of the gas in the enclosure or jacket and θ the difference in temperature between the body and its surroundings.

This was natural convection, i.e. it was not due to a forced draught. The term $\theta^{1\cdot233}$ is very close to $\theta^{\frac{5}{4}}$, a very much more recent result which has theoretical backing.

8. This illustrates a minor fault that occurs from time to time in his work, namely, too great a confidence in the *precision* of his experiments.

9. *Complete Works*, Vol. II, p. 267.

10. Tyndall, *New Fragments* (London, 1892), p. 160.

11. *Complete Works*, Vol. II, p. 333.

12. Ibid., p. 339.

CHAPTER 12

1. *An Inquiry Concerning the Source of the Heat which is Excited by Friction*, *Phil. Trans.*, LXXXVIII, and *Complete Works*, Vol. II, p. 471.

2. It is interesting to observe how the phrase 'Rumford was struck' has been continually used in textbooks on heat.

3. *Of the Nature of Things* (Everyman Edition), line. 419.

4. Francis Bacon, *Novum Organum*, Book II, Aphorism XX. See, e.g., the translation by Ellis and Spedding.

5. Quoted by Tyndall in *Heat, A Mode of Motion* (London), Sixth Edition, p. 36.

6. *A Collection of Several Pieces of Mr John Locke, never before printed or not extant in his Works* (London, 1720), p. 224. This quotation is taken from Locke's *Elements of Natural Philosophy* which is included in the collection referred to. The *Elements* are a series of concise statements which form a summary of some fields of elementary science. They were prepared for a pupil of Locke's and are very like the bare bones of a lecturer's course.

Locke in his *Essay concerning Human Understanding* makes the same assumptions about heat as he makes in the *Elements*, e.g. 'But if the Sensation of Heat and Cold be nothing but the increase or diminution of the motion of the minute Parts of our Bodies caused by the Corpuscles of any other body it is easy to be understood. . . .' (Sec. Ed. London, 1694), p. 63.

7. For Black's discussion, see *Lectures on the Elements of Chemistry* (Edinburgh, 1803), pp. 27, et seq.

8. He is careful to explain to the Fellows, in his paper, that he had not sacrificed a cannon in carrying out these experiments.

9. *Complete Works*, Vol. III, p. 42.

10. *Mémoires de l'Institut*, Classes des Sciences Mathematiques et Physiques, Vol. VI; and *Complete Works*, Vol. III, pp. 137–44.

11. *Complete Works*, Vol. III, p. 166.

12. They will be described later.

13. *Complete Works*, Vol. III, p. 208.

14. The fact was recorded by Cullen and the phenomenon investigated by Dalton.

15. This is probably an underestimate.

16. *A New System of Chemical Philosophy* (Manchester, 1808). See pp. 1, 98, 99.

17. Sanborn C. Brown, *American Journal of Physics*, Vol. 18, p. 367 (Article—'The Caloric Theory of Heat').

18. J. A. Paris, *The Life of Sir Humphry Davy* (London, 1831). If this statement is true Davy held these opinions before the publication of Rumford's first paper on the subject.

19. It might have been possible to claim, on lines already familiar, but without conviction, that the caloric arose from the diminution in volume of the ice on melting. Professor Andrade has argued that the success of the experiment was fortuitous (*Nature*, March 1935), in that the melting of the ice was mainly due to a gain of heat from outside sources and not to friction. It is indeed easy to show that under the conditions described a mechanism of about one-fifth H.P. working for ten minutes would be required to melt the ice. This is asking a lot.

20. J. Davy (ed.), *The Elements of Chemical Philosophy* (Collected Works, Vol. IV, p. 66). For an account of the experiments see Magie, *A Source Book in Physics* (New York and London, 1935), pp. 161–5.

21. For example, E. L. Youmans, *Memoir*, pp. 484, et seq.

As a footnote to this chapter it must be emphasized that the existence of the two theories in the first half of the nineteenth century did not prevent a good deal of progress in the mathematical theory of heat. On this point see E. Mendoza, 'The Historical Approach to the Mechanical Theory of Heat', *The School Science Review*, XLIV, p. 11.

CHAPTER 13

1. *Complete Works*, Vol. III, pp. 1–22, and *Phil. Trans.*, LXXXIX, pp. 179–94.

2. *New Fragments*, p. 169.

3. *Complete Works*, Vol. III, pp. 23–130.

4. Prévost, *Sur l'Équilibre du Feu* (Geneva, 1792).

5. The account given is over-simplified. Intensity, range and distribution of frequency are all involved.

6. *Complete Works*, Vol. III, p. 166.

7. No. 8, July 1804. Young had previously been viciously attacked.

8. The reference is not to the paper read before the *Institut* but to the paper sent to the Royal Society and published in *Phil. Trans.* (1804), XCIV, pp. 77–183.

9. 'If frigorific rays are to be considered as existing substances, of a nature essentially different from calorific rays, what can be less applicable than the case of vibrations differing from other vibrations only in degree

of strength? A frigorific ray can never, according to Count Rumford's theory, produce any of the effects of a calorific ray modify either as you please. But a slow undulation resembles a quick one in every particular and produces all the same effects in a smaller degree.' This is fair criticism.

10. *Complete Works*, Vol. III, p. 47.

11. *Nicholson's Journal*, 1799. This observation anticipated Mason's Hygrometer.

12. Mr Thomas Martin, in his valuable paper, 'The Experimental Researches of Benjamin Thompson', in the *Bulletin of the British Society for the History of Science* for October 1951, is in error on this point.

13. *An Experimental Enquiry into the Nature and Propagation of Heat* (London, 1804).

14. Loc. cit., p. 402.

15. Ibid., p. 552.

16. Vol. VII, p. 63.

17. E.g., on the history of the barometer, p. 46. 'When prejudice retires behind an entrenchment of invisibles and possibilities, we must abandon the pursuit. It is vain to contend with phantoms. When by the counsels of that illustrious martyr of science, Galileo, his ingenious disciple, Torricelli, performed the famous experiment of filling a sealed glass tube with mercury; the fact was so strikingly beautiful, and so completely decisive of the weight of the atmosphere, that to barely mention the cause might seem sufficient to have opened with enthusiasm the eyes of the learned world. The adherents of the *fuga vacui* were indeed sadly perplexed, unable to reply, yet resolute to maintain their opinion. But their champion, Father Linus, defying the power of argument, very gravely asserted that the mercury was suspended from the top of the tube by invisible threads. The good Father thus quieted the minds of the orthodox and their generation slept in peace.'

18. *Complete Works*, Vol. V, p. 1.

19. Pierre Bouguer (1698–1758).

20. Johann Heinrich Lambert (1728–1777). His book *Photometria* written in Latin was published in 1760.

21. I have discussed the question in an article in the *School Science Review*, 134, p. 43.

22. *Complete Works*, Vol. V, p. 27.

23. *The History and Present State of Discoveries relating to Vision, Light and Colours* (1772).

24. *An Enquiry into the Nature of Heat*, p. 162.

25. *Complete Works*, Vol. V, p. 75.

CHAPTER 14

1. *Complete Works*, Vol. V, p. 661.

2. Sanborn C. Brown, 'Scientific Drawings of Count Rumford at Harvard', *Harvard Library Bulletin*, Vol. IX, pp. 3, 350.

3. *Complete Works*, Vol. III, p. 258.

4. Ibid., Vol. III, p. 322.

5. Ibid., Vol. III, p. 370.

6. This simple procedure has kept Rumford's name in chapters on calorimetry in elementary textbooks on Heat. In introducing it he said: 'When we are making experiments to elucidate natural phenomena, it is always more satisfactory to avoid errors, or to compensate them, than to trust to calculation for appreciating their effects.' It is hardly necessary to add that compensation is exact only for a constant rate of rise of temperature.'

7. J. A. Thompson, *Count Rumford of Massachusetts* (New York, 1935).

CHAPTER 15

1. Much of the material for the first part of this chapter is provided by Rumford's letters to his daughter which are quoted *in extenso* by Ellis.

2. The Hon. Mrs Hugh Wyndham (ed.), *The Correspondence of Sarah, Lady Lyttelton* (1787–1870) (London, 1912).

3. *Les Salons d'Autrefois* (Paris, 1869).

4. *Memoir*, p. 568.

5. Ibid., p. 612.

6. J. A. Paris, *The Life of Sir Humphry Davy, Bart., Ll.D.* (London, 1831), Vol. II, p. 24.

7. Ibid., p. 24.

8. It is only fair to note that the date of publication of the relevant paper was 1807 and that Rumford's opinions may have hardened afterwards.

9. *London Athenaeum* (1935), 'Sketches from the Literature of the United States', p. 782.

Appendix

Miscellanius Observations upon the State of the Rebel Army:

Upon Sunday October 15th I saw 16 *flat-bottom'd* boats or *Batteaus* lying just below Cambridge Bridge, & two more were making in the yard—The workmen informed me that one was finished every day, and that more workmen were daily expected from Newbury.—These Boats are built of common deal Boards, & in general will contain from 50 to 60 Men, including the Rowers.—What number of them were to be made I could not learn.

It is generally supposed in the Rebel Army that an attack is designed upon either Charlestown, or Boston, or on both—and that these boats are preparing to transport Troops to those places—But many of the more intelligent and among these some of their principal Officers rather suppose these preparations are only to amuse Ye Kings Troops, and by keeping them continually alarm'd with apprehension of being attacked, prevent their going to distant parts of the Country to Ravage.—

About the 13th October a return was made of the number of Men, that all the boats of every denomination (exclusive of the flat-bottom'd boats) in the Rebel Camp, were capable of transporting—and I was told by a Person who saw said return that the total number was 550.

From the best information I have been able to get with respect to their *Military Stores,* the total quantity of *Gun-Powder* that they have in their Camp, (exclusive of what is distributed among the Troops) may be somewhere between 12 and 15 Tons.

The only *Magazines* on the left wing of the Army (that I know of) are the Powder House, a round stone building about half, or three quarters of a Mile N.W. of Winter Hill, over which a Subalterns Guard mounts—and a Cave in the W side of Prospect Hill, the entrance into which is defended by a small Trench & Parapet, which descends obliquely from the Fort down the side of the hill—This magazine is inaccessable from without, on account of the steepness of the hill on the W. side—But I apprehend that if a party could by any means come upon the rear of their encampment the Powder House might very easily be surprised, as it is at a very considerable distance from any of their Works, and is defended but by a small party—What quantity of Gun-Powder is contained in these two Magazines I have not been able to learn.—

On the N.W. side of Cambridge Common is the '*Laboratory*', round which two or three Companies are encamp'd, but I believe no considerable quantity of Powder is ever kept in this place, nor at any other place in or near Cambridge.

In Watertown at the distance of about half a Mile N from the meeting house is a school house which I am told is one of their principal Magazines of Gun Powder. The Company in Watertown furnish a Guard for it, and two Centries are constantly planted here in the day time, and four in the Night.

There was a house about half way from Cambridge to Watertown in which a considerable quantity of *Powder* was lodged about 3 months ago, over which a strong Guard was mounted, but I believe it has since been removed to Prospect and Winter Hill Magazines, 'tho I am not absolutely certain of it.

As to the quantity of *Powder* and the situation of the *Magazines* upon the right wing of the Army—I have never been able to get any satisfactory accounts.—I was lately told that a small, regular, square Redoubt which has lately been erected upon a very considerable eminence in the back part of Roxbury was built to defend a grand Magazine which was to be erected there, but I rather suppose it is designed as a Citidel, to command the Town and their other Works, which it is very well calculated to do.

As to *Shot* I believe the Rebels are in want of no kind of it, as large quantities of it, of every sort, have lately been cast in the Country—and the Furnaces are still employed in that service.—

Their *Canon* in general are excessively bad—many of which that are mounted, and planted are intirely useless—12 pieces, 18 and 24 pounders, which came from the Fort at Newport are really much more valuable than every piece of ordnance they have in their Camp. But they are not anxious to increase the quantity of their *Artilery* till they can have some certainty of a supply of *Gun Powder* which at present I believe they have not.

Their *Fire-Arms* in general are but very indifferent, and I believe two thirds of their Pieces at least are destitute of *Bayonets*—But there is a great number of *Armourers* in the Camp, who are constantly employed in making good these deficiencies. The Pieces in general are owned by the Soldiers, and are re-fitted at the expence of the Colonies.

Exclusive of 25 or 30 rounds of *Cartridge & Ball* which each Soldier has in his Cartouch Box. They have lately had a pound of *Buch shot* served out to each man to keep loose in his pocket, and make use occasionally—and I am told that every Soldier in the Camp is soon to be supplied with an additional quantity of 60 rounds of Cartridges which are to be carried in a leathern bag made for that purpose, and hung over the right shoulder by a strap.—

The *Officers* are universally armed with a *Musquet* and *Bayonet*, and some few of them have added a *sword*, a *Pike* or *Espantoon* I have never seen in their Camp and believe they make no use at all of these Weapons. The marks of distinction among them are as follows Viz—The *Commander in chief* wears a wide blue Ribbond between his Coat and waist-Coat, over the right shoulder and across the breast—*Major Generals* a Pink Ribbond in the same manner—*Brigadier Generals* a   Ribbond—And all *Aids du Camp* a green one—All *Field Officers* wear Red, Pink, or scarlet Cockades—*Captains* Yellow, or Buff Cockades and *Subalterns* Green ones—

Their *Works* in general are very extensive, and as strong as labour *alone* can make them, but *Engineers* are very much wanted in their Camp.

The *entrances* or *passage-way* into their Forts & Redoubts are all defended by Traverses, and in general there is a plank Bridge over the ditch which is drawn up & fast'ned by Chains to two posts even with the external face of the Parapet—which Bridge so drawn up intirely closes the passage into the Fort or Redoubt—And where they have no Bridges the entrances are defended by *Cheveau de Frise*.

The Army in general is not only very badly accoutered but most wretchedly *cloathed* and as dirty a set of mortals as ever disgraced the name of a Soldier—They have had no clothes of any sort provided for them by the Congress (except the detatchment of 1133 that are gone to Canada under Col. Arnold, who had each of them a new Coat, and a linen frock served out to them before they set out). Tho' the Army in general, and the Massachusetts forces in particular had encouragement of having Coats given them by way of bounty for inlisting—And the neglect of the Congress to fullfil their promise in this respect has been the source of not a little uneasiness among the Soldiers.—

They have no Women in the Camp to do washing for the men, and they in general not being used to doing things of this sort, and thinking it rather a disparagement to them, choose rather to let their Linen &c. rot upon their backs than to be at the trouble of cleaning 'em themselves. And to this nasty way of life, and to the change of their diet from Milk, Vegetables &c. to living almost intirely upon Flesh, must be attributed those Putrid, Malignant, and infectious disorders which broke out among them soon after their taking the field, and which have prevailed with unabating fury during the whole summer.

The leading men among them (with their usual art & cunning) have been indefatigable in their indeavours to conceal the real State of the Army in this respect, and to convince the World that the Soldiers were tolerably healthy. But the contrary has been apparent, even to a demonstration, to every person that has had but the smallest acquaintance with their camp— And so great was the prevalence of these disorders in the month of July that out of 4207 men who were stationed upon Prospect Hill no more than 2227 were returned fit for duty.—

The *mortallity* among them must have been very great, and to this in a great measure must be attributed the present weakness of their Regiments, many of wch were much stronger when they came into the Field.—But the number of Soldiers that have *died* in the *Camp* is comparatively small to those vast numbers that have *gone off* in the interior parts of the Country: For immediately upon being taken down with these disorders they have in general been carried back into the Country to their own homes, where they have not only died themselves, but by spreading the infection among their Relations & Friends have introduced such a general mortallity throughout New England as was never known since its first planting.—Great numbers have been carried off in all parts of the Country.—some Towns 'tis said have lost near one third of their inhabitants—and there is scarse a village in New England but has suffer'd more or less from the raging virulence of these dreadful disorders.—

Perhaps the intolerable heats, and continual droughts during the late summer, by inclining the Blood to a putrid state, and rendering it more easily susceptible of the infection may have contributed not a little to the spread of these diseases.—

Every article of *Provision* that is the natural produce of the Country is extremely cheap in the Camp; except the article of *Bread*, which is very far from being so, as the price of Corn of every sort is much raised on account of a very great scarsity of it, occasioned by the late drought.—Rye which used commonly to be Sold at 2/3 and 2/6, is now sold in many places at 4/-, & 4/6 pr. Bushel, and every other sort of grain in proportion.—But the Army expect to be supplied from the South ward.—

The best of fresh Beef is now sold at one penny three-farthings pr lb— and good Mutton from threehalfpence to twopence pr lb—But notwithstanding fresh Provisions are thus cheap and plenty, yet I have heard of no considerable Magazines that are forming.—

Many Capital *Medicines* are not to be bought in the Country—and in general those that are to be had are at an advanc^d price of 5 or 600 pr. Cent.— The price of *West India Goods* is raised in general from 70 to 100 pr. Cent— *English Goods* about as much (notwithstanding a resolve of the Congress to the contrary) and *Irish Linens* are not to be bought at any price.—

The great reason why fresh provisions of every sort are so remarkably plenty is the universal *scarsity of Hay* throughout the Country, occasioned by the late drought. The want of which article is so great that the farmers in general cannot possibly keep more than two thirds of their usual quantity of Stock alive during the Winter.—And if they do not kill them this fall, many of them must unavoidably perish by famine. But tho' this circumstance may make Provisions extremely cheap and plenty this year, yet it cannot fail to have a very different effect upon the next.—

The *Soldiers* in general are most heartily *Sick of the Service*, and I believe it would be with the utmost difficulty that they could be provailed upon to serve another Campaign.—The Continental Congress are very sensible of this and have lately sent a Committee to the Camp to consult with the General Officers upon some method of raising the necessary forces to serve during the Winter seasons; as the greatest part of the Army that is now in the field is to be disbanded upon the last day in December.—

Whether they will be successful in their indeavours to persuade the Soldiers to re-inlist, or not, I cannot say, but am rather inclined to think that they will; For as they are men possess'd of every species of cunning and artifice, and as their Political existance depends upon the existance of the Army, they will leave no stone un-turn'd to accomplish their designs.—

Notwithstanding the indefatigable indeavours of Mr. Washington, and the other Generals; and particularly of Assistant General Gates, to *arrange* and *discipline* the Army, yet any tolerable degree of *Order* and *Subordination* is what they are totally unacquainted with in the Rebel Camp.—And the doctrines of *independence & levellism* have been so effectually sown throughout the Country, and so universally imbibed by all ranks of men, that I apprehend it will be with the greatest difficulty that the inferior Officers, and Soldiers will be ever brought to any tolerable degree of Subjection to the commands of their Superiors.—

Many of their leading men are not insensible of this and I have often heard them lament that the existance of that very spirit which induced the common People to take up Arms and resist the authority of Great Britain should induce them to resist the authority of their own Officers, and by that means effectually prevent their ever making good Soldiers.—

Another great reason why it is impossible to introduce a proper degree of *Subordination* in the Rebel Army, is the great degree of *equallity* as to *birth, fortune* and *education*, that universally prevails among them. For men cannot bear to be commanded by others that are their Superiors in nothing but in having had the good fortune to get a Superior Commission, for which perhaps they stood equally fair. And in addition to this the Officers and men are not only in general very nearly upon a par as to birth, fortune,

&c.—but in particular Regiments are mostly commonly *neighbours* and *acquaintances*, & as such can with less Patience submit to that degree of absolute submission, and Subordination which is necessary to form a well-desciplined Corps.—

Another reason why the Army can never be well united and regulated is the *disagrement* and *jealousies* between the *different Troops* from the *different Colonies*; which must never fail to create disaffection and uneasiness among them. The Massachusetts forces already complain very loudly of the parti-ality of the General to the Virginians; and have even gone so far as to tax him with taking pleasure in bringing *their* Officers to Court Martials, and having them Cashired that he may fill their places with his friends from that quarter.—The Gentlemen from the Southern Colonies, in their turn, complain of the enormous proportion of New England Officers in the Army and particularly of those belonging to the Province of Massachusetts Bay, and say, as the cause is now become a common one, and the expence is general they ought to have an equal chance for Command with their neighbours.

Thus have these jealousies and uneasiness already begun which I think cannot fail to increase, and grow every day more and more interesting; and if they do not finally distroy the very existance of the Army (which I think they bid very fair to do) yet must unavoidably render it much less formid-able than it otherways might have been.—

Of all useless sets of men that ever incumbered an Army, surely *the boasted Rifle-men* are certainly the most so.—When they came to the Camp they had every Liberty and indulgence allow'd them that they could possibly wish for.—They had more pay than any other Soldiers—did no duty—were under no restraint from the commands of their Officers, but went when, & where they pleased, without being subject to be stopped or examined by any one, and did almost intirely as they pleased in every respect whatever.—But they have not answered the end for which they were designed in any one article whatever: For instead of being the best marksmen in the World, and picking off every Regular that was to be seen, there is scarsely a Regiment in Camp but can produce men that can beat them at shooting.—and the Army is now universally convinced that the continual fire which they kept up by the Week and Month together has had no other effect than to waste their amunition, and convince the Kings Troops that they are not really so formidable adversaries as they would wish to be thought.—

Mr Washington is very sensible of this, and has not only strictly forbid their passing the advanced Centries to fire at the Kings Troops, without particular Orders for that purpose, but has lately obliged them to do duty as other Troops. And to be sure there never was a more mutinous and undisciplined set of Villains that bred disturbance in any Camp.—

The whole number of these men in the Camp may be somewhere about 650—and I believe the total number of Troops, of every denomination in the Army, include Officers is very near upon 15000.—

Boston 4th November 1775   **B. T.**

Bibliography

Chief Sources

In the British Museum:
Various letters among the Hardwicke Papers, the Pelham Papers, and elsewhere.
A series of letters from Rumford to his publishers.
In the William L. Clements Library of the University of Michigan:
The Gage and the Germain Papers.
The Rev. George E. Ellis, *Memoir of Sir Benjamin Count Rumford.* Published in England by Macmillan & Co. (London, 1876); in America by Claxton, Remsen and Haffelfinger (Philadelphia, 1870).
The Historical Manuscripts Commission's Reports, especially those dealing with the Stopford-Sackville and the Royal Institution MSS.
In the Public Record Office:
Various letters and memoranda, especially in Home Office Papers, HO 42/2.
At the Royal Institution:
The Early Minute Books and sundry letters.
Rumford, *The Complete Works* of.
Published in London in 1876 by Macmillan & Co. (The numbering of the volumes is different in the American and English editions. In the present work the Memoir is Vol. I and is followed by Vols. II, III, IV, V. This accords with the English edition.)
Rumford's Journal of his stay in Paris in 1801 (Lady Palmerston's Copy), in the Library of the University of Birmingham.
In the Library of the Royal Society:
The unpublished manuscript diaries of Sir Charles Blagden (8 vols.).
Various letters, documents and original papers referred to in the text.

Other Sources

Bauernfeind, Article in *Allgemeine Deutsche Biographie*, Vol. 29.
Bibliothèque Britannique (Science et Arts).
Geneva, 1801 and after. Vols. XVII, XIX, XX, XXI, XXXIV.

Brian Connell, *Portrait of a Whig Peer* (London, 1957).

G. Cuvier, Éloge Historique, in *Recueil des Éloges Historiques*, Tome Deuxième (Paris, 1861).

K. Th. von Heigel, *Benjamin Thompson, Graf von Rumford*. Verlag der K. B. Akademie der Wissenschaften (München, 1915).

J. Johnston, *American Journal of Science and Arts*. Vol. XXXIII, January 1838.

H. Bence Jones, *The Royal Institution, Its Founder and its First Professors* (London, 1871).

J. Renwick, *The Life of Count Rumford*, in the Library of American Biography, conducted by Jared Sparks, Vol. XV (Boston, 1845).

J. Tyndall, *New Fragments* (London, 1892).

Thomas Young, *Miscellaneous Works* (ed. Peacock), Vol. II (London, 1855).

Other Biographies and Works containing Biographical Sketches of Rumford

Sanborn C. Brown, *Count Rumford* (New York, 1962).
A short biography, written for the Science Study Series, by an acknowledged expert.

March Cost, *The Countess* (London, 1963).
This is an historical novel dealing with the life of Sally—the Countess. It is based on much original material and gives a vivid picture of Rumford.

Dictionary of National Biography, Vol. LVI.

C. Harrison Dwight, Ph.D., *Sir Benjamin Thompson, Count of Rumford* (Cincinatti, 1960).

Lewis Einstein, *Divided Loyalties* (London, 1933).

Enciclopedia Universal Illustrada, Tomo LII.
Europeo–Americana.

Encyclopaedia Britannica (1946 ed.), Vol. 19.

Allen French, *General Gage's Informers* (Ann Arbor, 1932).
The late Mr Allen French was the first to make use of the famous 'spy' letter from among the Germain Papers.

William Garnett, *Heroes of Science* (London, 1885).
A short biography based in spirit and substance on Ellis's Memoir.

R. W. Hale, 'Benjamin Thompson: Count Rumford. His Romantic Career in Statesmanship and Science'. *New England Quarterly* (October 1928). *Technology Review*, 1931 (Illustrated).
Short, and only uses limited sources, but objective in approach.

Egon Larsen, *An American in Europe* (London, 1953).
   A popular biography which gives a fairly reliable picture of Rumford as a man.
Philipp Lenard, *Great Men of Science* (trans. by H. S. Hatfield) (London, 1933).
J. A. Thompson, *Count Rumford of Massachusetts* (New York, 1935).
   A modern biography which deals little with Rumford's scientific work, but quite vividly with his character and personal affairs.

A Select List of Articles and Books in which are contained Short Accounts of the Work, or References to the Life, of Count Rumford

C. Raymond Adams, 'Benjamin Thompson, Count Rumford', *Scientific Monthly*, LXXI, p. 380.
Randolph G. Adams, *The Papers of Lord George Germain*.
   The William L. Clements Library, University of Michigan.
Allgemeine Literatur Zeitung (1802).
Annual Register (London, 1780, 1798, 1800, 1814).
Thomas Bedford, *Basic Principles of Ventilation and Heating* (London, 1948).
Gerhard Berthold, *Rumford und die mechanische Warme theorie* (Heidelberg, 1874).—Very rare. This book gives a detailed account of the development of the dynamical theory of heat.
Blackwood's Magazine (Panaceas for Poverty), Vol. XIV, p. 637.
Sanborn C. Brown and K. Scott, 'Count Rumford: International Informer', *New England Quarterly*, Vol. 21, p. 1.
Sanborn C. Brown and E. W. Stein, 'Benjamin Thompson and the first Secret-Ink Letter of the American Revolution', *American Journal of Police Science*, 40, p. 627.
Sanborn C. Brown, 'Scientific Drawings of Count Rumford at Harvard', *Harvard Library Bulletin*, IX, p. 350.
Sanborn C. Brown, 'The Caloric Theory of Heat', *American Journal of Physics*, 18, p. 367.
Sanborn C. Brown, 'Count Rumford's Concept of Heat', *American Journal o, Physics*, 20, p. 331.
Sanborn C. Brown, 'Rumford Lamps', *Am. Phil. Soc. Proc.*, 96, p. 37.
Sanborn C. Brown, 'Count Rumford—Physicist and Technologist', *Proc. Amer. Acad. of Arts and Sciences*, 82, p. 266.
Chalmers's Biographical Dictionary, XXIX.
C. Harrison Dwight, 'Count Rumford: His Majesty's Colonel in Carolina', *South Carolina Historical Magazine* (Jan. 1956).
Edinburgh Review, IV, pp. 399–415; 415–19.

F. Edwards (Junior), *A Treatise on Smoky Chimneys* (London, 1868).
On the Extravagant Use of Fuel (London, 1869).
Chapter I is a short sketch of Rumford's life based on the *Biographie Universelle, Chalmers's Biographical Dictionary*, and the *Essays*.
Our Domestic Fireplaces, 2nd edition (London, 1864).
Margaret Fishenden, *House Heating* (London, 1925).
Gentleman's Magazine, LXX (1800).
A report of the first sitting of the Royal Institution.
Edward Gibbon, *The Autobiography and Correspondence of Edward Gibbon* (London, 1869).
M. Guizot, *Mémoires pour servir a l'Histoire de mon Temps* (Paris, 1859).
London Athenaeum, 1835.
Sketches of the Literature of the United States by the Rev. Timothy Flint.
Mailly, *Essai sur les Institutions de la Grande Bretagne et de l'Irlande* (Brussels, 1867).
The Essay on the Royal Institution is translated in the Annual Report of the Board of Regents of the Smithsonian Institution for the year 1872.
T. Martin, 'The Experimental Researches of Benjamin Thompson, Count Rumford', *The Bulletin of the British Society for the History of Science*, I, No. 6, 1951.
T. J. Mathias, *The Pursuits of Literature* (London, 1794)
Monthly Magazine or British Register, 1814, 1815.
Anne Cary Morris (ed.), *The Diary and Letters of Gouverneur Morris* (London, 1889).
New York Mercury, January 1872; April, 1782.
Nicholson's Journal, I, II, III, V, XI, XII.
Henry Onderdonk (Jnr.), *Documents and Letters, etc.* (New York, 1846).
Revolutionary Incidents, etc. (New York, 1849).
John A. Paris, *The Life of Sir Humphry Davy, Bart., Ll.D.* (London, 1831).
W. G. Perrin (ed.), *The Naval Miscellany*, III.
Contains letters written by Benjamin Thompson from *The Victory*.
Rivington's New York Gazette, 1782—various dates.
Giving matter quoted by Ellis.
Society for Bettering the Condition of the Poor. *Reports* for 1800 and 1801, London.
W. J. Sparrow, 'Benjamin Thompson and Lord George Germain', *University of Birmingham Historical Journal*, V, p. 138.
W. J. Sparrow, 'Count Rumford as a Spy', *Annals of Science*, 11, p. 320.
W. J. Sparrow, 'Rumford's Photometer', *The School Science Review*, No. 134, p. 43.

W. J. Sparrow, 'Count Rumford's Journal', *Arch. Int. d'Histoire des Sciences*, No. 42, p. 15.

W. J. Sparrow, 'Count Rumford', *Architectural Review*, CXXIII, p. 161.

W. J. Sparrow, 'Early Days at the Royal Institution', *Educational Review*, 6, No. 3, p. 202.

T. Pridgin Teal, *Designs of Fireplaces*.
A paper read before the Architectural Society of London, 1886.

Thomas Thomson (ed.), *Annals of Philosophy*, 1815.

John Tyndall, *Heat*, 6th edition (London, 1880).

K. D. C. Vernon, 'The Foundation and Early Years of the Royal Institution,' *Proceedings of the Royal Institution*, No. 179, 1963.

John Walcot, *The Works of Peter Pindar, Esq.*, IV, 'Epistle to Count Rumford' (London, 1802).

G. A. Ward (ed.), *The Journal and Letters of Samuel Curwen*, 4th edition (Boston, 1864).

Index

A

Achan, 38, 262
Acton, General, 266
Adams, C. Raymond, 287
Adams, Randolph G., 287
Adams, Samuel, 26, 43
Adams, The Honorable John, 195
Agriculture, Rumford and, 93
Aichner (Rumford's personal servant), 99, 146, 166, 246
Ambassador, The Turkish (to France), 159
America, 14, 18, 20, 22, 51-2, 53, 56, 62, 69, 96, 103, 118
American Academy of Arts and Sciences, 14, 173, 195-6
American Army, 37, 39, 41-2, 51, 55-7
American Colonies, 19, 26, 34
American Revolution, 27-65
Amiens, Peace of, 158, 163, 268
Ammerland See, 149
Anderson's Institution, 115
Andrade, E. N. da C., 273
Annual Register, The, 174, 263, 287
Appleton, John, 18, 21, 46
Arago, D-F, J., 160
Argand lamp, 178-80, 182, 253, 270
Arkwright, Sir Richard, 128
Armed Neutrality, The, 51
Armstrong, Sir Henry, 118
Army Reform, Thompson's Memorandum on, 79, 80, 81, 82, 83, 104
Artillery, 204-5
Atkinson, C. T., 266
Austria, 74, 79, 96, 101, 166
Austrian Netherlands, The, 74, 75, 82
Auteuil, 249, 252, 253, 257
Aylesford, The Earl of, 117, 267

B

Baader, J. von, 93-4
Babo, Professor, 86
Bach, J. S., 238
Bacon, Francis, 111, 215, 217, 223, 272
Baia, 192
Baldwin, Loammi, 19, 21, 26, 30, 31-2, 36, 37, 38, 98, 103, 143, 147, 148, 150, 165, 253
Baldwin, Mrs Loammi, 97, 100, 143
Baldwin, Stanley, 188
Ball, The Rev. Mr, 202
Banks, Lady, 99
Banks, Sir Joseph, 44, 77, 94, 99, 113-14, 116-17, 118, 120, 121, 122, 123, 126, 132, 134, 135, 138, 139, 150, 151, 156, 161, 162, 172, 194, 195, 233, 245, 259
Barnard, The Rev. Thomas, 19
Barnes, Thomas, 267
Barré, Colonel, 28
Basel, 101
Bassanville, Comtesse de, 250
Bath, 44, 70
Bauernfeind, von, 265, 271, 285
Baumgarten, The Countess of, 78, 144, 252
Baumgarten, Sophy, 146, 252
Bavaria, 71, 73, 74, 75, 76, 81, 83, 84, 85, 90, 92, 94, 95, 97, 101, 102-6, 107, 108, 109, 113, 128, 132, 133-4, 142, 143, 144, 153, 252
Bavarian Academy of Arts and Sciences, 78-9, 86, 105, 162, 166, 196, 252
Bavarian Succession, The War of, 74-5
Becker, Carl, 261

293